Course	Introduction to Biological Anthropology
Course Number	**ANTH 100**
Professor	Mark Griffin
	San Francisco State Univ
	ANTHROPOLOGY

http://create.mcgraw-hill.com

ISBN-10: 1121171591   ISBN-13: 9781121171596

Contents

Credits

Front Matter

CHAPTER 1

Biological Anthropology

Anthropologists study spiders, right?
—Anonymous Caller

f you asked twenty people to define anthropology, you would probably get twenty different answers. Anthropology is such a broad field that many people, understandably, are not sure just what an anthropologist studies. People have brought me rocks to identify and have asked me about the accuracy of the dinosaurs in *Jurassic Park*. One man even called me for information on black widow spiders—and he was referred to me by someone within the university where I teach.

In this chapter, we will define anthropology in general and then focus on the subfield of biological anthropology (also called *bioanthropology* or *physical anthropology*). Because fieldwork—where anthropologists make their observations and collect their data—is perhaps the best-known aspect of anthropology and is the part that attracts many students to the discipline, I will begin with a brief description of two of my fieldwork experiences.

As you read, consider the following questions:

What is anthropology, and what are its subfields?

What is biological anthropology?

How does the scientific method operate?

In what way is bioanthropology a science?

What are belief systems, and what is their relationship to scientific knowledge?

IN THE FIELD: DOING BIOLOGICAL ANTHROPOLOGY

Among the Hutterites

The wheat fields on either side of the long, straight road in western Saskatchewan, Canada, stretched as far as the eye could see. I found myself wishing, on that June day in 1973, that the road went on just as far. I was on my way to visit with my first real anthropological subjects, a colony of people belonging to a 475-year-old religious denomination called the Hutterian Brethren, or Hutterites.

Up to this point, I had not felt much anxiety about the visit. Accounts by other anthropologists of their contacts with Amazon jungle warriors and New Guinea headhunters made my situation seem rather safe. The Hutterites are, after all, people who share my European American cultural heritage, speak English (among other languages), and practice a form of Christianity that emphasizes pacifism and tolerance.

At this point, though, those considerations, no matter how reassuring they should have been, didn't help. Nor did the fact that I was accompanied by the wife of a local wheat farmer who was well known and liked by the people of this colony. I simply had that unnamed fear that affects nearly all anthropologists under these first-contact circumstances.

Finally, the road we traveled—which had turned from blacktop to dirt about 10 miles back—curved abruptly to the right and crested a hill. I saw below us, at the literal end of the road, a neat collection of twenty or so white buildings surrounded by acres of cultivated fields. This was the Hutterite colony, or *Bruderhof,* the "place where the brethren live" (Figure 1.1).

As we drove into the colony, not a soul was in sight. My companion explained that it was a religious holiday that required all but essential work to cease. Everyone was indoors observing the holiday, but the colony minister and colony boss had agreed to see me.

We entered one of the smaller buildings, which I recognized from pictures and diagrams of "typical" colonies as one of the residential buildings. The interior was darkened, in keeping with the holiday. A few minutes later, having gotten my bearings, I explained the reason for my visit to two men and a woman.

The men were dressed in the Hutterite fashion—black trousers and coats and white shirts—and they wore beards, a sign of marriage. The older, gray-haired man was the colony minister. The younger man, who happened to be his son, was the colony boss. The woman, the minister's wife, also dressed in the conservative style of the Hutterites and related

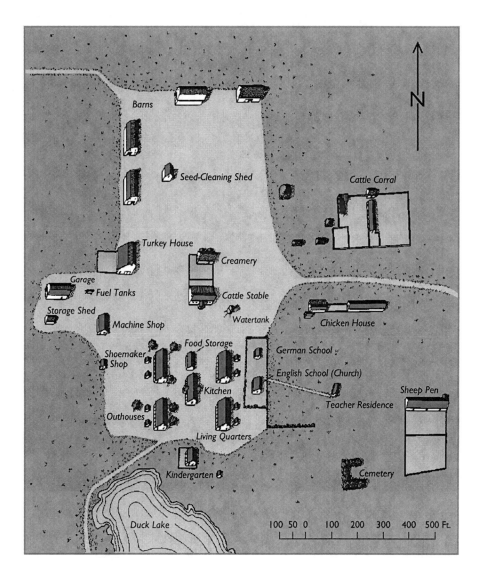

FIGURE 1.1
Diagram of a typical Hutterite colony. The variety of buildings and their functions are indicative of the Hutterites' attempt to keep their colonies self-sufficient and separate from the outside world.

groups. She wore a dress with a white blouse underneath. Her head was covered by a polka-dot kerchief, or *shawl*, as they call it (Figure 1.2).

My contacts, the wheat farmer and his wife, had arranged the visit and had already given the Hutterites an idea of what I wanted to do. But if the colony members didn't like me or my planned study, they could still decline to cooperate. The three listened in silence as I went through my well-rehearsed explanation. When I had finished, they asked me only a few questions. Was I from the government? (My study involved using fingerprints as hereditary traits—a now outdated method—and they

FIGURE 1.2
Hutterite women in typical dress.

apparently associated fingerprinting with law enforcement and personal identification.) Did I know Scripture? (My equivocal answer created no problem.) What would I use this study for? Was I going to write a book? Did I know so-and-so, who had been there two years ago and done medical examinations?

I expected them to confer with one another or ask me to come back when they had decided if they would allow me to conduct the study. Instead, the minister, who was clearly in charge, simply said, "Today is a holiday for us. Can you start tomorrow?"

And so, for the next month I took part in my personal version of fieldwork—taking fingerprints, recording family relationships, observing colony life, and getting to know the Hutterites of this and one other Canadian Bruderhof (Park 1979; Figure 1.3).

FIGURE 1.3

Author (*right*) and Hutterite informant. I already had the beard, but it was suggested that I keep it so that I would look more familiar to the Hutterite children.

What exactly had brought me 1,300 miles from my university to the northern plains, to this isolated community of people whose way of life has changed little over the past 475 years and whose lifestyle and philosophy differ so much from those of North Americans in general? Essentially, it was the same thing that takes anthropologists to such locations as the highlands of New Guinea, the caves of the Pyrenees, and the street corners of New York City: the desire to learn something about the nature of the human species.

In my case, I was pursuing an interest I had developed early in graduate school—to study the processes of evolution and how they affect humans. I was curious about two of these processes: gene flow and genetic drift (see Chapter 4 for details). Both topics had been described half a century earlier, but their workings and importance, especially with regard to living human populations, were still poorly understood.

To examine the actions of these processes on human populations and to determine their roles in human evolution, I needed to find a human group with a few special characteristics. The group had to (1) be genetically isolated, (2) be fairly small as a whole but with large families, and (3) consist of individual populations that resulted from the splitting of earlier populations.

The Hutterites exhibited all these characteristics. I discovered them through library research on genetically isolated groups. My opportunity to study them was greatly enhanced by a stroke of luck. A fellow graduate student was the daughter of the wheat farmer and his wife who became my "public relations advisors."

A Hawaiian in Connecticut

Exactly twenty years after my fieldwork with the Hutterites, I found myself standing over an open grave in an old cemetery in the wooded hills of northwest Connecticut. Our team of anthropologists was hoping to find the remains of a native Hawaiian who had been buried here in 1818 and who was now, after 175 years, going home.

A few weeks earlier, Nick Bellantoni, the Connecticut State Archaeologist (and a former student of mine), had called me with a fascinating story. In 1808 a young Hawaiian named Opukaha'ia (pronounced *oh-poo-kah-hah-ee'-ah*) escaped the tribal warfare that had killed his family by swimming out to a Yankee whaling vessel, where he was taken on board as a cabin boy. Two years later, he ended up at Yale University in New Haven, Connecticut. He took the name Henry, converted to Christianity, and became a Congregational minister who helped build a missionary school in Cornwall, Connecticut. His dream was to return to Hawai'i and to take his new faith to the people there (see his portrait in Figure 1.6).

Sadly, Henry's dream was never realized. He died in a typhoid epidemic in 1818 at the age of 26, but his vision inspired the missionary movement that was to change the history of the Hawaiian Islands forever. His grave in Cornwall became a shrine both for the people of his adopted land and for visiting Hawaiians, who would leave offerings atop his platform-style headstone (Figure 1.4).

Nearly two centuries after his death, a living relative of Henry's had a dream that she would honor Henry's final wish to return to his native land. After almost a year of raising funds and making the necessary arrangements, her dream was to come true. And this is where anthropology comes in.

Old New England cemeteries tended to be inexact in the placement of headstones relative to the bodies buried beneath them, and the acidic New England soil is unkind to organic remains. Both logically and legally,

FIGURE 1.4
Grave of Henry Opukaha'ia.

this was a job for the state archaeologist, and Nick wanted my help in recovering and identifying whatever remains we might be lucky enough to find. He also wanted my help, it turned out, in moving several tons of stone.

Henry's tomb had been carefully and lovingly assembled by the people of Cornwall. They had placed the inscribed headstone on a pedestal of fieldstone and mortar. We dismantled this with care, labeling each stone and diagramming its position, since it was to be rebuilt in Hawai'i by a stonemason. Under the pedestal and going down about 3 feet into the ground, we uncovered three more layers of fieldstone, which acted as a foundation for the monument and protection for the coffin and the remains we hoped were still below. When all the stones had been removed and we were into a layer of sandy soil, Nick worked alone, delicately scraping away the dirt inch by inch (Figure 1.5).

Late on the second day of our excavation, the remnants of the coffin came into view. In fact, the wooden coffin itself had long since decayed. All that was left was the dark stain of its outline in the soil. We began to despair of finding much else, but an hour later Nick's trowel grazed

FIGURE 1.5
Nick Bellantoni excavating the grave of Henry Opukaha'ia. The pattern on the floor of the excavation marks the coffin outline.

something hard, and in a few minutes the apparent remains of Henry Opukaha'ia saw the light of day for the first time in 175 years.

We soon learned that the skeleton was virtually complete. But was it *Henry*? As Nick slowly freed each bone from the soil and handed it up to me (see chapter-opener photograph), we recorded it and compared it with what we knew of Henry from written descriptions and a single portrait. The skeleton was clearly that of a male and, at first glance, conformed to that of a person in his late 20s of about the right size. Henry had been described as being "a little under 6 feet," and the long bones of the arms and legs appeared to be just a bit shorter than mine (I'm 6 feet 1 inch), though much more robust. The skull, however, confirmed our identification. As the dirt was brushed away, the face of Henry Opukaha'ia emerged, the very image of his portrait. (The family has requested that, for religious reasons, photographs of Henry's remains not be published.)

FIGURE 1.6
Reverend David Hirano, from Hawai'i, speaks over the remains of Henry Opukaha'ia at his "homegoing" celebration in Cornwall, Connecticut. The *koa*-wood coffin, *ti* leaves, and flowered *lei* all have symbolic meaning in Hawaiian culture.

We spent two more days with the bones, this time in the garage of a Hartford funeral home. We cleaned, photographed, measured, and described each bone. Finally, we placed each bone in its proper anatomical position in spaces cut into heavy foam rubber that lined the bottom of a *koa*-wood coffin, specially made and shipped from Hawai'i. The following Sunday, we attended a memorial service in Cornwall, and then Henry's remains began their long journey back home (Figure 1.6).

WHAT IS BIOLOGICAL ANTHROPOLOGY?

My experiences as a biological anthropologist range from examining the esoteric detail of evolutionary theory to using my knowledge of the human skeleton for a very personal endeavor. These are just two examples of the many things that biological anthropologists do.

Defining Anthropology

Biological anthropology (or **bioanthropology** or **physical anthropology**) needs to be defined within the context of anthropology as a whole, and doing this is both simple and complex. **Anthropology,** in general, is defined as the study of the human **species.** Simply put, anthropologists study the human species as any zoologist would study an animal species. Using a **holistic** approach, we look into every aspect of the biology of our subject—genetics, anatomy, physiology, behavior, environment, adaptations, and evolutionary history—stressing the interrelationships among these aspects.

The holistic approach is the hallmark of anthropology. We understand that all the facets of our species—our biology, our behavior, our past, and our present—interact to make us what we are. But some topics are so complex that they need to be studied separately—just as you may be taking courses in history, economics, psychology, art, anatomy, and so on. What anthropologists do, though, is seek the connections among these subjects, for in real life they are not absolutely separate.

But here's where it gets complicated. The most characteristic feature of our species' behavior is **culture,** and cultural behavior is not programmed in our genes, as is, for example, much of the behavior of birds and virtually all of the behavior of ants. Human culture is learned. We have a biological potential for cultural behavior in general, but exactly *how* we behave comes to us through all our experiences. Take language, for example. All humans are born with the ability to learn a language, but it is the language spoken by our respective families and our broader cultures that determines what language we will speak.

Moreover, cultural knowledge involves not just specific facts but also ideas, concepts, generalizations, and abstractions. For example, you were able to speak your native language fairly fluently before you were ever formally taught the particulars of its grammar. You did this by making your own generalizations from the raw data you heard and the rules they followed, that is, from the speech of others and from trying to make yourself understood. Even now when you speak, you are applying those generalizations to new situations. And each situation—every conversation you have, every essay you write, every book you read—is a new situation.

In addition, because culture exists in the context of human social interactions, it must be shared among members of a social group. The complexity of cultural ideas requires this sharing to involve symbols—agreed-upon representations of concepts and abstractions. Human language, of course, is symbolic, as are many visual aspects of our cultures.

biological anthropology
A subfield of anthropology that studies humans as a biocultural species.

bioanthropology
Another name for biological anthropology.

physical anthropology
The traditional name for biological anthropology.

anthropology The biocultural study of the human species.

species A group of organisms that can produce fertile offspring among themselves but not with members of other groups.

holistic Assuming an interrelationship among the parts of a subject.

culture Ideas and behaviors that are learned and shared. Nonbiological means of adaptation.

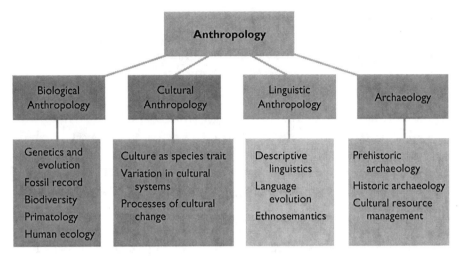

FIGURE 1.7
Major subfields of anthropology with some of their topics. The topics of each subfield may be applied to various social issues (see Chapter 15); this is collectively called *applied anthropology.*

In short, culture is highly variable and flexible. It differs from society to society, from environment to environment, and from one time period to another. It even differs in its details from one individual to another. We continually modify our cultural behaviors to fit the unique circumstances of our lives.

So another characteristic of the field of anthropology is its **biocultural** approach. That is, anthropology seeks to describe and explain the interactions between our nature as a biological species and the cultural behavior that is our species' most striking and important trait. We will encounter many examples of these interactions as we continue.

But all these different dimensions make the study of the human species complex and challenging, and so anthropology, the discipline that takes on this challenge, is typically divided into a number of subfields (Figure 1.7). Biological anthropology looks at our species from a biological point of view. This includes all the topics covered in this book. **Cultural anthropology** is the study of culture as a characteristic of our species and of the variation in cultural expression among human groups. This includes human language, although sometimes **linguistic anthropology** is considered a separate subfield. **Archaeology** is the study of the human cultural past and the reconstruction of past cultural systems. It also involves the techniques used to recover, preserve, and interpret the material remains of the past. The theoretical basis for these activities is the study of the relationship of material culture with cultural systems as a whole.

biocultural Focusing on the interaction of biology and culture.

cultural anthropology A subfield of anthropology that focuses on human cultural behavior and cultural systems and the variation in cultural expression among human groups.

linguistic anthropology A subfield of anthropology that studies language as a human characteristic and attempts to explain the differences among languages and the relationship between a language and the society that uses it.

archaeology A subfield of anthropology that studies the human cultural past and the reconstruction of past cultural systems.

The Specialties of Bioanthropology

Each subfield has many specialties. For biological anthropology, these specialties are best expressed in terms of the questions we seek to answer about human biology:

1. What are the biological characteristics that define the human species? How do our genes code for these characteristics? Just how much do genes contribute to our traits? How much are traits shaped by the environment? How does evolution work, and how does it apply to us? (These were the questions I was pursuing in my study of the Hutterites.)

2. What is the physical record of our evolution? This is the specialty referred to as **paleoanthropology,** the study of human fossils based on our knowledge of skeletal biology, or **osteology.**

3. What sort of biological diversity do we see in our species today? How did it evolve? What do the variable traits mean for other aspects of our lives? What do they *not* mean?

4. What can we learn about the biology of our close relatives, the non-human **primates,** and what can it tell us about ourselves? This specialty is called **primatology.**

5. What do we know about **human ecology,** the relationships between humans and their environments?

6. How can we apply all this knowledge to matters of current concern? This is often called **applied anthropology** and can refer to all the subfields. (The exhumation of Henry Opukahaʻia is an example.)

Individual biological anthropologists undertake numerous and diverse studies. I took fingerprints of members of a centuries-old Christian group to learn something about the processes of evolution that have affected our species. Paleoanthropologist Donald Johanson led the team that discovered and identified the famous fossil "Lucy," a 3.2-million-year-old human ancestor. Paleontologist Elwyn Simons studies fossils of nonhuman primates that go even further back in evolutionary time—to the dawn of the apes more than 30 million years ago. Other anthropologists study living nonhuman primates. Shirley Strum, Barbara Smuts, and Linda Fedigan, for example, have all observed troops of baboons to understand what their behavior can tell us about our own.

Clyde Snow is a **forensic anthropologist.** He applies his knowledge of the human skeleton to solving crimes and identifying missing persons. He has worked to identify the remains of death-squad victims in Argentina

paleoanthropology A specialty that studies the human fossil record.

osteology The study of the structure, function, and evolution of the skeleton.

primates Large-brained, mostly tree-dwelling mammals with three-dimensional color vision and grasping hands. Humans are primates.

primatology A specialty that studies nonhuman primates.

human ecology A specialty that studies the relationships between humans and their environments.

applied anthropology Anthropology used to address current practical problems and concerns.

forensic anthropologist A scientist who applies anthropology to legal matters.

and has tried (so far without success) to locate the bones of Butch Cassidy and the Sundance Kid in Bolivia.

Melvin Konner has examined the lifestyles of contemporary **hunter-gatherers,** including their diet and exercise, to show how those lifestyles differ (mostly for the better) from those of people in industrial societies. And Jim McKenna has studied infant sleep behavior across cultures to determine whether sleeping apart from or with (co-sleeping) their parents is better for babies.

We'll discuss these people and their studies, and many more, as we survey the field of bioanthropology. As we do, keep in mind that what connects these varied activities is their focus on *learning about human beings as a biocultural species*.

The studies of bioanthropologists are also connected in that they are all scientific. In many cases, they may not seem to fit the common conception of science. Most anthropologists don't wear white lab coats or work with test tubes and chemicals. Many anthropologists study things that can't be directly observed in nature or re-created in the lab because they happened in the past. But bioanthropology *is* a science, just as much as chemistry, physics, and biology. We'll see how this is so, and we'll also look at some nonscientific ways in which people try to understand their world.

BIOANTHROPOLOGY AND SCIENCE

A popular image of a scientist is that of a walking encyclopedia. Science is often seen as fact collecting. While it's fair to say that scientists know a lot of facts, so do a lot of nonscientists.

Facts are certainly important to science. They are the raw material of science, the data scientists use, collected through observation and experimentation. But the goal of science is to relate and unify facts in order to generate, eventually, broad principles known as **theories. Science,** in other words, is a method of inquiry, a way of answering questions about the world. But how does science work? Is science the only valid and logical method for explaining the world around us?

Science

The world is full of things that need explaining. We might wonder about the behavior of a bird, the origin of the stars in the night sky, the identity of a fossil skeleton, the social interaction of students in a college classroom,

hunter-gatherers Societies that rely on naturally occurring sources of food.

theory A well-supported general idea that explains a large set of factual patterns and predicts other patterns.

science The method of inquiry that requires the generation, testing, and acceptance or rejection of hypotheses.

or the ritual warfare of a society in highland New Guinea. As people, we strive to understand such phenomena, to know why and how these things occur. As scientists, we must answer these questions according to a special set of rules—the **scientific method.**

The Scientific Method Involves a Cycle of Steps The most basic step of the scientific method is asking the questions we wish to answer or describing the observations we wish to explain. We then look for patterns, connections, and associations so that we can generate educated guesses as to possible explanations. These educated guesses are called **hypotheses.** In other words, we try to formulate a *general* explanatory principle that will account for the *specific* pieces of real data we have observed and want to explain. This process of reasoning is called **induction.**

Next comes the essence—indeed the defining characteristic—of science. We must attempt to either support or refute our hypothesis by testing it. Tests may take many forms, depending on what we are trying to explain, but basically we reverse the process of induction and go from the general back to the specific by making predictions: *If* our general hypothesis is correct, *then* what other specific things should we observe? This process is called **deduction.** For example, we look for

Repetition: Does the same phenomenon occur over and over?

Universality: Does the phenomenon occur under all conditions? If we vary some aspect of the situation, will the phenomenon still occur? How might different situations change the phenomenon?

Explanations for exceptions: Can we account for cases where the phenomenon doesn't appear to occur?

New data: Does new information support or contradict our hypothesis?

If we find one piece of evidence that conclusively refutes our hypothesis, the hypothesis is disproved, at least for the moment. (But even then, the hypothesis may not be dismissed entirely. Newton's hypothesis that light consists of particles was discounted for centuries until twentieth-century quantum mechanics showed that light is, in fact, particles that have the properties of waves.) But if a hypothesis passes every test we put it to, we elevate it to a *working hypothesis* and use it as a basis for further induction and testing. Notice that I didn't say we *prove* a hypothesis. Good science is skeptical, always looking for new evidence, always open to and, indeed, inviting change. The best we should honestly say about most hypotheses is that, so far, no evidence has been found that *disproves* them.

When, through this process, we have generated an integrated body of ideas, we have a theory. In science, *theory* is a positive term. Theories are

scientific method The process of conducting scientific inquiry.

hypotheses Educated guesses to explain natural phenomena.

induction Developing a general explanation from specific observations.

deduction Suggesting specific data that would be found if a hypothesis were true.

called *theories* because they are general ideas that explain a large number of phenomena and are themselves made up of interacting and well-supported hypotheses. All the facts of biology, for instance, make sense within the general theory of evolution—that all life has a common ancestry and that living forms change over time and give rise to new forms by various natural processes.

Some Common Misconceptions about Science   A theory is not the end of the scientific method. No theory is complete. For example, some force we call *gravity* exists, and we know so much about it that we can accurately predict phenomena—from the motion of stars and planets to the trajectory of a spacecraft. But we still don't understand how gravity works and how it originated and separated from the other forces of nature. In other words, we still have hypotheses to test to arrive at a complete theory of gravity.

Another popular misconception of science is that it studies only visible, tangible, present-day things—chemicals, living organisms, planets and stars. But notice that gravity is neither visible nor tangible. We can't see gravity, but we know it exists because all our deductive predictions support its existence. We see gravity work every time we drop an object or jump up in the air and come back down to earth instead of flying off into space. We logically predict that if gravity is the property of objects with mass, the bigger the object the more its gravity. We saw this clearly when we watched the astronauts walk around on the moon; they were literally lighter (about one-sixth their earthly weight) because the moon, being smaller than the earth, has less gravity. We also see the increased effects of the gravity of very massive objects (Figure 1.8). We can even explain exceptions *within the context of our general idea*. The reason a helium-filled balloon seems to violate gravity can be explained by the existing theory of gravity: helium is less dense than the surrounding air and so responds relatively less to the earth's gravity. In other words, the helium is lighter than the surrounding air and so a slightly greater pressure on the bottom of the balloon than on the top causes the balloon to rise.

Similarly, past events can't be seen or touched. They can't be experimented on directly or repeated exactly. The evolution of plants and animals is an example. But again, we know that evolution occurs because the theory has passed all our tests. The theory of evolution explains observations of the real world. We have observed everything we predicted we would *if* evolution occurred. (We'll look more closely at how science has generated and supported the theory of evolution in Chapter 3.)

I noted earlier that scientists may begin their investigations at any step in the cycle of the scientific method. For instance, we might have

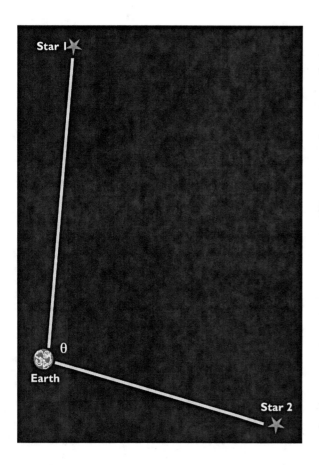

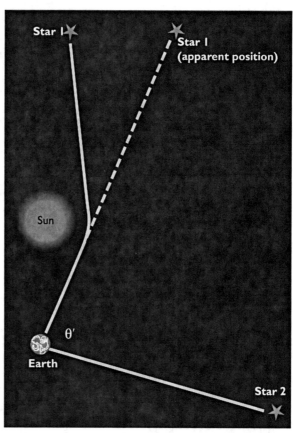

FIGURE 1.8
Light bent by gravity. Einstein predicted in 1905 that a strong gravitational field could bend light. His prediction was verified in 1919, when light from stars that should have been blocked by the sun could be seen during a solar eclipse. The effect is greatly exaggerated in these drawings.

a flash of inspiration for some overarching concept that might explain many different phenomena. In other words, we might dream up a potential theory. We then, of course, would have to go through all the other steps: making observations, generating individual hypotheses, and testing those hypotheses. As an example, Albert Einstein was pondering the nature of light waves when he came up with the idea of the equivalence of energy and mass, his famous formula $E = mc^2$. It was only later that this relationship was experimentally verified and all its implications and applications were understood.

Science Is Conducted in a Cultural Context   We must acknowledge that scientists are members of their societies and participants in their cultures. Thus, science—as objective as we try to make it—is always constrained by what we already know, by what we still don't know, by the technology available to us to gather and test data, by existing theories, and even by certain influential social or cultural trends.

For example, I remember back in the mid-1950s, when one of my elementary school teachers pointed out that the east coast of South America and the west coast of Africa seemed to potentially fit together like a giant jigsaw puzzle (Figure 1.9). Of course, she had said, there's no

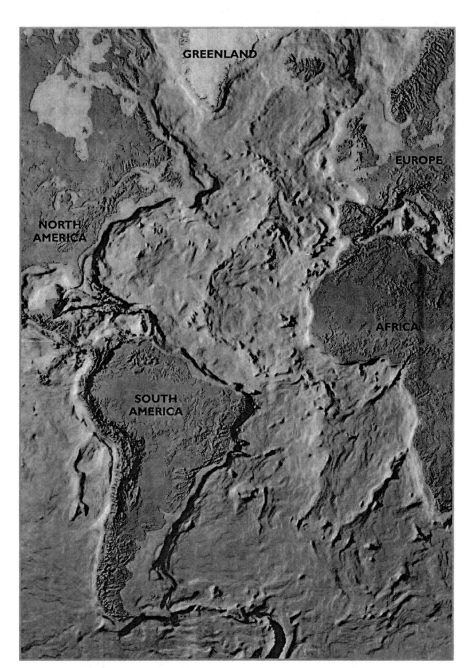

FIGURE 1.9
Topographic map of the Atlantic Ocean floor showing the correlating outlines of the edges of the Eastern and Western Hemispheres. Also shown is the Mid-Atlantic Ridge—evidence for the plate tectonics that pushed the once-connected continents apart.

way the continents could move around, so it must just be a coincidence. In fact, she was reflecting our scientific knowledge of the time. There was plenty of geological and fossil evidence suggesting that the continents had moved around, but although the idea of continental drift had been proposed in 1912, there was no mechanism to explain it. Beginning in the 1960s, however, new technologies gave us new evidence that provided such a mechanism. We now have a well-verified theory of continental drift by the process of plate tectonics.

An interesting example of an influential social trend comes from a hypothesized explanation for the famous Salem witch trials in Massachusetts in 1692, when a group of young girls accused some adults of witchcraft, with the result that twenty people were executed. The hypothesis suggested that the people of Salem had consumed bread made from grains tainted with ergot, a fungus that contains alkaloids, some of which are derivatives of lysergic acid, which in turn is used in the synthesis of the hallucinogenic drug LSD. In other words, maybe the young girls who made the witchcraft accusations were inadvertently having an "acid trip." Not surprisingly, this explanation arose and found popularity in the 1960s, a period associated in part with the so-called drug culture. Although the idea showed up as recently as 2001 in a public-television documentary, there is no evidence to support it.

These examples show us why scientific skepticism is so important and why we should always question and re-examine even our most well-supported ideas. Science answers questions about our lives and about the world in which we live; however, for an answer to be defined as scientific, it must be testable—and must be tested. Put another way, it must be possible to find data that could *disprove* it. For an answer to be accepted, it must pass all tests and be refuted by none.

Belief Systems

For most human societies throughout most of our species' history, many questions could not be addressed scientifically. Some questions about the world, even in a technologically complex society such as ours, remain beyond the scope of science. Scientific inquiry, as powerful and important as it is, doesn't answer everything.

Science does not, for example, tell us how to behave. In our society, we treat medical matters scientifically. But science does not, and cannot, inform us how best to apply medical knowledge. Who should practice medicine? How are medical practitioners trained and administered by society? How should they be compensated? What should their relationship be with their patients? Is everyone equally entitled to medical care? Society and the medical profession answer these questions through laws and regulations. One version of the Hippocratic oath (there are several forms) taken by doctors says, in part, "I will not permit considerations of religion, nationality, race, party politics or social standing to intervene between my duty and my patient."

And there are questions that can never be answered by science—matters such as the meaning of life, the existence of a higher power, the proper social relationships among people within a society, and the purpose of one's own life. All these sorts of questions are addressed by **belief systems**—religions, philosophies, ethics, morals, and laws. Belief systems differ from science in that they cannot be tested, cannot be disproved. Their truths are taken on faith, and that, of course, is the source of their power. They provide stable bases for our behavior, for explanations of what is beyond our science, and for the broad, existential questions of life.

Belief systems change, but they change only when *we* decide to change them, either as a society or as individuals. Two of us with opposite views on the existence of a supreme being could debate the issue endlessly, but no scientific test could support or refute either view. If I were to change my mind on the matter, it would be because of a personal decision. A supreme being is not to be found in a test tube or seen through a telescope.

Belief systems don't apply only to these big questions. I had a friend in graduate school from a West African society that is polygynous—men may have several wives. Having more than one wife is normal in his society, whereas in mine, one wife (at least one at a time) is the norm. We discussed the pros and cons of these two systems at length one day, but we never, of course, arrived at any "answer." His belief was the norm for his society, as was mine for my society. We each took it on faith that this was so.

Although we often perceive science and belief systems as being eternally and inevitably at odds with one another, nothing could be further from the truth. Indeed, conflicts do arise when a belief system asserts scientific validity for a claim that is not scientifically valid or verifiable (see Chapter 5). But it should be apparent that for a society to function, it needs both scientific knowledge and beliefs, because neither by itself addresses all the questions.

belief systems Ideas that are taken on faith and cannot be scientifically tested.

Contemporary Reflections

Is Evolution a Fact, a Theory, or Just a Hypothesis?

It may surprise you that the answer is "all of the above." Evolution, as a broad topic, incorporates theory, fact, *and* hypothesis. This is because the scientific method is not a nice, neat, linear series of steps from first observation to final all-encompassing theory. Rather, science works in a cycle, and the inductive and deductive reasoning of science is applied constantly to the different aspects of the same general subject. Data and hypotheses are always being re-examined, and each theory itself becomes a new observation to be questioned, tested, explained, and possibly changed.

A theory is a well-supported idea that explains a set of observed phenomena. Evolution is a theory in that all our observations of life on earth—fossils, the geological formations in which they are found, and the biology of living creatures—make sense and find explanation within the concept of evolution, the idea that living things change through time and that organisms are related as in a huge branching tree, with existing species giving rise to new species.

Moreover, there is so much evidence in support of evolution that this tried-and-tested theory may reasonably be considered a fact. Of course, new data could conceivably change that, but with an idea as well supported as evolution, it is highly unlikely. A good analogy is the accepted fact that the earth revolves around the sun and not, as people thought for so long, the other way around. But how do we *know* the earth revolves around the sun? It certainly appears upon daily observation to do just the opposite. We accept the heliocentric (sun-centered) theory because there is so much data in its support. It makes so much sense and explains so many other phenomena that we consider it a fact and take it for granted, never giving it much thought on a regular basis. I would be very surprised to read in tomorrow's newspaper that some new evidence refuted the idea. Similarly, that evolution occurs and accounts for the nature of life on earth is, for all intents and purposes, a fact.

But that fact poses more questions. A big one (the one that confronted Darwin) is *how* evolution takes place. The fact of evolution now becomes a new observation that requires explanation through the generation of new hypotheses and the subsequent testing and retesting of those hypotheses. Darwin proposed a mechanism he called *natural selection* and then, over many years, examined this hypothesis against real-world data. The mechanism of natural selection is now so well supported that we call it, too, a fact.

But an overall explanation for how evolution works—a theory to explain the observed fact of evolution—is far from complete. We know that mechanisms in addition to natural selection contribute to evolution. The relative importance of all these mechanisms is still being debated. The broad picture of evolution—the "shape" of the family tree of living things—is a matter of much discussion. The specific genetic processes behind all evolutionary change are really only beginning to be revealed as new technologies are letting us look at the very code of life. In other words, we are still examining hypotheses to account for how evolution takes place and for what happened in evolutionary history.

Evolution—like any broad scientific idea—involves a complex and interacting web of facts, hypotheses, and theories. It is the never-ending nature of scientific inquiry that can make science so frustrating—but also so exciting and so important in the modern world.

SUMMARY

Anthropology is the biocultural study of the human species. Cultural anthropology studies human culture, cultural systems, and their variation. Our species' most characteristic feature today is our cultural behavior, which is expressed in a great variety of ways among different societies.

The majority of human cultural systems that ever existed did so in the past and so have left us only meager physical remains of their presence and nature. Archaeology recovers and interprets these remains.

Biological anthropology studies the human species the way biology studies any species, examining our biological characteristics, our evolution, our variation, our relationship with our environment, and our behavior, including our ability to have culture.

Bioanthropology, as a scientific discipline, asks questions about the human species and then attempts to answer them by proposing hypotheses and by testing those hypotheses, looking both for evidence in their support and for anything that would refute them.

Scientific knowledge is important for any society, but it must be mediated by the nonscientific values of belief systems—the untestable ideas of philosophy, law, and religion that are taken on faith. Societies need both science and belief systems, interacting in harmony, to fully function.

QUESTIONS FOR FURTHER THOUGHT

1. Anthropologists have special responsibilities when studying other human beings. What sorts of issues do you think I had to take into account when conducting my research among the Hutterites? What issues would have been involved in the exhumation of Henry Opukaha'ia? Consider another culture you are familiar with, and imagine what particular issues would be involved in studying it as an anthropologist.

2. Because of anthropology's wide scope of interests and its overlap with other scholarly disciplines, anthropologists have sometimes been described as "jacks of all trades and masters of none." How would you respond to this?

3. Our impression that science and belief systems are naturally at odds with one another comes largely from cases in which the two areas are forced into conflict—when, for example, a religious belief is said

to refute a scientific idea or a scientific idea is said to undermine a belief. Can you give an example of such a conflict? How would you resolve the conflict, given what you now understand about these two areas of inquiry?

KEY TERMS

biological anthropology

bioanthropology

physical anthropology

anthropology

species

holistic

culture

biocultural

cultural anthropology

linguistic anthropology

archaeology

paleoanthropology

osteology

primates

primatology

human ecology

applied anthropology

forensic anthropologist

hunter-gatherers

theory

science

scientific method

hypotheses

induction

deduction

belief systems

SUGGESTED READINGS

For more personal experiences of biological anthropologists, see part 1 of my *Biological Anthropology: An Introductory Reader*, sixth edition. *(Complete publication details of the suggested readings appear in the "References.")*

For more information on the Hutterites, see John Hostetler's *Hutterite Society*.

For a longer discussion of the nature of science and the scientific method, see Kenneth L. Feder's *Frauds, Myths, and Mysteries: Science and Pseudoscience in Archaeology*, sixth edition, and for even more detail see *Understanding Scientific Reasoning*, by Ronald N. Giere. The relationship between science and belief systems is nicely covered by John Maynard Smith's article, "Science and Myth," in the November 1984 issue of *Natural History*. A more philosophical discussion can be found in *Rocks of Ages: Science and Religion in the Fullness of Life*, by Stephen Jay Gould.

The field of anthropology in general is covered in my *Introducing Anthropology: An Integrated Approach,* fourth edition, and in a collection of contemporary articles edited by Aaron Podolefsky and Peter Brown, *Applying Anthropology: An Introductory Reader,* fifth edition.

I've written an extended version of the story of Henry Opukaha'ia, "The Homegoing," which appears in *Lessons from the Past: An Introductory Reader in Archaeology,* by Kenneth L. Feder. See also "The Life, Death, Archaeological Exhumation and Reinterment of Opukaha'ia (Henry Obookiah), 1792–1818," by Nicholas Bellantoni, Roger Thompson, David Cooke, Michael Park, and Cynthia Trayling in the Fall 2007 issue of *Connecticut History.*

For an update on the Hutterites, see "Solace at Surprise Creek" by William Albert Allard in the June 2006 *National Geographic.*

CHAPTER

The Evolution of Evolution

One touch of Darwin makes the whole world kin.
—George Bernard Shaw

Evolution and its application to the human species—how we descended from nonhuman ancestors, how we have changed over time into modern *Homo sapiens*, and how we are still changing—is a central theme of bioanthropology. As noted in Chapter 1, the *fact* of evolution is well supported by scientific examination—the idea has passed every scientific test applied to it. Scientists, however, are still debating the details of evolution and refining the *theory* that explains exactly how evolution operates. It took some time, though, for the scientific method to be applied to this idea.

How did our knowledge of the history of living organisms move from the realm of belief systems to the realm of science?

How did the scientific evidence for evolution develop?

"ON THE SHOULDERS OF GIANTS": EXPLAINING THE CHANGING EARTH

The Englishman Charles Darwin (1809–1882) is usually, and correctly, associated with our understanding of biological evolution (Figure 2.1). He is also popularly given credit for the very idea of evolution and for explaining and therefore proving it. This, however, is not entirely correct. Like any great scientific accomplishment, Darwin's was based on the work of many who came before him. He stood, as Isaac Newton said of himself, "on the shoulders of giants." Darwin's genius was in being able to take massive amounts of data and assorted existing ideas and, using an imagination possessed by few humans, put them all together into a logical, cohesive theory

FIGURE 2.1
Portrait of Charles Darwin in 1869 by famed photographer Julia Margaret Cameron.

evolution   Change through time; here, with reference to biological species.

that made sense of the world and that could be examined by the methods of science.

The idea of **evolution** is simple enough: species of living things change over time, and under the right circumstances this change can produce new species of living organisms from existing ones. This idea was not new in Darwin's time. Anaximander, a Greek philosopher and astronomer of the sixth century BC, proposed that humans had arisen from other forms of life. He incorrectly thought we arose directly from fish, but rather than explaining his idea in supernatural terms, he used reasoning to explore the question of how animals survive in their environments, a question that would form the cornerstone of Darwin's idea (Harris, 1981).

The Biblical Context

Many others over the next two thousand years also contemplated the origins of living things, but the modern story of evolutionary theory really began in seventeenth-century Europe, where the influence of the Bible was felt in all aspects of life, including science. Specifically, the ancient Judeo-Christian creation story—Adam and Eve, the Garden of Eden, the Flood and Noah's ark—was generally considered to be literally true. Thus, it was thought that the entire universe was created by supernatural processes over a period of six days and that, except for the matter of the great flood, the earth and its inhabitants were pretty much the same now as they were when created. One scholar, Irish archbishop James Ussher (1581–1656), used the assumption of biblical truth, as well as certain historical records, to help him calculate the date of the Creation and thus the age of the earth. In 1650 he reckoned that the Creation began at noon on Sunday, October 23, in the year 4004 BC. The earth was thus about 6,000 years old.

The literal interpretation of the Bible, in turn, was probably influenced by two old but pervasive ideas that go back to Plato and Aristotle, Greek philosophers of the fourth and fifth centuries BC. One idea is called *essentialism*—the notion that there is an ideal, or essential, form of every natural entity and that the variations we see are largely inexact copies of the ideal. Applied to biblical creation, essentialism promoted the idea that one ideal form of each living thing had been created and that the present-day variations—breeds of animals or races of people—are mostly departures from those ideals.

The second idea is called the *great chain of being*. It says that since there is an ideal, the various forms of things are not just a list of equals but are arranged in a ladder or chain, from least complex to most complex and from least perfect to most perfect. There are two different creation stories in Genesis, one in which humans are created last, after all the animals (Genesis 1), and one in which humans are created first (Genesis 2). Whichever order one accepts, however, there is the clear implication that humans are the most perfect form of creation. As we will see, these two philosophical ideas would also have a strong influence on the later science of evolution, even to the present day.

The Framework of "Natural Philosophy"

Dependence on the Bible for knowledge of the natural world was not to last. About the time Ussher was making his calculations, others were beginning to seek knowledge about the earth from the earth itself. What these "natural scientists," or "natural philosophers," saw forced them to reconsider what seemed to be the obvious lessons from the book of Genesis.

The Evidence for Change Accumulates   Another seventeenth-century scientist, Robert Hooke (1635–1703) recognized **fossils** of plants and animals—once thought to be mere quirks of nature—as the remains of creatures that had become extinct or that still existed but in different form. Living things, in other words, had changed.

Moreover, Hooke attributed these extinctions and changes to the fact that the earth itself had been continually undergoing change since the Creation. He even proposed a naturalistic explanation for Noah's flood; it was, he said, probably caused by earthquakes. So, since the earth is in a continual state of change, so are its inhabitants, changing as their environments are altered or becoming extinct if that alteration is too great.

Evidence for this idea of a changing earth came from the examination of the layers of rock and soil below the earth's present surface. These layers are the earth's **strata** (singular, *stratum*), and their study is called **stratigraphy** (Figure 2.2). One of the earliest scientists to discuss this was a Dane, Nicholas Steno (1638–1686). He suggested that the strata represented layers of sediments deposited by water in a *sequence*, the lower layers earlier and the higher layers later. The nature of the rock and soil of each stratum, and its fossil contents, showed the natural conditions at the time the stratum was deposited: what creatures existed, whether the area was under sea or on land, and so on. It became clear that neither the earth nor its inhabitants were stable and unchanging.

Catastrophism Was an Attempt to Reconcile the Evidence with a Biblical Time Frame   Steno and Hooke, however, still believed in a

fossils Remains of life-forms of the past.

strata Layers; here, the layers of rock and soil under the earth's surface.

stratigraphy The study of the earth's strata.

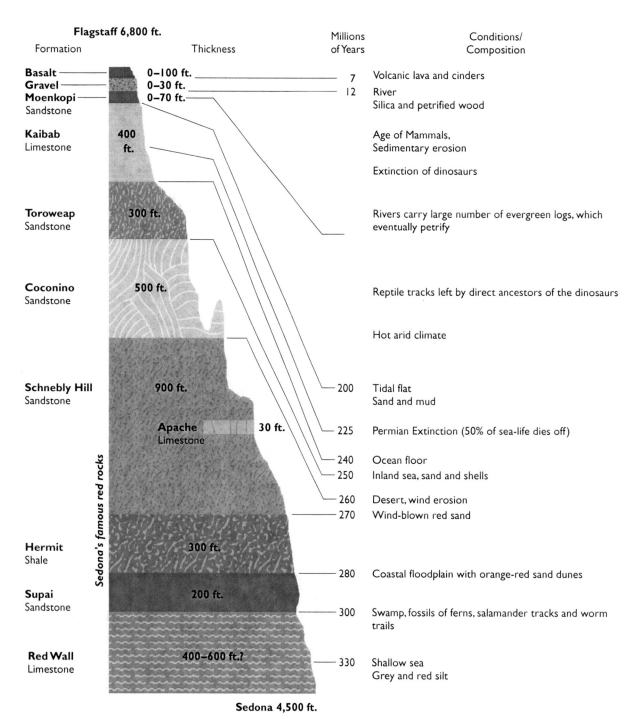

FIGURE 2.2
This geological cross section of the area around Sedona and Flagstaff, Arizona, shows the variation in composition and thickness of the strata and some of the events represented in those strata.

biblical chronology. To Steno, the water-deposited layers of the stratigraphic sequences represented two events—the original water-covered earth on which God created land and plants and animals (Genesis 1) and the waters of Noah's flood (Genesis 6–8). The geological record, however, shows a vast amount of change, and the Bible provides only 6,000 years of the earth's history. So much change in such a short time, thought Steno and Hooke, required the presence of global catastrophic events such as earthquakes and volcanoes. Steno and Hooke and others who subscribed to this explanation are often referred to as **catastrophists.**

One well-known proponent of catastrophism was the French naturalist Georges Cuvier (1769–1832). Cuvier thought that a "prototype" of each creature had been created and that it and its environment had been planned to fit each other. The influence of essentialism is obvious here. Cuvier believed that differences in climate could bring about alterations in these prototypes but that such changes were limited, producing minor variations in the created types. He also thought that he could reconstruct the prototypes by using fossil remains of creatures. He compared the fragments of ancient creatures to living ones to try to picture what the whole organism looked like. In so doing, he pioneered the method known as **comparative anatomy,** still used today to infer missing parts of fossil organisms.

But Cuvier also realized that life on earth had undergone major changes. He believed that the entire plan of the Creation had been changed several times by the Creator and that the changes were manifested in a series of global catastrophes that brought about the extinction of existing forms of life and prepared the way for newly created forms. In other words, he accepted that the world had changed but not that it had evolved, and not that new forms of life were modifications of older forms. Moreover, since humans were included only in the latest Creation (although Cuvier did admit that they might have been around before), there was the implication that humans were somehow the Creator's highest, most perfect form of living thing—an idea clearly influenced by the great-chain-of-being concept.

Uniformitarianism Ushers in the Modern Approach Catastrophism enjoyed a degree of popularity because it seemed to reconcile natural evidence with a biblical time frame. But strict catastrophism did not stand up to further scientific observation and examination. The French scholar Comte Georges-Louis Leclerc de Buffon (1707–1788) concluded that although catastrophic events do occur, they are rare and so "have no place in the ordinary course of nature." Instead, the earth's history is mainly explained by "operations *uniformly* repeated, motions which succeed one another without interruption" (emphasis mine). Thus, much of the

catastrophists Those who believe that the history of the earth is explained by a series of global catastrophes, either natural or divine in origin.

comparative anatomy The study of physical features—shared or different—among animal species, used to reconstruct a fossil species from fragmentary remains.

earth's geological history could be explained by normal, everyday, uniform processes—the things taking place before our eyes, such as erosion and deposition of sediments in water. This idea is called **uniformitarianism.** For such processes to account for all the changes recorded in the earth's strata, however, the earth would have to be older than 6,000 years. Buffon was among the first to propose a longer history for the planet.

A Scotsman, James Hutton (1726–1797), elaborated on the idea. Hutton saw the processes of deposition and erosion as part of a self-regulating system: Erosion produced the soil in which plants grew. Plants, in turn, fed animals and humans (for whom, he thought, all this had been created in the first place). New land was continually being formed under the sea from sediments produced by erosion, which would ultimately provide new sources of soil. And so on. Again, such a system would require far more than 6,000 years, and Hutton suggested that the earth was much older. Indeed, he thought it was virtually timeless, having "no vestige of a beginning—no prospect of an end."

The English surveyor and geologist William Smith (1769–1839) formalized the description of the evidence for change in the earth—the strata and their fossil content. Smith, whose work earned him the nickname "Strata," documented the patterns of strata and fossils across England, Wales, and Scotland and produced the first geological map of any area of the world (Figure 2.3).

Charles Lyell (1797–1875), born in Scotland the year Hutton died, expressed an extreme version of uniformitarianism. He advocated, as had Hutton, the uniformity of processes throughout time, that is, that present-day processes are the key to explaining the past. He also believed that the rate of geological change was uniform—slow and steady through countless eons, with no need to invoke global catastrophes.

But he also believed that the earth itself was fairly uniform across time, that the earth has been, and always will be, basically the same. Changes certainly occur, but they occur, said Lyell, just in the details, not in the overall appearance of the earth or in its life-forms. Moreover, these changes occur in great cycles. He thought, for example, that dinosaurs, though extinct at the moment, would eventually reappear.

At this point, it would be a good idea to briefly describe what modern scientific knowledge has to say about these issues. We now agree with the major parts of the uniformitarian position:

1. Processes that formed and changed the earth in the past—as seen in its stratigraphic record—are the same processes that take place in the present.

uniformitarianism The idea that present-day geological processes can also explain the history of the earth.

FIGURE 2.3
William Smith's 1815 map, titled "A Delineation of the Strata of England and Wales, with Part of Scotland . . ." The original, more than 6 by 8 feet, is at the Geological Society of London.

2. By studying the stratigraphic record, we can reconstruct the history of the earth.

3. For known geological processes to account for the changes recorded in the strata, an immense amount of time would have been required; we know now that the earth is about 4.5 billion years old (Figure 2.4).

FIGURE 2.4
Utah's Bryce Canyon shows the results of geological processes, especially the laying down of strata and subsequent erosion, over millions of years.

We also now understand that Lyell was far too restrictive in his idea about uniform rate. Not all processes are slow and steady. Catastrophic events may seem relatively rare to us, but they do take place and have occurred many times during the history of the earth. Even Lyell acknowledged that most are localized events, such as volcanoes and earthquakes that affect the geology and life of a particular area. However, some events are catastrophic on a global scale. At least five major catastrophes have occurred during the 3.5-billion-year history of life on earth—in one case, bringing about the extinction of over 95 percent of the earth's species. The most famous of these cataclysms (though not the biggest) occurred 65 million years ago, when an asteroid collided with the earth and caused such radical environmental change that 75 percent of the world's marine species became extinct, along with many terrestrial species, including the dinosaurs (see Chapter 6). These are not the regular series of biblically associated catastrophes proposed by Steno, Hooke, and Cuvier; rather, these catastrophes occur irregularly and are of completely natural origin. They have, nonetheless, radically altered the history of the planet.

Today we understand that Lyell's idea about the earth changing only in its details and in great cycles is also incorrect. The earth's history is a complex chain of events leading to other events, a continual sequence of changes—major and minor—never to be repeated. The dinosaurs are extinct; they will never return.

Despite what turned out to be some incorrect notions, Lyell's influence was great. Not only did he expand on the work of Hutton and others, he also began the explicit examination of geological data, bringing it fully into the realm of natural science. For example, he attempted to estimate the age of the Mississippi Delta (Figure 2.5). Because the rate of deposition of sediments at the mouth of the river can be measured and because the size of the existing deposit in the delta can be estimated, the time required for the delta to be formed can be reckoned. Assuming a uniform rate of deposition, Lyell

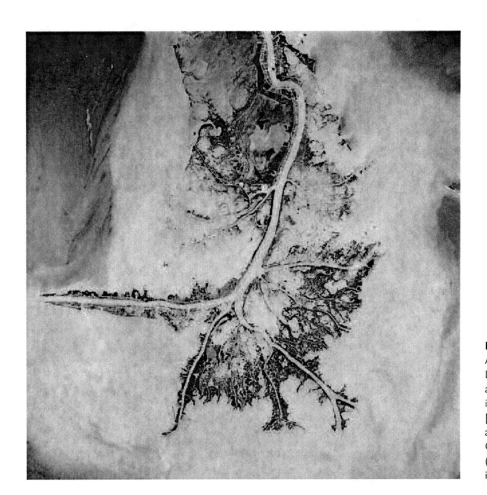

FIGURE 2.5
Aerial view of the Mississippi Delta. By estimating the amount of material deposited in the delta (the delta-shaped [Δ] deposit of sand and soil at the mouth of a river), Charles Lyell concluded (although incorrectly) that it was 100,000 years old.

arrived at an age of about 100,000 years (1873:44–47). (Lyell was incorrect; the delta is not that old. It is only about 7,000 years old. Deposition rates are not constant, nor were existing measurement techniques precise enough.)

Through the work of Hooke, Steno, Hutton, Smith, and Lyell—and many others—the study of the earth shifted from the supernatural to the natural. Scientists sought data about earth's history from the earth itself, not from the presuppositions of belief systems. As a result, by the early nineteenth century, our world was viewed through the interacting perspectives of constant change brought about by observable processes over vast amounts of time.

Lyell put these ideas down in his three-volume *Principles of Geology*, first published between 1830 and 1833. The book was highly influential. It was enthusiastically received by supporters of the uniformitarian approach, strongly criticized by those who continued to explain earth's history as a series of global catastrophes, and pored over by those still examining the data. Among those weighing Lyell's ideas was a young British naturalist, Charles Darwin, who took the first volume of Lyell's book with him as he embarked, in 1831, on a round-the-world voyage of scientific exploration.

"COMMON SENSE AT ITS BEST": EXPLAINING BIOLOGICAL CHANGE

Darwin's Predecessors

The view of life on earth as static and unchanging is exemplified by the work of Carl von Linné (1707–1778), better known to us as Carolus Linnaeus, whom we will discuss in detail in Chapter 7. Linnaeus, who devised the system of scientific names we still use to classify living things, initially thought that all species of plants and animals had been divinely created in their present forms and numbers. But Linnaeus, a keen observer of nature, came to recognize (as had Hooke before him) that some sort of change had taken place—that fossils, for example, represented species that had become extinct and that new species could arise.

Gradually, then, through the observations and interpretations of all the scientists discussed so far, it became clear that life on earth had undergone change, just as had the earth itself, and that this change required scientific explanation using a uniformitarian approach. But this idea—then referred to as the *transmutation of species*—was a more controversial matter than the idea of a changing earth. For if other forms of life had arisen and changed over eons of time by uniform natural processes, then it followed that the same should apply to humans. So, even after it became obvious that life had "evolved" (as we now phrase it), just *how* this had taken place mattered a great deal.

There were many who addressed this issue from a uniformitarian position, including Charles Darwin's grandfather, Erasmus Darwin (1731–1802), but one of the most influential was the French naturalist Jean-Baptiste de Lamarck (1744–1829). Lamarck emphasized Hooke's conclusion that plants and animals are **adapted** to their environments; that is, each kind of living organism has physical traits and behaviors that allow it to survive under a given set of natural circumstances. When environments change—as the stratigraphic record shows they do—organisms must change if they are to continue to exist.

Lamarck was quite correct that organisms undergo "possibly very great" change and that this change is connected to the environment. He erred, however, in his explanation of how this change occurs and in his idea that change is **progressive,** going from imperfect to perfect by a process of increasing complexity. This is another example of the influence of the great-chain-of-being concept. It should be obvious which species Lamarck thought was the most perfect and complex. This was the appeal of the idea of progressive evolution: if life itself changed through time, at least *we* were what it was changing toward.

Lamarck's mechanism for this progressive change is called the **inheritance of acquired characteristics,** an old idea that Lamarck formalized in his 1809 *Philosophie zoologique.* He wrote:

> When the *will* guides an animal to any action, the organs which have to carry out that action are *immediately stimulated* to it by the influx of *subtle fluids.* . . . Hence it follows that numerous repetitions of these organised activities strengthen, stretch, develop and *even create* the organs necessary to them. . . . Now every change that is wrought in an organ through habit of frequently using it, is subsequently *preserved by reproduction.* . . . Such a change is thus handed on to *all succeeding individuals* in the same environment, without their having to acquire it in the same way that it was actually created. (Harris 1981:116–17; emphases mine)

As a famous (and probably overused) example, Lamarck explained the long necks and legs of giraffes in the following way: In the past, giraffes were short, but some environmental change altered their food source, placing the foliage they ate high up in the trees. Confronted with this problem, each giraffe was able to stretch itself enough to reach the leaves. This greater height was automatically passed on to the giraffes' offspring, which had to make themselves even taller. And so on (Figure 2.6).

adaptation The state in which an organism is adjusted to and can survive in its environment through its physical traits and behaviors. Also, the process by which an organism develops this state through natural processes.

progressive In evolution, the now-discounted idea that all change is toward increasing complexity.

inheritance of acquired characteristics The incorrect idea that adaptive traits acquired during an organism's lifetime can be passed on to its offspring.

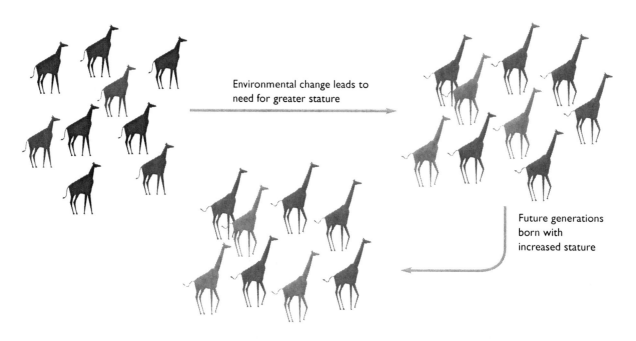

Environmental change leads to
need for greater stature

Future generations
born with
increased stature

FIGURE 2.6

Lamarck's model of inheritance of acquired characteristics applied to the evolution of long necks and tall bodies in giraffes. In the past, giraffes were short, but environmental change altered their food source, placing the foliage they ate high up in the trees. Confronted with this problem, *each giraffe* was able to stretch its neck and legs enough to reach the leaves. This greater height was automatically passed on to the giraffes' offspring, which had to make themselves even taller, and so on, giving rise to the 18-foot-tall giraffes of today.

One reason that Lamarck's idea was popular was that it was one of the first detailed, lengthy, scientific treatments of evolution. Lamarck even spelled out how he used the scientific method by specifying the data that would be required to falsify his model. It was also a comfortable explanation for an uncomfortable topic. It had become clear that life was capable of change over time. At least, according to Lamarck's hypothesis, life changed in a particular (and very human-oriented) direction, and it changed by a process that was unfailing and dependent on something inherent to the organism—Lamarck called it "will." It even followed that no organisms ever become extinct. Creatures represented only by fossils were simply creatures that had undergone so much change they now looked very different.

But observation and logic produced some major objections to Lamarck's concept. Traits acquired during an organism's lifetime cannot be inherited by its offspring. A bodybuilder's children will not automatically be born with bulging muscles. Further, it was hard to see how an organism's "will" could change its color or produce a new organ or make a giraffe taller. And just what is the "subtle fluid" that is supposed to bring all this about?

Charles Darwin

Charles Darwin was born (in 1809, the same year Lamarck's book was published) into a world that accepted the *fact* of biological change but was still in search of a *mechanism* for that change. Although many, including Lamarck, held to a uniformitarian position, others, such as Cuvier, still adhered to a catastrophic explanation. It was Darwin who would provide the mechanism that has withstood over a century and a half of scientific examination.

The story of Darwin's life and scientific work is a fascinating one (see the list of biographies in this chapter's "Suggested Readings"). For the purpose of our story, however, we can simply say that Darwin recognized an important fact not fully appreciated by many of his predecessors or contemporaries. In his work in his native England and especially on his famous voyage around the world on the HMS *Beagle* (1831–1836; Figure 2.7), Darwin realized the incredible degree of variation that exists within each living species (Figure 2.8). If Lamarck were correct, one would expect every member of a particular species to look pretty much the same because they all would have responded identically to the same environmental circumstances. Darwin saw that this was clearly not the case. Variation always exists, no matter how well adapted a species might be. What tipped Darwin

FIGURE 2.7
Route of Darwin's voyage aboard the HMS *Beagle* from 1831 to 1836. This trip provided Darwin with observations and thoughts vital to his formulation of the theory of natural selection. Especially famous and important was his visit to the Galápagos Islands in the eastern Pacific.

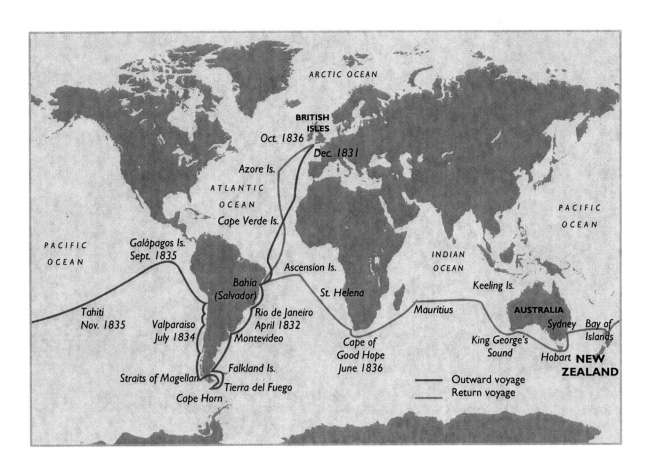

FIGURE 2.8

Variation within a population represents the raw material for natural selection. The tiger swallowtail butterflies (*upper right and bottom*) are members of the same species. The dark tiger swallowtail is a mimic of the pipe-vine butterfly (*left*), which is protected from predation by its foul taste.

off to this fact of nature were his observations of domestic species such as pigeons, carefully bred for certain features but still showing physical variation every generation. Therefore, in each generation, breeders would have to choose for mating only those individuals possessing the features they desired, using the assumption that offspring tend to resemble parents. The goal was to eliminate undesirable traits and accumulate desirable ones.

Darwin also took a clue from the work of English economist Thomas Malthus (1766–1834). Malthus argued that human populations, if unchecked, increase at a more rapid rate than do resources. Thus, there is competition within any population over those resources, and this is what keeps populations in check.

Darwin reasoned that the same things happened in nature. Some of the natural variation within a species would make a difference in the success, or **fitness,** of individuals. The better-adapted individuals would tend to be more reproductively successful. Their traits would be passed on to more offspring than would those of the less well adapted. Over time, then, some traits would accumulate while others would decrease in frequency or even be eliminated. If the environment to which a species is adapted changes, it stands to reason that the fitness value of certain traits might also change, so the process described might proceed in a different adaptive direction—what was once adapted might now be neutral or perhaps even poorly adapted.

So, while Lamarck thought that variation *arose when it was needed,* Darwin understood that variation *already existed.* Because Darwin lived before the processes of genetics were understood, he did not know where this variation came from, but his observations showed it was a fact; and he realized that nature, like a plant or animal breeder, "selects" better-adapted individuals for more successful reproduction. Darwin called this process **natural selection.**

Thus, according to Darwin's model, giraffes didn't become steadily taller and taller in response to one environmental change. Rather, over many millennia, various environmental factors selected for certain expressions of many traits, resulting today in these tallest of living mammals.

Several important ideas follow from natural selection:

1. It becomes clear that evolution by natural selection has no particular direction. Organisms do not "progress" to increasingly complex forms, as Lamarck thought, but evolve to simply stay adapted to their environments or, if possible, become readapted to changed environments. Variation is not "willed." It results from random processes that we now understand from the study of genetics (see Chapter 3).

fitness The relative adaptiveness of an individual organism, measured ultimately by reproductive success.

natural selection Evolutionary change based on the differential reproductive success of individuals within a species.

2. It is also clear that such a process, using random rather than directed or "willed" variation, is not foolproof. Species do become extinct, usually when the environment changes so extensively or rapidly that none of the existing variation within a species is adaptive. Extinction is, in fact, the norm. Nine-tenths of all species that have ever lived are now extinct.

3. It follows that *new* species can arise from this basic process. If populations within a species become environmentally separated, these populations will exist under different selective pressures—different traits will be differently adapted to each environment. Moreover, different variations will be produced in each population. Natural selection will have different raw materials to work with. Over time, then, a single species may give rise to one or more new species. This, in fact, was what Darwin was ultimately trying to explain, as indicated by the title of his most famous work, *On the Origin of Species by Means of Natural Selection,* first published in 1859. (See Chapter 5.)

Darwin's idea generated some controversy, which was perhaps why he delayed publishing his book. We know he understood natural selection sometime in the late 1830s, yet it was not until more than twenty years later that he made it public. Even then, he did so only because a younger, less well-known naturalist, Alfred Russel Wallace (1823–1913), independently came up with the same idea, and Darwin was urged by friends to rush his conclusion into print.

The controversy centered not around the idea of uniformitarian evolution itself—which was generally well accepted by that time—but around the fact that Darwin's idea, unlike Lamarck's, did not involve a particular progressive direction nor the direct control or will of the organism. Darwin also acknowledged extinction. These ideas were not always comfortable. But to Darwin's surprise, by the time his book sold out on its first day of publication, the scientific community and much of the informed public were ready to accept the idea, even with its implications. Natural selection—the mechanism of evolution—was hailed as a major scientific breakthrough and remains today a classic example of scientific reasoning, what Darwin's friend Thomas Henry Huxley called "common sense at its best."

The Modern Theory of Evolution

At about the time Darwin was writing *Origin of Species,* a monk in what is now the Czech Republic was answering Darwin's question about the source of variation. After years of undocumented research on several species of

Contemporary Reflections

Has Science Dehumanized Society?

To many, the story recounted in this chapter is one of science *versus* belief systems, specifically religious belief. A popular assessment of Darwin's contribution is that by "proving" evolution he "disproved" the Bible. As we will see in Chapter 5, there is still a substantial contingent today that feels that the very idea of evolution is antireligious.

And it's not just the science of evolution. From Mary Shelley's *Frankenstein* (published in 1818) to modern blockbuster movies such as *Jurassic Park*, science in general is seen as a potential evil, something that is far too easily abused and that, when abused, wreaks havoc on people and their societies. People often use the phrase "playing God" when referring to scientific endeavors—genetics studies in particular—that they perceive as affronts to human spirit and individuality. Science is blamed for many of today's social and environmental ills—and there *are* plenty of them—from global climate change to radioactive contamination to the proliferation of weapons of mass destruction.

There are three errors in this view of science. First, although science has put forth and scientists have embraced ideas that resulted in human suffering, one of the hallmarks of science is its ability for self-correction. The eugenics movement, for example—which held that many human behaviors were hereditary and that therefore selective breeding could improve the species—resulted (even in the United States) in the forced sterilization of many individuals who were deemed less fit because of some characteristic that society felt undesirable (below-average intelligence, for instance, or having borne illegitimate children). This practice is abhorrent, but through scientific progress we now know much more about the nature of human heredity, and such mistakes are at least unlikely in the future.

Second, this view of science ignores the fact that *anything* may be a danger if used incorrectly or for nefarious purposes. One has but to examine world history to see that religious ideals are not always put to positive use. Indeed, many of today's bloody hostilities are the result of religious conflict—often involving religions that specifically prohibit the taking of human life.

Third, in focusing on the negative results of science, we all too easily forget about the positive results. Today's most vocal critics of science still promote their ideas on television and over the Internet; they travel in airplanes and enjoy all the medical and nutritional benefits of a modern scientific society. The astronomer Carl Sagan (1934–1996) once asked a group of people how many of them would not be alive today if it weren't for modern medical technology. Most raised their hands. (I tried this with a class of undergraduates, average age about 20, and still about half raised their hands.)

But didn't Darwin set the stage for this seeming conflict by disproving the Bible with his theory of evolution? Not at all. He *did* show that one literal interpretation of one part of one book of the Bible failed to account for observations of biology in the real world. In no way, however, did his idea of evolution refute a whole religious worldview, nor need it conflict with one's personal sense of the spiritual.

It is not knowledge or ideas, scientific or otherwise, that are dangerous; it is *how* they are used that matters. Ignorance, however, is dangerous, and it is ignorance that dehumanizes us.

TABLE 2.1
Early Figures in Evolutionary Theory (before 1900)

	Approx. Date of Publication	Contribution
James Ussher (1581–1656)	1650	Calculation of the age of earth, using biblical data
Robert Hooke (1635–1703)	1660s–90s	Fossils as evidence of change Importance of environmental change
Nicholas Steno (1638–1686)	1669	Stratigraphy
Carolus Linnaeus (1707–1778)	1758	System of scientific names Recognition of extinction and possibility of new species
Comte Georges-Louis Leclerc de Buffon (1707–1788)	1749	Uniformitarianism Longer time frame for age of earth
James Hutton (1726–1797)	1795	Uniformitarianism Natural cycles Longer time frame for age of earth
Jean-Baptiste de Lamarck (1744–1829)	1809	Adaptation Inheritance of acquired characteristics Progressive evolution
Thomas Malthus (1766–1834)	1789	Relationship between population and resources
William Smith (1769–1839)	1815	First geological map showing strata
Georges Cuvier (1769–1832)	late 1700s, early 1800s	Ideal prototypes Climatic alterations Extinction Catastrophism
Charles Lyell (1797–1875)	1830–33	Uniformitarianism Scientific investigation
Charles Darwin (1809–1882)	1859	Natural selection Origin of species
Gregor Mendel (1822–1884)	1860s	Laws of inheritance
Alfred Russel Wallace (1823–1913)	1859	Natural selection

plants and animals, Gregor Mendel (1822–1884) derived the basic laws of genetics by experimenting with pea plants in the garden of his monastery. These laws (which we'll cover in the next chapter) not only explained one source of biological variation but also showed why and how offspring tend to resemble their parents. Basic laws of genetics and biological variation are crucial to natural selection and the origin of new species.

Mendel died in relative obscurity (Darwin never learned of his work), and his writings languished in libraries until 1900, when they were rediscovered independently by three European scientists who realized that Mendel's work carried implications far beyond some interesting facts about pea plants. They understood that genetics filled in those pieces that Darwin acknowledged were missing from his process.

During the twentieth century, the history of evolutionary theory became more complex, with many more scientists refining and adding to the theory. Among the most important were R. A. Fisher (1890–1962), J. B. S. Haldane (1892–1964), and Sewall Wright (1889–1988), all of whom, mostly in the 1930s, helped show how Mendelian genetics, biological diversity, and natural selection interact in evolution. The result of their work has become known as the *modern synthesis*, after a 1942 book by another figure in the field, Julian Huxley (1887–1975).

Among the first to conduct evolutionarily oriented experiments on living species, in this case the well-known fruit fly, was Theodosius Dobzhansky (1900–1975), who was also interested, as was Darwin, in the origin of new species. This was an interest as well of Ernst Mayr (1904–2005), who helped establish the definition of *species* as a group of interbreeding organisms.

George Gaylord Simpson (1902–1984) focused on the paleontological record and the overall pace and pattern of evolutionary history. These were also major interests of Stephen Jay Gould (1941–2002), whose work we'll look at in Chapter 5.

But all the work of the past hundred years has been built on the thoughts and discoveries of Darwin, Lyell, Hooke, and many others. All the men and women whose investigations have led to our modern theory of evolution (which we will cover in the next three chapters) would freely agree that they have stood on the shoulders of these giants (Table 2.1).

NOTE: Since the topic of this book is the human species, it may have struck you that one-half of our species—namely, women—is distinctly missing from the preceding historical discussion. This has nothing to do with differences in intellect and everything to do with the social, educational, and occupational limits placed on women until fairly recently. (Remember, women have been able to vote in the United States for less than 100 years.) Simply put, no women played major roles during most of the history of evolutionary theory. This is largely true for science in general. Women who were involved in the sciences early on were often amateurs, such as Mary Anning (1799–1847), an English naturalist and fossil hunter, and Beatrix Potter (1866–1943), a fungi expert better known as the creator of Peter Rabbit and other beloved characters of children's literature. Women scientists of the past were also considered anomalies and sometimes linked to men, such as the French chemist Marie Curie (1867–1934), often mentioned along with her husband, Pierre (1859–1906).

In the twentieth century, women became more prominent in the sciences. A few notable examples from the biological sciences are Barbara McClintock (1902–1992), who won a Nobel Prize for her work in genetics; Rosalind Franklin (1920–1958), who probably *should* have shared a Nobel with James Watson and Francis Crick for discovering the structure of DNA; and Dian Fossey (1932–1985), Jane Goodall (b. 1934), and many other women involved in primate studies and other aspects of biological anthropology (whom we shall meet later on).

SUMMARY

The Judeo-Christian belief system, as set down in and interpreted from the Bible, was long seen as both a belief system and a source of literal knowledge. As scholars began looking more objectively at nature itself, however, their observations and the rational conclusions they drew from them showed clearly that knowledge of the heavens, the earth, and the earth's inhabitants required the methods of science. As the scientific method was applied to the study of the earth, scientists gradually learned to give up their presuppositions.

Charles Darwin, adhering faithfully to the spirit of scientific methodology, was able to synthesize his observations and thoughts with those of many others and to formulate a theory that made possible the work that has led to our modern knowledge of the nature and evolution of living things.

QUESTIONS FOR FURTHER THOUGHT

1. The scientific research and ideas of many early biologists and geologists were influenced by philosophical concepts. Do you think such influences ended with people like Darwin? Can you think of a modern scientific matter that may be influenced by beliefs?

2. Whereas biological evolution is not Lamarckian, the evolution of culture is. How so?

3. There are those who say that certain areas of scientific research should be avoided either because their results might be misused or because the facts generated might be unpleasant. What sorts of research do you think these people might be referring to? How would you respond to such cautions?

KEY TERMS

evolution	strata	catastrophists
fossils	stratigraphy	comparative anatomy

uniformitarianism

adaptation

progressive

inheritance of acquired characteristics

fitness

natural selection

SUGGESTED READINGS

The history of the study of evolution is covered in C. Leon Harris's *Evolution: Genesis and Revelations*, which contains numerous sections from original works, and in John C. Greene's *The Death of Adam*. The impact of Darwin's work on modern knowledge in general is the theme of Philip Appleman's *Darwin: A Norton Critical Edition*, second edition.

There are a number of good biographies of Darwin. I especially like *Charles Darwin: A New Life*, by John Bowlby, and *Charles Darwin: Voyaging* and *Charles Darwin: The Power of Place*, by Janet Browne.

For online access to Darwin's writings, see http://darwin-online.org.uk and www.darwinproject.ac.uk.

See the November 2005 issue of *Natural History*, nearly all of which is devoted to Darwin and evolutionary theory, and "Darwin's Big Idea," by David Quammen, in the November 2004 issue of *National Geographic*. See also "Darwin's Enduring Legacy," by Kevin Padian, in the 7 February 2008 *Nature*.

For more on the fascinating life and work of Alfred Russel Wallace, see *Bright Paradise: Victorian Scientific Travelers*, by Peter Raby; *In Darwin's Shadow: The Life and Science of Alfred Russel Wallace*, by Michael Shermer; and "Missing Link," by Jonathan Rosen in the 12 February 2007 *New Yorker*.

William "Strata" Smith's eventful life is chronicled in Simon Winchester's *The Map That Changed the World: William Smith and the Birth of Modern Geology*.

Paleontologist and science historian Stephen Jay Gould wrote many wonderful essays about the history of evolution and other scientific topics and the personalities involved. These can be found throughout his books *Ever Since Darwin, The Panda's Thumb, Hen's Teeth and Horse's Toes, The Flamingo's Smile, Bully for Brontosaurus, Eight Little Piggies, Dinosaur in a Haystack, Leonardo's Mountain of Clams and the Diet of Worms, The Lying Stones of Marrakech*, and *I Have Landed*. These are all highly recommended.

CHAPTER

The Processes of Evolution

*I am convinced that Natural Selection
has been the most important, but not the
exclusive, means of modification.
—Charles Darwin*

One of the scientists who "rediscovered" Mendel's work in 1900 was the Dutch botanist Hugo de Vries (1848–1935). De Vries had been trying to explain the variations that sometimes spontaneously appear in plants (and, of course, in animals)—such as a single flower of the wrong color or one that is much smaller or larger than other members of its species. At that time breeders called these oddities "sports." De Vries called them *mutations*. When he read about Mendel's experiments, de Vries realized that these mutations resulted from sudden changes in Mendel's "factors." We now say that a mutation is any change in the genetic mechanism.

With de Vries's contribution, all the major pieces were in place to articulate the *synthetic theory of evolution*. It may be stated as follows:

A particulate genetic code is initially responsible for the form and function of an organism. Mutations in the coding portion of DNA continually add genetic, and therefore phenotypic, variation to a species. Other processes provide additional genetic and phenotypic variation. Phenotypic variation is affected by the process of natural selection, where the better-adapted individuals will be more reproductively successful and will thus disproportionately pass on their phenotypic traits to future generations. The results of natural selection are the maintenance of a species' adaptive relationship to existing environmental conditions, the potential alteration of a species' phenotypic variation under circumstances of changing environmental conditions, and, ultimately, the development of new species.

Put differently, in the wonderfully concise phrase of Richard Dawkins (2005), evolution is

the nonrandom survival of randomly varying hereditary instructions for building embryos.

As research continued throughout the twentieth century, scientists realized that other processes also play roles in the production of the variation on which natural selection acts. Research still goes on into the relationships and relative importance of all these processes in the evolution of species.

In this chapter, we will address the following questions:

What are species?

What are the processes of evolution?

How do these processes interact to bring about evolution as we understand it today?

SPECIES: THE UNITS OF EVOLUTION

We observe evolution as the change in species over time and the development of new species. Evolution does not take place in individuals. Evolution takes place in *populations* of organisms, and the basic population in nature is the species.

A species may be defined as *a population of organisms whose members can, under natural circumstances, freely interbreed with one another and produce fertile offspring.* Humans and chimpanzees, despite our genetic similarity, cannot (even under *unnatural* circumstances) interbreed and produce offspring, because our two species have different numbers of chromosomes. But any two normally healthy humans of opposite sex, no matter how different they may appear phenotypically, can reproduce and generate fertile offspring. Thus, all human beings are members of a single species, *Homo sapiens*.

But it's not always so clear cut. Horses and donkeys can mate and produce offspring, known as mules. But mules are nearly always sterile. Two mules can't reproduce and make more mules. Thus, horses and donkeys are considered separate species that are unable to combine their genetic endowments for more than one generation.

In captivity, lions and tigers have been known to produce hybrid offspring that are, in many cases, fertile. But lions and tigers don't interbreed in the wild. Although their ranges overlap in India, the specific environmental **niche** of each animal is different, as are their behaviors, including mating behavior. Thus, lions and tigers are separate species.

Domestic dogs and wolves can and will mate and produce hybrid offspring that are fertile. Your family pooch is now lumped into *Canis lupus* and is, technically, a wolf, even though some breeds of dogs are so small that they could not mate with wolves, let alone carry and give birth to the fetuses of such matings. (Coyotes and jackals are also able to

niche The environment of an organism and its adaptive response to that environment.

FIGURE 4.1
Wolflike and very unwolflike dogs. The German shepherd (*left*) closely resembles the wolf, an ancestor of all dog breeds. The miniature poodle (*right*) bears little resemblance to that ancestor. Both breeds, however, are genetically the same as wolves and could potentially interbreed with them.

hybridize with dogs and wolves, but those two groups are still given different species names.)

It is not surprising to us that humans and chimps are separate species because, very simply, we don't *look* like the same species, although we do differ in only a small percentage of our genes. Horses and donkeys, on the other hand, do look pretty similar yet are different species. Lions and tigers look like different species but can still produce fertile offspring, although only under artificial conditions. And some breeds of dogs look so similar to wolves as to obviously belong to the same species, although other breeds only faintly resemble their wild ancestors (Figure 4.1).

If the species is the natural basic unit of evolution, then why is the distinction among various species sometimes so vague? Why aren't all species equally distinct? And why are scientists who specialize in classifying species (called **taxonomists**) sometimes at odds with one another over which populations belong to the same species?

taxonomists Scientists who classify and name living organisms.

FIGURE 4.2
This child with Down syndrome has the characteristic facial features that are some of the multiple phenotypic effects of the presence of the extra chromosome 21. This girl has just won medals in swimming at a Special Olympics event.

point mutations
Mutations of a single base of a codon.

chromosomal mutations
Mutations of a whole chromosome or a large portion of a chromosome.

The answer to all these questions is that while the origin of new species from existing species usually happens relatively quickly, it does not happen instantly. It is a *process* that takes place over time (a subject we'll examine in Chapter 5). Thus, there is usually a period when an emerging species still can interbreed with its ancestral species and is therefore difficult to define. For the moment, however, we will think of species as distinct, discrete units, and we will now describe those processes that produce evolutionary change within species and that, ultimately, bring about the origin of new species.

THE FOUR PROCESSES OF EVOLUTION

Mutations: Necessary Errors

A mutation is any change in the genetic code. Some mutations involve a single incorrect base in a codon (one letter of one word). These are known as **point mutations.** Some point mutations are inconsequential, but some result in the wrong amino acid in a protein, which could have disastrous results for the organism. (An example is sickle cell anemia, a genetic disease, which we'll cover at the end of this chapter.)

Other mutations involve a whole chromosome or a large portion of one. These are called **chromosomal mutations.** They are almost always deleterious because many genes are involved. For example, humans who have three copies of chromosome 21, instead of the usual pair, have trisomy 21, or Down syndrome, which results in mental retardation and other phenotypic effects (Figure 4.2). This mutation most commonly results when a pair of parental chromosomes fail to segregate in the production of gametes.

Mutations are random. They occur continually, but exactly *what* mutation occurs is totally unpredictable. Some mutations are the result of environmental influences such as cosmic radiation, other forms of radioactivity, or chemical pollutants. Most, however, are simply mechanical errors that occur during the complex process of gene replication at cell division or during the even more complex process by which the genetic code is read, translated, and transcribed into proteins. They are occurring in the cells of your body as you read this sentence. Most affect just the individual, since they cannot be passed on. The process of aging, for example, is partly due to an accumulation of cells with mutations that make them in some way abnormal, though they are still alive and able to divide.

The only mutations that concern us in an evolutionary sense are those that occur in the gametes or in the specialized cells that produce gametes. These mutations are the ones that are passed on to future generations.

Because mutations are mistakes—deviations from the normal genetic code—many mutations in coding regions are deleterious. Such mutations produce a phenotypic result that is abnormal and therefore, to one degree or another, maladaptive. Individuals with such traits may not be as reproductively successful as most members of their species, and so the mutant gene or genes will not be passed on as often, if at all. In other words, natural selection will select *against* those genes. But mutations may also produce alleles that are neutral, making no difference to an individual's fitness, or they may produce alleles that result in even *better-adapted* phenotypes and are thus selected *for* by being passed on more often.

Mutation, in other words, adds genetic variation to a species' **gene pool.** Mutations are the price living things pay for the process of evolution. Without mutation—if the first life-forms had reproduced themselves absolutely without error—nothing would have changed, and the first living things would be the *only* living things. Mutations are thus one of the basic processes of evolution. They are necessary errors.

Natural Selection: The Prime Mover of Evolution

By now, you should have a pretty good idea of how natural selection operates. Genetic variation within a species results in phenotypic variation. Much of a species' phenotypic variation may make little difference to the fitness and reproductive success of individuals. We have come to see that nature is more tolerant of variation than Darwin thought. He felt that *every* variation made a difference. We now know this is not the case.

At the same time, however, some phenotypic variation *does* make a difference. How much of a difference, of course, depends on what traits are important for the adaptation of a particular species to a particular environment at a particular time. What's adaptive for one species—say, large size or a certain color—will not necessarily work for even a closely related species. As environments change, a trait that *was* adaptive for a species may no longer be adaptive, or a trait that was once neutral, or even nonadaptive, may now be adaptive.

Darwin's Finches Provide a Striking Example of Natural Selection in Changing Environments   Rosemary and Peter Grant and their colleagues (Grant and Grant 2000, 2002, 2008; Weiner 1994) have studied the famous birds of the Galápagos Islands collectively known as Darwin's finches for over thirty years (Figure 4.3; see also Figure 5.3). Among the important adaptive features of these birds are their beaks, which have evolved to help each species of finch exploit particular food sources. In

gene pool   All the alleles in a population.

FIGURE 4.3
The medium ground finch, *Geospiza fortis,* was one of the species of Darwin's finches studied by Rosemary and Peter Grant and their colleagues.

1977 there was a severe and nearly yearlong drought on one of the small islands that the Grants' team was using as a study area. Insects virtually disappeared, and the only plant seeds available were larger than average and had tougher than average exteriors to preserve their moisture. The finches on the island suffered a serious food shortage.

The next year, when the rains returned, the researchers found that just one finch in seven (a mere 14 percent) had made it through the drought. Moreover, the surviving birds of one species common to the island (the medium ground finch) were 5 to 6 percent larger than those that had perished and had beaks that were slightly (in fact, less than a millimeter) longer and deeper than the average before the drought. These are not big differences on a human scale, but the beak-size difference helped some of the finches crack open the larger, tougher seeds during the drought, enabling them to survive. As a result, many more males survived than females, because they are about 5 percent larger overall than females.

Now, however, because evolution takes place across generations, it had to be seen if this change would be passed on to the offspring of the surviving finches. This was, indeed, the case. It is the female finches who select males for mating. The males selected by the few surviving females were the largest and had the deepest beaks. As a result, the finches of the next generation were both larger and had beaks that were 4 to 5 percent deeper than the average before the drought. Moreover, when conditions, and thus food sources, returned to normal for a time, the average beak size decreased over several generations toward its previous dimensions. Larger beaks were no longer a distinct advantage and so were no longer selected for. These changes showed natural selection in action. Because of the severity of the situation, it took place rapidly enough for human observers to measure and record it.

There Are Several Important Implications of Natural Selection It is important to note that in the case of the finches, as in any example of natural selection, the variation that proved useful under changed circumstances was already present. It did not appear when it was needed or because it was needed. The finches that survived *already* had larger bodies and beaks; they did not develop these after the drought altered their food source. It was, in other words, already an aspect of their variation, although only a small number of finches possessed large beaks and bodies because under usual conditions they conferred no distinct advantage and may even have been disadvantageous. This is the essential difference between Lamarck's inheritance of acquired characteristics and Darwin's natural selection.

It follows from these points that natural selection is not always successful in maintaining a species' adaptation and survival in the face of environmental change. If a change is too rapid or too extensive, the natural variation within a species simply may not be enough to provide any individuals with sufficient reproductive success to keep the species going. Natural variation within a species cannot predict what environmental change may take place in the future. Adaptation to change is a matter of luck. Indeed, for over 90 percent of all species that have ever existed, luck has run out; they are extinct.

Recognition that extinction is commonplace was another reason for Charles Darwin's delay in making his idea of natural selection known to the public. Natural selection does not produce change in a particular direction, nor is it always successful in ensuring the survival of a species. Darwin thought, perhaps correctly at first, that these implications were too uncomfortable for most people to accept. By 1859, however, the Victorian world of rapid social, industrial, economic, and political transformation had come to accept change as the norm, for nature as well as for itself. Moreover, the logic of *Origin of Species* was so lucid and well presented that its conclusions were seen as obvious. Darwin's book was a best seller, and his idea was, except for a few holdouts, well accepted.

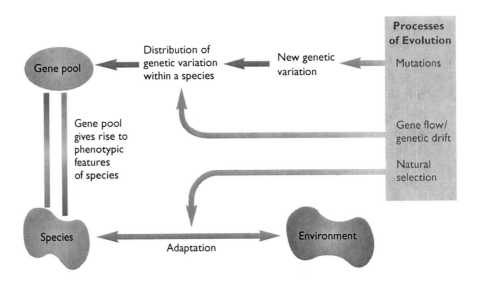

FIGURE 4.4

Processes of evolution. A species is in an adaptive relationship with its environment. This relationship is maintained by natural selection. Environments, however, are constantly changing, so the adaptive characteristics of a species change through time. In addition, the gene pool of a species is always changing, altering the phenotypes on which selection acts. Processes that alter a species' gene pool are also, by definition, processes of evolution. Mutation provides new genetic variation by producing new alleles or otherwise altering the genetic code. Gene flow and genetic drift mix the genetic variation within a species, continually supplying new combinations of genetic variables.

Mutation and natural selection are the major processes of evolution. Mutation provides new genetic variation. Natural selection selects phenotypes for reproductive success based on their adaptive relationship with the environment. But because evolution is technically defined as genetic change, two other processes must also be considered as processes of evolution: gene flow and genetic drift (Figure 4.4).

Gene Flow: Mixing Populations' Genes

By definition, members of a species can and do interbreed with one another. The members of a species, however, are usually unevenly distributed over that species' range. Populations within a species can be to some degree separated from other populations by environmental barriers, geographic distance, or, in the case of our species, social and cultural distinctions such as political, religious, and ethnic boundaries. Such populations are called **breeding populations.** Individuals tend to find mates within their own breeding population (Figure 4.5).

breeding populations
Populations within a species that are genetically isolated to some degree from other populations.

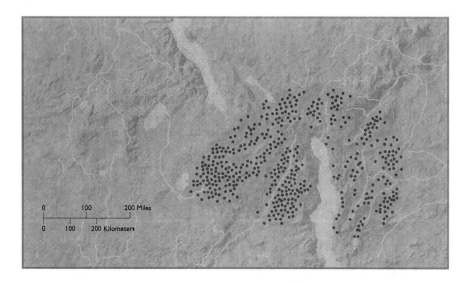

FIGURE 4.5
Breeding populations. The members of a species of lowland, nonaquatic animal (represented by the dots) are unevenly distributed within that species' range because of mountain and water boundaries. The separate population concentrations—the breeding populations—may show genetic and phenotypic differences.

Although belonging to the same species, breeding populations may exhibit genetic differences for two reasons. First, breeding populations may exist in somewhat different environmental circumstances from each other, as illustrated in Figure 4.5. Natural selection will have been favoring different phenotypes, and thus different allele frequencies, in adaptive response to these environments.

Second, other genetic events (such as mutations and the evolutionary processes we're about to discuss) tend to be concentrated within breeding populations because that is where breeding is concentrated. What happens genetically in one breeding population will differ from what happens in another.

However, because breeding populations *are* still members of one species, interbreeding between them does take place as populations and individuals migrate and as neighboring populations exchange genes. This is called **gene flow.** When members of different breeding populations interbreed, new genetic combinations are produced in the offspring. In other words, genes within a species "flow" among the populations of that species, altering the distribution of genes and thus phenotypic variation of the species as a whole (Figure 4.6).

This process of evolution is particularly effective in a mobile species such as ours, with populations that are continually moving around and mixing genes. For example, about half of all Hutterite marriages (see Chapter 1) take place between colonies, with the bride moving to the colony of her husband. The woman thus brings her genes into the population and contributes them to subsequent generations. In one of the colonies I visited, 70 percent of the female parents came from other colonies, and marriages involving these women produced nearly 60 percent of the children of

gene flow The exchange of genes among populations through interbreeding.

FIGURE 4.6
Simple example of gene flow where two populations merge. The dots represent the relative frequencies of two alleles.

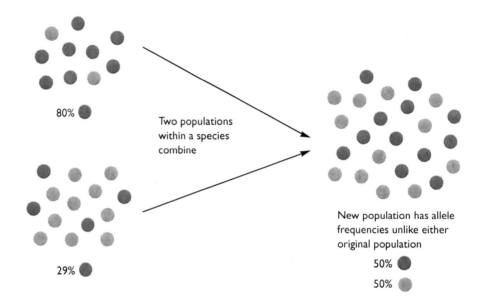

80%

Two populations within a species combine

29%

New population has allele frequencies unlike either original population

50%

50%

the next generation. Changes from one generation to the next in a Hutterite colony are greatly affected by this continual mixing, or flowing, of genes among populations, and it is the same for the human species as a whole.

Genetic Drift: Random Evolution

Fission and the Founder Effect   One form of genetic drift can be demonstrated by the following experiment: Take 100 coins and arrange them so that 50 heads and 50 tails are showing. Mix them up and without looking (that is, at random) set aside 10 coins. The 10 coins you've chosen will probably *not* be 5 heads and 5 tails, 50 percent of each as in the original group. The odds are against it (about 4:1). Your sample of 10 will probably not be representative of the whole population of coins. It will probably be a nonrepresentative sample, and this effect is called **sampling error.**

Similarly, when a population within a species splits, each new population will exhibit a nonrepresentative sample of the genes, and therefore the phenotypes, of the original. The splitting of a population is called **fission** (Figure 4.7). When one of the new populations is drawn from a small sample of the parental population, it will be strikingly different genetically (as with the coins above). This phenomenon is called the **founder effect.**

The Hutterites again provide an example. Because of their high birthrate—an average of 10 children per family—colonies soon become so large that there are administrative problems and duplication of labor specialists. At this point, a colony will fission, or "branch out," as they put it. As a result, the 3 original North American Hutterite colonies, founded

sampling error   When a sample chosen for study does not accurately represent the population from which the sample was taken.

fission   Here, the splitting up of a population to form new populations.

founder effect   Genetic differences between populations produced by the fact that genetically different individuals established (founded) those populations.

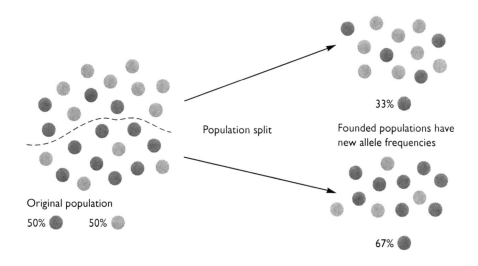

FIGURE 4.7
Fission and the founder effect.

33%

Population split

Founded populations have new allele frequencies

Original population

50%   50%

67%

in 1874 and 1875, have become more than 380. As I saw in my study, these cases of fissioning and the founder effect had significantly altered the biological diversity among colonies.

In fact, the North American Hutterite colonies as a whole are an example of an extreme case of the founder effect. Only 300 Hutterites immigrated from Russia, and of those, only 90 contributed genes to future generations. Thus, most of the more than 35,000 present-day Hutterites trace their genes back to fewer than 100 ancestors. A founder population that comprises a small percentage of an original group is known as a **bottleneck.** In this case, the bottleneck was the result of the movement of a small number from one hemisphere to another. Other bottlenecks may result from an epidemic or a natural disaster.

The founder effect can have interesting and sometimes tragic results. In a population of 333 Pennsylvania Dutch, nearly one-third (98) were found to have the gene for Tay-Sachs disease, a fatal condition that kills recessive homozygotes by their fourth year of life (see also Chapter 15). The high frequency of this lethal recessive allele can be explained by the fact that these 333 people were all descended from one couple who founded the group in the nineteenth century. One of them, no doubt, by sad circumstance, carried the gene (Diamond 1991).

Fission, the founder effect, and gene flow are particularly important in the evolution of our species. They are processes caused by population movement, and our species is among the most mobile. We'll return to this topic in Chapters 12 and 14.

Gamete Sampling   Another form of genetic drift is called **gamete sampling.** Just as genes are not sampled representatively when a population

bottleneck   A severe reduction in the size of a population or the founding of a new population by a small percentage of the parent population that results in only some genes surviving and characterizing the descendant population.

gamete sampling   The genetic change caused when genes are passed to new generations in percentages unlike those of the parental generation. An example of sampling error.

fissions, they are not sampled representatively when two individuals produce offspring. An organism passes on only one of each of its pairs of genes at a time, and only chance dictates which one will be involved in the fertilization that produces a new individual.

For example, refer back to the Punnett square of Figure 3.8, where two heterozygotes for the taster trait produce four children. Understand that those four possible genotypes are just *probabilities*; that is, the two heterozygotes have a one-quarter chance of producing a homozygous dominant, a one-half chance of producing heterozygotes like themselves, and a one-quarter chance of producing a nontasting homozygous recessive. It's quite possible (the odds are 1 in 128) that they could produce four homozygous dominants; it all depends on what sperm fertilizes what egg:

Tt × Tt ⟶ TT, TT, TT, TT

Note that the recessive allele has, just by chance, been completely lost. But what if another set of heterozygous parents produce four homozygous recessives? The effect is balanced:

Tt × Tt ⟶ tt, tt, tt, tt

Combined, there is genotypic change but no overall genetic change. The four parents have 50 percent of each allele as do the eight offspring. No allele has been lost. Neither allele has gained in percentage.

This is what might happen in a large population—the sampling error would be balanced. But in small populations, the size of a colony of Hutterites, for example, the change produced by one set of parents, such as in the first case above, would probably not be balanced by another set of parents.

The percentages of alleles, then, may change at random across generations, "drifting" in whatever direction chance takes them. The change may be great enough that certain alleles may be completely lost, while others may reach a frequency of 100 percent—all with no necessary relationship to natural selection based on the fitness of those alleles.

SICKLE CELL ANEMIA: EVOLUTIONARY PROCESSES IN ACTION

We can now take the ideas covered in Chapters 2 and 3 and see how they work in a real example. Sickle cell anemia is a genetic blood disorder; it is often associated with Africans and African Americans because it is found in high frequency in a band across the center of Africa. It is also found in North Africa, Southwest Asia, India, and Southeast Asia.

Genetics and Symptoms

Sickle cell anemia is the result of a mutation affecting hemoglobin, the protein on the red blood cells that carries oxygen from the lungs to the body's tissues. Hemoglobin is made up of two pairs of amino acid chains, the alpha chain of 141 amino acids and the beta chain of 146. Mutations can occur all along the codes for these proteins. But if the codon CTC for glutamic acid mutates to CAC for valine in the sixth position of the beta chain—one particular wrong word in a sentence of 287 words—an abnormal form of hemoglobin results.

When this abnormal form is present and stress, high altitude, or illness lowers an individual's oxygen supply, the red blood cells take on peculiar shapes, some resembling sickles (Figure 4.8). These misshapen cells cannot carry sufficient oxygen to nourish the body's tissues and can block

FIGURE 4.8
Normal red blood cells and one with the abnormal shape (*bottom left*) that results from the presence of hemoglobin with one incorrect amino acid. Such cells fail to transport oxygen properly to the body's tissues.

Contemporary Reflections

Are Humans Still Evolving?

As asked by most people, the question has two meanings. Perhaps the most common refers to the direction of future human evolution; in other words, how will we look in so many millions of years? As our minds do more and more of our work—and our bodies do less and less—will we eventually be great big heads atop short, spindly bodies? (This is the image we are often given of aliens from more advanced civilizations. Think of *Close Encounters of the Third Kind*, *E.T.*, or *The X-Files*.)

The answer to the first meaning of the question is, obviously, who knows? Evolution is so complex, so dependent on multiple, interacting series of events, that there is really no way of predicting the evolutionary future of any species, especially ours, with its ability to control its behavior, the environment, and, indeed, its genes through culture. If we could take a time machine back to the Cambrian period 543 million years ago and look at its animal life (see Figure 6.5), made up mostly of primitive arthropods (ancestors of modern insects, spiders, and crustaceans), who would predict that a rare little wormy creature only about 2 inches long, called *Pikaia*, would be the earliest-known representative of the chordates, the important group of organisms now represented by fish, amphibians, reptiles, birds, and mammals (Gore 1993; Gould 1989)?

A second, more sophisticated meaning of the question concerns whether we humans have stopped our evolution by so controlling our environment that natural selection is no longer in operation, that genetic variation is no longer an important factor in reproductive success. There are two parts to the answer. First, as we discussed, there are processes other than natural selection that bring about genetic change from generation to generation in a species. Our control over our environment certainly won't halt the processes

capillaries. Symptoms include fatigue, retarded physical development in children, increased susceptibility to infection, miscarriage, fever, and severe pain. Sickle cell kills about 100,000 people a year, 85 percent of whom die before their 20s. Those who live longer experience constant pain and have very low reproductive rates. In terms of evolutionary fitness—that is, reproductive success—sickle cell anemia may be considered nearly 100 percent fatal. (It should be noted that there have been breakthroughs in the treatment of this disease, including a means of repairing the message from the DNA so that it produces normal hemoglobin. This new technique, however, remains out of reach for most people suffering from the disease.)

The abnormal allele (S) for sickle cell is an example of a codominant allele. An individual who is homozygous for the allele (SS) will have sickle cell anemia. A heterozygote, who inherits one sickle cell allele and one allele for normal hemoglobin (AS) will possess about 40 percent abnormal hemoglobin. These people are said to have the sickle cell *trait*. In extreme of mutation, gene flow, and genetic drift. Indeed, one might argue that we have increased mutation rates through some of our environmental manipulations and that our increasing mobility makes gene flow ever more powerful. So, by its genetic definition, evolution will always be taking place in our species.

But have we buffered ourselves against natural selection? For some genetically based characteristics, yes, we have. Remember that fitness is measured against a particular environment. If, through culture, we change the environment, we then change the adaptive fitness of certain phenotypes and thus of the genes that code for them. If I had lived in, say, *Homo erectus* times (1.8 million to 100,000 years ago), I'd no doubt be dead by now. If my infected appendix hadn't killed me (which it would have), my nearsightedness would have prevented me from being a very effective hunter or gatherer. Our present environment, however, has available all sorts of techniques and devices to improve one's eyesight. I wear glasses and see my optometrist once a year, so my poor vision (which, for the sake of the example, we'll say has a genetic basis) does not put me at any survival or reproductive disadvantage. You can probably think of dozens of other examples.

We have not, however, completely eliminated all relevant genetic variation. There are plenty of genes for diseases that place severe, or absolute, limits on a person's ability to reproduce and thus pass on those genes. Tay-Sachs disease, for example, is lethal well before reproductive age. Sickle cell anemia lowers reproductive rates in the few individuals who live long enough to reproduce.

And let's end on a hypothetical note (keeping in mind my precaution about predicting future evolution). There could well be some genetic variables that will make some difference in reproductive success in the near future. Suppose there is genetically based variation in humans' abilities to withstand less-than-optimal air quality or severely crowded living conditions or high levels of noise pollution. As these conditions worsen, it is certainly conceivable that genes for such tolerances will become more frequent as their possessors become less reproductively affected by the modern environment.

conditions of low oxygen, they may experience symptoms of the disease but usually not as severe as homozygotes and with a great deal of variation from person to person. The heterozygous condition is not normally fatal.

For a disease that kills its victims, usually without allowing them to pass on their genes, sickle cell is found in unexpectedly high frequencies in parts of the world (Figure 4.9), in some areas as high as 20 percent. One would expect such an allele to be selected against and to virtually disappear.

The Adaptive Explanation

The answer to this puzzle is a perfect example of the complexity of natural selection. Not only do heterozygotes experience less severe episodes of the disease, they also have a resistance to malaria, an often fatal infectious disease caused by a parasitic single-celled organism and

FIGURE 4.9
Distribution of frequencies of the sickle cell allele. Compare this with the map of endemic malaria (Figure 4.10).

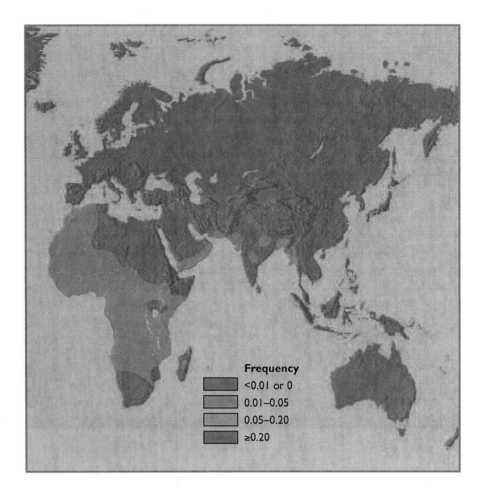

Frequency
<0.01 or 0
0.01–0.05
0.05–0.20
≥0.20

transmitted by mosquitoes. Malaria, though now treatable, still infects over 400 million and kills 1 million to 3 million people a year, mostly African children younger than 5. Red blood cells with abnormal hemoglobin (recall that heterozygotes have about 40 percent of these cells) take on abnormal shapes when infected by the malaria parasite and die, thus failing to transport the parasite through the body. Sickle cell is thus found in highest frequencies where malaria is found in highest frequencies (Figure 4.10).

Now, if heterozygotes are the healthiest in such environments and thus are relatively more successful at passing on their genes, then more sickle cell alleles will be inherited than would be expected if sickle cell had no benefit in any environment. Whenever two heterozygotes mate, they stand a one-quarter chance of producing an individual with normal hemoglobin, a one-quarter chance of producing an offspring who will die from

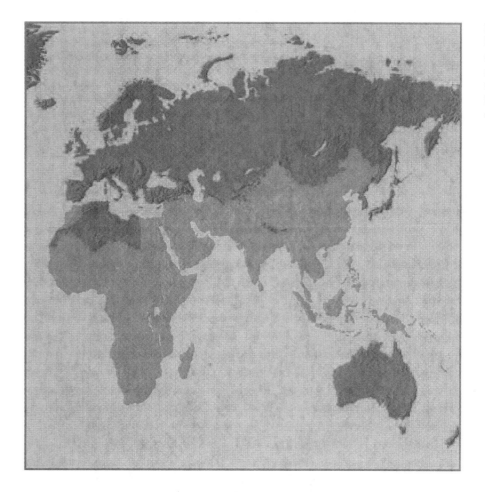

FIGURE 4.10
Distribution of endemic (consistently present) malaria. Compare with the map showing high frequencies of the sickle cell allele (Figure 4.9).

sickle cell, and a one-half chance of producing an offspring who will die neither from sickle cell nor from malaria but who will possess one sickle cell allele that can be passed on (Figure 4.11). This shows dramatically how adaptive fitness is related to specific environmental conditions. Even a lethal allele may be adaptive under certain circumstances.

Other Relationships

The connection between sickle cell and African Americans is an example of the founder effect. African Americans can trace most of their ancestry back to the populations from West Africa that provided much of the slave trade to North America. The African American population was thus, in part, founded by individuals from an area where sickle cell already existed in high frequencies.

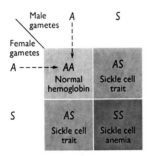

FIGURE 4.11

Punnett square for sickle cell anemia, showing the potential offspring of two heterozygotes. Because heterozygotes have an adaptive advantage in malarial areas but stand a one-quarter chance of producing an offspring with sickle cell anemia, the allele for sickle cell is maintained and passed on in such populations and the disease exhibits high frequencies.

But sickle cell is less frequent among African Americans than it is among certain populations of Africans. Moreover, sickle cell is not limited to persons of African descent in this country. One only has to have the alleles to have the disease. Persons of largely European American background can also have sickle cell. Both these facts can be explained partly as a result of gene flow. There has been a good deal of genetic mixing between European Americans and African Americans over the past several hundred years. The addition of European genes would have lessened the frequency of the sickle cell allele in African Americans, because Europe is largely free of the disease. The presence of the disease among a small number of persons of largely European descent might be the result of their having an ancestor of African descent who carried the allele. Of course, the mutation that produces the sickle cell allele can occur in people of any geographic or ethnic background, European Americans included.

Moreover, because malaria is less common in the United States and Canada than in central Africa, there has been less of an adaptive advantage in possessing the sickle cell trait. Natural selection has thus been producing lower frequencies of the sickle cell allele, even in persons whose ancestors are from one of the areas of highest frequency.

Finally, while we're on the subject, there is evidence (Livingstone 1958; Pennisi 2001; Relethford 2003) that the frequency of malaria increased when people began farming in Africa several thousand years ago. Clearing and planting the land provides the sunlight and the pools of stagnant water that are ideal breeding grounds for the mosquitoes that carry the malaria parasite. An increase in malaria would result in an increased selection for the sickle cell allele, which, in heterozygotes, confers an immunity to the infectious disease.

Thus, the full story of this lethal disease shows the interaction of the forces of evolution and involves not only the genetics behind the cause of the disease but also a single-celled parasite, an insect, and human demographic and cultural practices. The story of sickle cell is a perfect example of the holistic perspective of anthropology.

SUMMARY

A basic theory of evolution involves the production of new genetic variation by mutation and the continual mixing of that variation at reproduction. Gene flow and the forms of genetic drift (fission, the founder effect that results from fission, and gamete sampling) act to randomly change allele frequencies within populations of a species. The resulting phenotypic variation becomes the raw material for natural selection that selects individuals for reproductive success, thus accumulating adaptive traits across generations and decreasing the frequency of poorly adapted traits.

The basic unit of evolution is the species, an interbreeding population that is reproductively isolated from other populations. Because the evolution of new species is a process that occurs over time and at differing rates, species are not always equally distinct from one another and can often be difficult to define.

The processes of evolution are

1. *Mutation*—mistakes in the genetic mechanism that add new variation to a species' gene pool.

2. *Natural selection*—the differential reproduction of individuals based on the relative adaptive value of their traits.

3. *Gene flow*—the mixing of genes as populations within a species move about and interbreed.

4. *Genetic drift*—the splitting of populations to found new populations with new percentages of alleles (fission and the founder effect) and the nonrepresentative sampling of genes as each new generation is produced (gamete sampling).

Sickle cell anemia is an example of not only the processes of evolution at work but also anthropology's holistic approach—the search for connections among the various aspects of its subject.

QUESTIONS FOR FURTHER THOUGHT

1. Domestic dogs are now classified in the same species as wolves, but we humans have been able to produce through selective breeding hundreds of different dog breeds, each with its own phenotype

and behavioral attributes—many decidedly unwolflike. Given what you know about the processes of evolution, how do you think we've accomplished this?

2. Severe bottlenecks can pose serious problems for species. We are seeing this now among cheetahs and elephant seals. What do you think the problem is with a severe bottleneck, in some cases even after the species regains a fairly large population? Why is it actually threatening some species with extinction?

3. If I were an African American planning on having children, I might want to be screened to see if I were heterozygous for sickle cell. (I could be without ever having exhibited noticeable symptoms.) But since I am a European American, there is statistically little need for me to do so. Some people object to such reasoning, saying that it is potentially racist because it makes an assumption about one's health based on one's race. What do you think? Do you know of any other diseases that are statistically linked to certain populations?

KEY TERMS

niche	gene pool	fission
taxonomists	breeding	founder effect
point mutations	populations	bottleneck
chromosomal	gene flow	gamete sampling
mutations	sampling error	

SUGGESTED READINGS

An extended discussion of genetics and evolutionary processes within the context of anthropology can be found in John H. Relethford's text, *The Human Species: An Introduction to Biological Anthropology*, seventh edition. It includes a chapter on sickle cell and many additional examples of evolution in action within human populations.

A highly technical but very readable text on all aspects of evolution is *Evolution*, second edition, by Mark Ridley. The nature of species and the evolutionary processes that affect them are nicely covered in Edward O. Wilson's *The Diversity of Life*, a book about the importance of maintaining the biological diversity of the planet.

The research on Darwin's finches and the people who conducted it are the subjects of Jonathan Weiner's Pulitzer Prize–winning *The Beak of the Finch: A Story of Evolution in Our Time*. For an update, see Peter and Rosemary Grant's *How and Why Species Multiply: The Radiation of Darwin's Finches*. For what happened after the drought, see "Competition Drives Big Beaks Out of Business," by Elizabeth Pennisi, in the 14 July 2006 issue of *Science*.

For another informative example of the subtleties of natural selection in action, see "Why Do Cave Fish Lose Their Eyes?" by Luis and Monika Espinasa in the June 2005 issue of *Natural History*. Also look at the entire November 2005 issue of that magazine.

For a discussion of the definition and origin of species, which also relates to the next chapter, see Stephen Jay Gould's article "What Is a Species?" in the December 1992 issue of *Discover*. See also the article of the same name by Carl Zimmer in the June 2008 *Scientific American*.

For more examples of natural selection among humans, see "Positive Natural Selection in the Human Lineage" by P. C. Sabeti et al., in the 16 June 2006 *Science*.

CHAPTER

The Origin of Species and the Shape of Evolution

> *Endless forms most beautiful and most
> wonderful have been, and are being
> evolved.*
> *—Charles Darwin*

The examples of evolution in action that we discussed in the previous chapter—the finches responding to climatic changes in the Galápagos and populations of our own species interacting with malaria—focused on changes within single species. Darwin's book, however, was titled *Origin of Species*. What Darwin was ultimately trying to explain was how new species arise, the "mystery of mysteries" as he called it in his introduction.

We will address the following questions in this chapter:

How do existing species give rise to new species?

How do the processes of evolution contribute to the origin of new species?

How do species diversify?

What does the "family tree" of species look like?

NEW SPECIES

Species are, by definition, reproductively isolated from other species. Members of two species cannot mate and produce fertile offspring. Members of the same species can. What prevents interbreeding between species?

Reproductive Isolating Mechanisms

Any difference that prevents the production of fertile hybrid offspring between two populations under natural conditions is called a **reproductive**

isolating mechanism. These isolating mechanisms fall into several general categories (based on Dobzhansky 1970):

1. *Ecological adaptation.* Members of the populations are adapted to different environmental niches. Even though their ranges may overlap, their specific niches don't—as is the case with lions and tigers in India.

2. *Seasonal.* Mating within each population or the flowering of plants of two related species takes place at different times of the year.

3. *Sexual.* Behaviors that attract one sex to the other (called *courtship behaviors*) are different in the two populations.

4. *Mechanical.* The organs of reproduction (genitalia or flower parts) are incompatible.

5. *Different pollinators.* In flowering plants, different species, even if closely related, attract different insects, birds, or bats to facilitate pollination.

6. *Gamete isolation.* The cells of reproduction may be incompatible or may not be able to survive within the body of a member of the other species, thus preventing fertilization even if mating takes place.

7. *Hybrid inviability.* Fertilization may occur, but the hybrid zygotes do not survive.

8. *Hybrid sterility.* Hybrids survive but do not produce functional gametes. Mules are normally an example, although in rare cases they are fertile.

The origin of new species, then, is the evolution of *any* of these differences between populations that prevent the production of fertile offspring. As biologist Edward O. Wilson puts it, "In order to spring forth as a species, a group of breeding individuals need only acquire *one* difference in *one* trait in their biology. . . . When that happens, a new species is born" (1992, 68; emphases mine).

How do such differences arise? It is important to understand that reproductive isolating mechanisms do not evolve *in order* to produce a new species. It is an accident when the differences in traits are isolating mechanisms. The differences themselves evolve through the processes of mutation, gene flow, genetic drift, and natural selection acting differently on different populations.

reproductive isolating mechanism Any difference that prevents the production of fertile offspring between members of two populations.

Processes of Speciation

Most Species Evolve in Separate Environments   To take the simplest model, a species inhabits a wide geographic range, and populations at

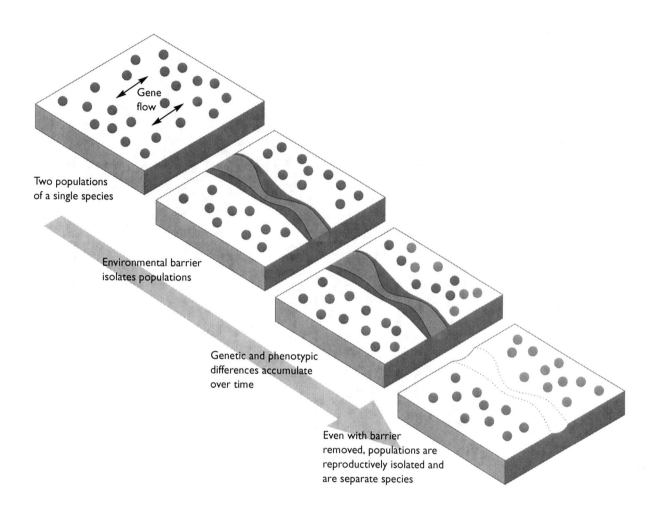

Two populations
of a single species

Gene
flow

Environmental barrier
isolates populations

Genetic and phenotypic
differences accumulate
over time

Even with barrier
removed, populations are
reproductively isolated and
are separate species

FIGURE 5.1
Simple example of speciation
through environmental
isolation.

opposite ends of the range exhibit slightly different adaptive responses to
particular environmental circumstances (Figure 5.1). Now, some environmental change—say, a river changing its course, the destruction of some
important resource, or the advance of a glacier—splits the species, geographically isolating one population from another. Over time, each population will continue to adapt to its environment but without being able to
exchange genes with the other population. In other words, there will be
no gene flow. Each population will accumulate different genetic and phenotypic traits. Quite possibly one or more of these traits will, by chance, be
a reproductive isolating mechanism. If at some later point the geographic
barrier were removed and the two populations *could* mix, they would not
be able to interbreed. They would be separate species, and we would say
that **speciation** had occurred.

speciation The evolution
of new species.

FIGURE 5.2
Two cichlids of different species, one from Central America and one from South America, illustrating the sometimes slight differences in color that the cichlids themselves respond to in mate selection.

Species Can Evolve within the Same Environment   Even if there are no distinct geographic barriers separating portions of a species, speciation can still take place. For example, in Nicaraguan lakes there are two closely related species of cichlid fishes that are distinguished by color (Figure 5.2). Since cichlids mate according to color, these two groups don't hybridize. They apparently evolved from an original species when a new color arose through mutation, and, because of the importance of color in mate choice, those with the new color were reproductively isolated (Kirkpatrick 2000).

In another striking example, Johnson et al. (1996) have indicated that the basin of Lake Victoria in East Africa was completely dry only 12,000 to 14,000 years ago (ya*). And yet there are 500 distinct but closely related species of cichlid fishes in the lake, species found *nowhere else*. Clearly all

---

*By convention, I will use the following abbreviations throughout the remainder of the book: *ya* for "years ago," *mya* for "million years ago," and *bya* for "billion years ago."

these species have arisen fairly recently from, according to DNA studies, a single ancestral species. Apparently, cichlids are poor swimmers that prefer certain habitats and don't move around much. They may also have a tendency not to select mates outside their local group. So small populations could quickly become isolated, and this could account for what seems to be the world's fastest speciation rate in a vertebrate (Yoon 1996a).

Major Mutations Can Cause Speciation Occasionally speciation may be accelerated when a breeding group within a species shares a mutation with extensive phenotypic effects. Such mutations are called **macromutations.** Most macromutations are, as you would expect, deleterious. But by chance, some macromutations might be neutral or even beneficial. In such a case, they would be retained by natural selection, and they might serve to very rapidly make a small population within a species adaptively isolated from the rest of the species. Speciation is given a "head start" by the macromutation, especially if it involves a gene that influences the development of an individual during its life. A mutation of one of these genes could have important consequences for the structure and function of the adult organism.

In fact, a relatively new area of study called *evolutionary developmental biology*—"evo-devo" for short—focuses on a special type of such mutations. Evo-devo is based on growing data suggesting that there are a small number of genes shared by all animals that control important steps in individual development (Orr 2005b). The same gene that triggers the development of eyes in fruit flies, for example, also does the same in mice. A gene for plumage color in birds is the same as one for hair pigmentation in humans. A gene that triggers the building of beaks in birds triggers faces in us.

But how do the same genes translate into such different phenotypes? Rather than resulting from an alteration in the proteins the genes code for, the phenotype is affected by *when* and *where* the genes are expressed, and this, in turn, is controlled by noncoding DNA, which acts as "switches" that turn specific genes on and off at certain times in certain cells. In other words, according to evo-devo, evolution is more a matter of mutations in this switcher DNA than in the coding genes. By way of an analogy, think of those Magnetic Poetry Kits: from a box containing a limited number of words (genes), you can create countless lines (phenotypes) simply by changing (switching) the order and combination (the when and where) of the words.

The processes of evolution that bring about genetic and phenotypic variation are constantly in action (see Figure 4.4). So are the processes

macromutations
Mutations with extensive and important phenotypic results.

that alter environmental circumstances. It stands to reason, then, that the conditions that produce new species are ever-present and that speciation must be a very common occurrence indeed.

THE EVOLUTION OF LIFE'S DIVERSITY

Our Family Tree

No one is sure how many species of living things inhabit the earth, and we have no idea how many have *ever* lived on this planet. There are about 1.5 million *named* species living today; the total is certainly many times that number, possibly 100 million.

Even in modern times, new species are still being discovered. In the 1990s, seven new monkey species were found in Brazil. New species of small mammals, mostly rodents and bats, are described at an average rate of sixteen per year. In 2002 a whole new order of insects was discovered. (Orders are groups of many related species. See Table 7.1.) New species of bacteria are being found by the thousands, including some recently discovered bacteria living in small spaces within rocks nearly 2 miles below the surface of the earth and at temperatures of more than 235°F.

Indeed, some microbes (single-celled organisms) that live at extreme conditions in superheated water near volcanic vents on the ocean floor or in water so salty it would kill most creatures have been shown to be far more common than previously thought. Genetic tests of these and other microbes have shown them to belong to a whole new branch of life and have indicated that microbes compose the bulk of the world's *biomass*— a measure of the weight of organic matter (Gould 1996a). The actual number of species in the world must be, as one scientist put it, "staggering."

Despite the great array of living creatures, however, there is a high degree of similarity among them all. All living things use the same genetic code; they are built from the proteins that are the products of that code, using the same basic twenty amino acids. We assume, then, that life on earth had a single origin. This being the case, all those millions upon millions of species have descended from a common ancestor and have come about by the process of speciation.

Adaptive Radiation

For a potential new species to persevere, it must survive the adaptive trials of natural selection. Put another way, it must have the ecological opportunity to be able to adapt to its environment. When such opportunities are extensive, speciation may take place numerous times, and a group of related species may spread into a number of niches. This spread of related species is called **adaptive radiation.** Evolution has been a story of the adaptive radiation of species into different environments and the subsequent actions of the processes of evolution on those species.

Ecological opportunities come about and can foster adaptive radiation under three general circumstances:

1. When an environment supports no similar and therefore competing species

2. When extensive extinction empties a set of environments of competing species

3. When the new group of related species are adaptively **generalized** (as opposed to **specialized**) and are able to disperse successfully into different niches and displace species already there

Darwin's Finches Had No Competition   Darwin's finches (introduced in Chapter 4) are a group of thirteen related species that inhabit the Galápagos, the volcanic archipelago of some nineteen islands in the Pacific about 600 miles west of Ecuador (Figure 5.3). This was one of Darwin's stops on his voyage around the world. There is a fourteenth related species that lives on Cocos Island, north of the Galápagos.

From a small group of original migrants of an ancestral species, blown out to the islands from the mainland of Central or South America no more than 3 mya, these birds have radiated into niches that were pretty much unoccupied by other birds. Today there are species of ground-dwelling finches that feed on seeds of different sizes and have bills shaped accordingly. There are several species that feed on cactus and several that live in trees and eat insects. Their beaks, too, as noted in Chapter 4, are adapted for the specific foods they eat. One species is a tool-user, holding a cactus spine or twig in its bill and using it to probe for insects in tree trunks. The ground finches on two of the smaller islands peck the skin of larger birds and drink the surfacing blood. Not surprisingly, they are referred to as "vampire finches." Moreover, there is new evidence that beak form influences the songs of the various finch species, which could also affect species distinction (Podos 2001).

In fact, birds in general are an example of adaptive radiation into empty niches. Birds first evolved some 150 mya from a group of dinosaurs (Figure 5.4). There was little competition for species possessing the new attributes of feathers and, for some, flight. This evolutionary novelty

adaptive radiation The evolution and spreading out of related species into new niches.

generalized Here, species that are adapted to a wide range of environmental niches.

specialized Here, species that are adapted to a narrow range of environmental niches.

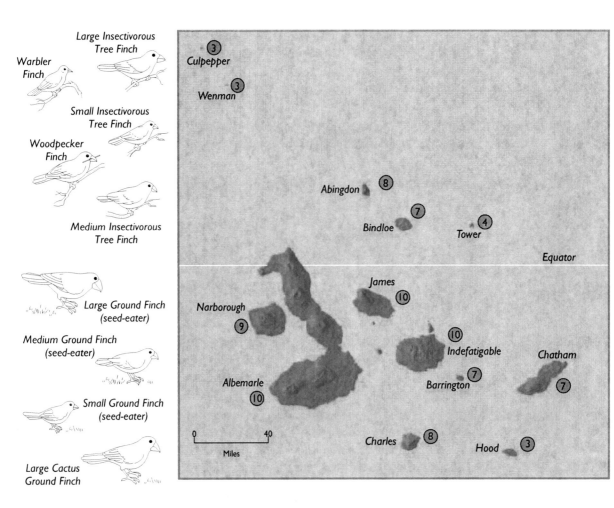

FIGURE 5.3
The various species of Darwin's finches evolved when small groups from an original species underwent adaptation to the varying environmental conditions found throughout the Galápagos Islands. The numbers on the map represent the number of finch species found on each major island. The bird drawings illustrate some of the variations observed among the species of Darwin's finches.

radiated into a wide variety of niches, resulting currently in about 9,000 species of birds of incredible diversity. All are variations on the same basic theme.

Mammals Benefited from a Major Extinction   While mammals were already diverse during the time of the dinosaurs, the asteroid strike of 65 mya that killed off the dinosaurs and many other species opened up new niches for the survivors. The mammals (as well as surviving birds) radiated rapidly, and by about 40 mya the groups of mammals we recognize today had evolved.

The Primates Are a Generalized Group   We can look to our own group of mammals, the primates, for examples of species that were able to radiate because they were generalized and could fairly easily disperse

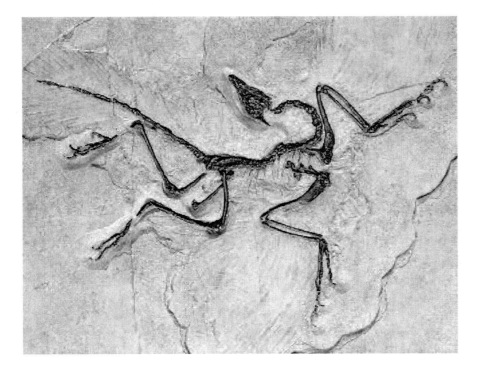

FIGURE 5.4
Fossil remains of *Archaeopteryx* ("ancient bird"), about 150 million years old. This is essentially a small bipedal dinosaur with feathers. The feathers, modifications of dinosaurian scales, are an example of an alteration in a species' genetic makeup that eventually gave rise to a whole new group of organisms.

into diverse niches. When monkeys first evolved, about 40 mya, they proved more generalized than their **prosimian** ancestors, the earliest primates. The monkeys were larger-brained, **diurnal** (as opposed to the largely **nocturnal** prosimians), and well adapted to an active **arboreal** life, eating a mixed diet of leaves, fruits, and insects. As the monkeys underwent speciation and radiated into new niches, they displaced the prosimians. In the New World (Central, South, and North America), there are only monkeys (prosimians apparently became extinct in North America). In the Old World (Europe, Africa, and Asia), prosimians were pushed into marginal areas. A few species live on the mainland of Africa and the mainland of Southeast Asia, but most inhabit isolated islands of Southeast Asia and the island of Madagascar, which separated from mainland Africa prior to the monkeys' evolution (see Chapter 10 for more detail).

On a smaller scale, we will see this pattern repeated when we look more closely at our own evolution. At least once during the evolution of our group of primates, a new and more generalized species of human (in the nontechnical sense) spread geographically and ecologically, displacing an existing human species (see Chapters 10, 11, and 12).

prosimian A primate with primitive features, most closely resembling the ancient primates.

diurnal Active during the day.

nocturnal Active at night.

arboreal Adapted to life in the trees.

THE SHAPE OF THE FAMILY TREE

What is the pattern of speciation, and what, as a result, is the shape of the evolutionary family tree of species?

Darwinian Gradualism

Charles Darwin felt that natural selection was directly responsible for speciation and that it was a process of almost unlimited power. He said that natural selection brought about "the accumulation of innumerable slight variations, each good for the individual possessor." He added:

> What limit can be put to this power, acting during long ages and rigidly scrutinizing the whole constitution, structure, and habits of each creature,—favoring the good and rejecting the bad? I can see no limit to this power, in slowly and beautifully adapting each form to the most complex relations of life. (1869:556)

In other words, Darwin saw natural selection as "fine-tuning" each species to its environment, constantly favoring or rejecting any difference among individuals, no matter how "slight." This constant selection eventually changes one species so much that it may be considered a new species. In addition, such constant selection, Darwin said, will also produce variation among populations within a species in response to slight differences in their environments. He referred to these populations as "varieties." Eventually, selection brings about such marked distinctions in varieties that two or more new species branch from the old one. These species, said Darwin, "are only well-marked varieties, of which the characters have become in a high degree permanent" (1869:561).

According to this model, referred to as **Darwinian gradualism,** the family tree of species has relatively few gracefully diverging branches (Figure 5.5). These represent the slow but steady pace at which individual species change through time and at which populations within species slowly become distinct from one another under the "scrutiny" of natural selection. The tree of evolution represents, in Darwin's words, "an interminable number of intermediate forms . . . linking together all the species . . . by [fine] gradations" (1869:547). In modern terms, we would say that most of the evolutionary change we see, in a broad geological time frame, is the result of **microevolution,** steady natural selection expanded through and accumulating over time.

Darwinian gradualism
The view, held by Darwin, that evolution is slow and steady with cumulative change.

microevolution
Evolutionary change within a single species through time.

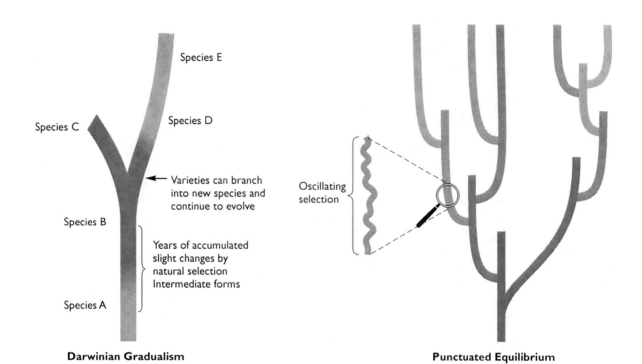

Darwinian Gradualism   **Punctuated Equilibrium**

Punctuated Equilibrium

Here, however, Darwin's model has been challenged. For one thing, the fossil record has failed to show fine gradations for all evolutionary lines. Instead, fossil species often tend to remain relatively stable for long periods of time, and changes—new species—show up rather suddenly.

The origin of our own group did not occur slowly and steadily, gradually producing a humanlike form from an apelike one. The first accepted human fossils, from over 4 mya, are, to exaggerate only slightly, apes that stood upright (see Chapter 10). The change was not gradual but was focused on bipedalism and was quick enough so that few other evolutionary changes had time to occur. (It is important to remember that "quick" in evolutionary perspective is, of course, a relative term and may mean *tens* of thousands of years or more.)

Second, there is the problem of determining at which point in the microevolution of one species enough change has occurred to warrant calling it a new species. In fact, if species are defined as natural populations capable of interbreeding, then there is *no point* in a species' evolution when a member of one generation could not interbreed with a member of the previous generation. As Stephen Jay Gould put it (2002b:775),

FIGURE 5.5

Models of evolution through geological time. According to Darwinian gradualism, the evolution of species through time is a slow, steady process. By contrast, according to the punctuated equilibrium model, major evolutionary change is the result of speciation, the branching of new species from existing ones. Individual species change relatively little through time, although natural selection still acts constantly to maintain a species' adaptation to its environment.

Contemporary Reflections

Are There Alternatives to Evolution?

All the information about the theory of evolution presented in Chapters 2, 3, and 4 has been developed and tested, using the methods and principles of science, over the past several hundred years by many people and from many different perspectives. Evolution is so well supported that we consider the basic idea to be a fact, and it is the central concept of all biology, although we continue to apply the scientific method to our investigation of specific details.

So it is truly astounding that some people, even today, question the fact that evolution has actually occurred, and many of these people base their questioning on religious belief. Why is this a problem? Think back to our discussion of science from Chapter 1. Science and belief systems are both important for the operation of any society, and, ideally, they operate in harmony with one another. They are still, however, distinct realms of knowledge, distinguished by the *testability* of science and the *faith* of belief.

But what about ideas that have characteristics of both? Suppose someone holds a scientific idea (an idea that is testable) but treats it as a belief by taking it on faith and by not recognizing the results of tests that refute it. Here's an example: there are people who believe that the lines on the palms of your hands and on your fingers hold information about your personal character and even, perhaps, about your future. This belief is called palmistry, and its precepts are quite scientifically testable. In fact, I examined them scientifically (Park 1982–83) and they failed. But will palmists all over the country close up shop because some anthropologist says their ideas are false? Hardly. Palmists take their ideas on faith. In other words, they treat a scientifically testable idea like a belief system. Thus, palmistry is a **pseudoscience,** or "false science."

Although pseudoscientific ideas such as palmistry, astrology, and the power of crystals may be harmless enough, other examples have implications that may not be so benign. Some pseudoscientific ideas find support within established belief systems. There are—believe it or not—still people who think the earth is flat and who refuse to acknowledge the masses of scientific evidence to the contrary (Schadewald 1981–82). This belief stems in large part from the literal interpretations of several biblical passages, for example, Matthew 4:8: "Again, the devil taketh him [Jesus] up into an exceeding high mountain, and sheweth him all the kingdoms of the world. . . ." How, the flat-earthers ask, could Jesus have seen all the kingdoms of the earth unless the earth were flat?

Although most people recognize the allegorical sense of this and similar passages in both testaments of the Bible, there is a danger that some might find the issue terribly confusing. On the one hand, scientific evidence—not to mention photographs taken from space—tells us unequivocally that the earth is a sphere. On the other hand, an interpretation of the chronicles of two major religions seems to say the earth is flat. Must one choose between science and religion? There are those who think so, and in the process, both science and belief suffer.

The idea of a flat earth is utterly ridiculous, but there is another pseudoscience, relevant to our topic here, that is far more complex and difficult to evaluate. It's called **scientific creationism.** It proposes that the entire universe, including the earth and all its inhabitants, was created spontaneously by untestable supernatural forces around 10,000 ya. Except for minor changes within "kinds" of plants and animals (breeds of dogs, for example, or regional varieties of a wild species), no changes in living organisms have occurred. Certainly no *new* species have arisen. But, we might ask, what about the layers of rock and soil

FIGURE 5.6
Strata of the Grand Canyon in Arizona. Scientific creationists contend that these strata and all the fossils they contain are the results of the biblical flood. Scientific data show that the canyon's strata represent geological and biological events that took place over nearly 2 billion years. (See also Figure 2.2.)

and the fossils they contain? According to supporters of scientific creationism, those resulted from "a primeval watery cataclysm" (Morris 1974:22), a great flood in other words (Figure 5.6).

Sound familiar? It should. This argument derives directly from one literal interpretation of the first eight chapters of the book of Genesis, and it is clearly in direct opposition to all the data and ideas accumulated and tested by science. More than 200 years of scientific inquiry tell us that the universe, including the earth and its inhabitants, arose through knowable, natural processes. The universe is approximately 13 billion years old, the earth 4.5 billion years old, and life on earth roughly 3.6 billion years old. Living organisms do change through time, and species give rise to new species. The geological and fossil records are the records of these billions of years of change. We've been covering the evidence, data, and arguments for evolution in these last few chapters.

Scientific creationism is thus a pseudoscience—a testable set of ideas that even in the face of contrary evidence is accepted on faith. But scientific creationism goes further. Its proponents claim its ideas are, indeed, supported by scientific evidence that also refutes the accepted theory of evolution. That the creation model coincides with one interpretation of Genesis merely shows, they say, the scientific accuracy of the Bible. Because advocates of scientific creationism claim both models are scientific, they feel both should be taught in science classes as viable alternative explanations for the origin and diversity of life.

The argument is persuasive, especially in a society like ours, concerned with religious freedom and with our American sense of fair play and equal time. *But equal time is for equivalent things.* There is not a single shred of scientific evidence in support of the creation model.

To teach scientific creationism alongside evolution would be to violate the religious freedoms of those who do not subscribe to a strict creationist interpretation. It would also badly confuse those trying to learn how science really operates and what conclusions about our world science has arrived at. The distinction between science and belief would be blurred, interfering with the harmonious and important relationship between the two.

Recently, a new twist on this problem has surfaced with a new degree of complexity and, thus, a potential for unquestioned acceptance. It is generally referred to as **intelligent design.** It comes in several forms, but one will capture the idea. This version of intelligent design says that the basic chemistry of life—the cell, with its DNA, resultant proteins, and myriad reactions—is far too complex to have evolved naturally and so *must* have been designed by some intelligent entity. The more involved arguments use statistics to convey the great odds against putting together just the right combination of molecules that we now know are needed for life. Intimidated by such large numbers, many people accept the proposed improbability, if not impossibility, of life evolving by natural processes.

There are two problems with this idea. First, the initial improbability of something happening doesn't *preclude* its happening. What was the probability at my birth that I would eventually become a biological

pseudoscience
Scientifically testable ideas that are taken on faith, even if tested and shown to be false.

scientific creationism
The belief in a literal biblical interpretation regarding the creation of the universe, with the connected belief that this view is supported by scientific evidence.

intelligent design The idea that an intelligent designer played a role in some aspect of the evolution of life on earth, usually the origin of life itself.

"A true continuum cannot be unambiguously divided into segments with discrete names."

It would seem, then, that evolutionary change over great spans of time is not the result of gradual change *within* species, but rather the result of new species *branching from* existing species, the process of **macroevolution.** Indeed, natural selection is not the creative "scrutinizing" force that Darwin envisioned but a more conservative force, eliminating what doesn't work adaptively and allowing to reproduce what does. Change *within* a species is limited.

This does not mean that natural selection has *no* effect on a species over time. Traits that are important may change as environmental conditions change. Recall the changes in beak size among the Darwin's finches that the Grants and their team studied. The data indicate that a slight difference in beak size among members of one species—as little as a millimeter or two— can be of adaptive importance during sudden, prolonged, or radical environmental changes such as droughts. The average expression of important traits of a species, then, may change back and forth as environmental conditions anthropologist teaching at this university and, at this moment, writing a textbook? The answer is: infinitesimally small! And yet it happened, through all the contingent facts of my personal history—all the little things, many of them conscious decisions but many random, unpredictable, and accidental, which led to other things, and so on.

Similarly, for the evolution of life, a billion years or so passed from the formation of the earth to the first evidence of life (think of how long a billion years is). There are so many molecules, so many combinations of molecules to make compounds, so many individual chances for things to come together in different variations that we couldn't begin to even estimate the number. Among the things that did occur was the chemical combination, under just the right circumstances, that set in motion the chain of events that led to what we now call *life*. In other words, an intelligent designer is *not necessary*.

The second problem is that an intelligent designer is not a scientific (that is, testable) idea. The proposal of an intelligent designer based on supposed rational, scientific evidence (biochemistry and statistics) is just a thinly disguised version of scientific creationism. It ignores the majority of empirical evidence and substitutes an idea that cannot be tested, that *must* be taken on faith. There may well *be* some designer behind the universe we see, but a belief in such a designer is not a *substitute* for a scientific explanation of that universe.

The quality of our lives now and in the future depends on the continued progress of our testable scientific knowledge, mediated by the values of our belief systems. We need to understand what these two areas of knowledge are and how they interact, and we must promote free access to and sharing of all knowledge.

change. This is called **oscillating selection.** But it is adaptive variation around a norm, rather than continual change in a particular direction.

The role of natural selection is basically to maintain the adaptation of a species to its environment. Natural selection is not the author of evolution so much as the editor. Thus, species normally change little over the course of their tenure on earth, and new species seem to arise fairly quickly as a result of the isolation of populations within species through geographic or ecological separation, mutation, or a combination of these. Natural selection, of course, *then* plays an important role in screening the isolated population in terms of adaptive fitness.

We may describe this model of evolution as follows: The adaptive equilibrium of species with their environments is punctuated (interrupted) by the branching of a new species from a population of the parent species. The parent species, in the meantime, may remain unchanged, at least for a time. This model is called **punctuated equilibrium** and is represented not by a tree with gracefully diverging branches but by a bush with many twigs (see Figure 5.5). These twigs are evolution's experiments, potential new species.

macroevolution The branching of new species from existing species.

oscillating selection Adaptive variation around a norm, rather than in one direction, in response to environmental variation in a species' habitat.

punctuated equilibrium The view that species tend to remain stable and that evolutionary changes occur fairly suddenly through the evolution of new species branching from existing ones.

Many twigs are short, since the species they represent became extinct in a short time. Some are longer, however, and give rise to yet more new species.

So, the evolution of life on earth, on the broad scale of geological time, cannot be depicted as a ladder or a chain representing the steady march of progress toward complexity, as Lamarck and other early scientists believed. Nor is it a gracefully branching tree, as Darwin pictured it. Instead, it is, in the words of Stephen Jay Gould (1994b:91), a "luxuriant bush," more complex than we will probably ever know—a "blooming and buzzing confusion" (1985:355).

SUMMARY

The evolution of new species is the result of the interacting processes of genetic variation, natural selection, and environmental change. New species arise when a population within an existing species becomes isolated. Among the differentiating traits that result, some may act as reproductive isolating mechanisms, meaning that even if the populations once again have the opportunity to interbreed, they will not be able to do so. They will have become separate species.

The process of speciation, occurring countless times over the billions of years of life's history, has produced the incredible array of life-forms we know today and see in the fossil record. When species have the opportunity, they are able to adaptively radiate into new niches, and increased diversity is the result. It must be remembered, however, that all these forms are variations on the single theme of life that originated on this planet. All life, through speciation and adaptive radiation, is descended from a single origin.

We can depict evolution as a luxuriant bush, dense with innumerable twigs, each representing a new species. We use the bush as a metaphor for evolution for two reasons. First, we realize that the conditions for speciation are continuous, so that speciation has probably taken place more often than we can imagine. Second, we understand that Darwin's model of the origin of species, driven by the steady, gradual "fine-tuning" of natural selection, is not accurate. Natural selection is a conservative force, acting largely to maintain a species' adaptation. What produces new species is geographic or genetic isolation, and these processes act relatively quickly. In other words, evolutionary change on a geological time frame is the result of macroevolution, not microevolution.

QUESTIONS FOR FURTHER THOUGHT

1. Does the conflict between scientific creationism and mainstream evolutionary science mean that we must choose between science and religion? Are the two realms of knowledge, with regard to this subject, incompatible?

2. Consider the processes of evolution and speciation. Can you think of any examples of these processes in action today? How are human influences on the world part of these processes?

3. The result of adaptive radiation is biodiversity. Human actions are threatening the rich biodiversity of the planet. Is there a real problem with this, beyond the loss of some interesting or attractive species? How might diversity in and of itself be vital to the health of the planet?

KEY TERMS

reproductive isolating mechanism

speciation

macromutations

adaptive radiation

generalized

specialized

prosimian

diurnal

nocturnal

arboreal

Darwinian gradualism

microevolution

pseudoscience

scientific creationism

intelligent design

macroevolution

oscillating selection

punctuated equilibrium

SUGGESTED READINGS

You should certainly have a look at the book that began our modern understanding of evolution, Darwin's *Origin of Species*. The last chapter, "Recapitulation and Conclusion," nicely summarizes his arguments and provides a good idea of his style.

A wonderful book on evolutionary processes, the origin of new species, and the variety of living things is Edward O. Wilson's *The Diversity of Life*.

For more on Darwin's finches, see Jonathan Weiner's *The Beak of the Finch*.

A nice piece on the evo-devo model is "Turned On," by H. Allen Orr, in the 24 October 2005 *New Yorker*.

One of the originators of the model of punctuated equilibrium is biologist Stephen Jay Gould, and many of his articles concern that model. Try "The Episodic Nature of Evolutionary Change" and "Return of the Hopeful Monster," both in *The Panda's Thumb*. Gould has also addressed the shape of the evolutionary tree. See his informative books *Wonderful Life* and *Full House* and his article in the October 1994 *Scientific American*, "The Evolution of Life on the Earth."

For what many consider the last word on evolution, see Gould's magnum opus, his 1,433-page *The Structure of Evolutionary Theory*. Although his tome is beyond the scope of this book, it bears noting that Gould not only modifies Darwin's gradualistic view of evolution as a whole, as described in this chapter, but he also argues for two other changes. First, where Darwin saw species as the focus of selection, Gould notes that selection (that is, differential reproductive success) can take place at other levels as well—from the cell, to the population within a species, to species themselves, even to whole groups of species. Second, while Darwin saw adaptation through natural selection as the main process of evolution, Gould shows that the relationships between organisms and the various components of their environments flow in many directions. Organisms, in his words, are "interactors" and not just "replicators." We (that is, organisms) change the environments to which we are adapted as the environments change us.

For an idea of the arguments of the scientific creationists, try *Evolution: The Fossils Say No!* by Duane T. Gish. For a refutation of scientific creationism, go once again to Stephen Jay Gould and a series of articles on the subject in *Hen's Teeth and Horse's Toes*. A good example of the intelligent-design argument is *Darwin's Black Box,* by biochemist Michael J. Behe. For a discussion, see the January–April 2002 issue of *Reports of the National Center for Science Education*.

See H. Allen Orr's article on intelligent design, "Devolution," in the 30 May 2005 *New Yorker*.

The National Center for Science Education, Inc. (NCSE) works to support the teaching of evolution and to increase public understanding of evolution and science. It publishes "Reports of the NCSE," which contain interesting and useful articles on all aspects of this topic. Its Web site is www.natcenscied.org.

The relationship between science and philosophical ideas, brought out so powerfully by the issue of scientific creationism, is addressed in Kenneth Miller's *Finding Darwin's God* and in Stephen Jay Gould's

Rocks of Ages; for a very broad discussion, see *Consilience,* by Edward O. Wilson.

Data continue to come in about the cichlids of Lake Victoria. Among other things, it appears that some of the named cichlid species are not entirely reproductively isolated; that is, they are still in the process of real speciation. However, because of the increasingly murky waters of the lake, many cichlids can't discern color differences and are mating with members of other populations. This is gradually increasing gene flow and thus decreasing the variability of these fishes. See Erica Goldman's piece in the 31 January 2003 *Science,* "Puzzling Over the Origin of Species in the Depths of the Oldest Lakes." At the same time, color differences and visual adaptations to them might be contributing to the evolution of new species. See "In Sight of Speciation," by Mark Kirkpatrick and Trevor Price, in the 2 October 2008 issues of *Nature.*

CHAPTER 6

A Brief Evolutionary Timetable

And there is no new thing under the sun.
—Ecclesiastes 1:9

Anthropology focuses on one group of organisms, humans and our direct ancestors, and deals mostly with a single species, *Homo sapiens*. Humans, in a broad, nontechnical sense, have been around for 5 or 6 million years. Depending on one's interpretation (see Chapter 12), our species has inhabited the earth for 2 million years at most. Although this seems like a long time, it is really just the last tick of the earth's evolutionary clock, four-hundredths of 1 percent (0.04 percent) of the history of our planet, and one-hundredth of 1 percent (0.01 percent) of the estimated history of the universe. If the history of the universe were reduced to a single year, our species would not show up until after 11:30 p.m. on December 31.

So, although we focus on *us*, we need to appreciate the fact that all the processes of evolution apply to all forms of life on earth and that the idea of evolution—change through time—applies to the whole history of the universe.

Before we focus on ourselves, our close relatives, and our immediate ancestors, we need to put human evolution in context, to see it as part of a long and ongoing series of changes that began maybe 13 bya.

Following are two questions we will consider in this chapter:

What is the history of the universe, the earth, and life on earth?

What processes and events have affected the overall history of the earth and life on earth?

FROM THE BEGINNING: A QUICK HISTORY

The origin of the universe is shrouded in mystery. We don't, in all honesty, really know exactly how old it is, although 13 billion years is a recent estimate. We do know, however, that the universe is expanding in all directions. All the galaxies in the universe (an estimated 50 billion) are constantly traveling farther away from each other. A logical conclusion from this fact is that the universe began as an incredibly tiny, dense, and hot speck (the proper term is a *singularity*) composed of pure energy that would one day become all the energy and space and matter—including us—of the universe we know.

At the beginning of time—we'll use 13 bya—this speck began to expand, an event commonly called the Big Bang, although it wasn't really an explosion. It was more like a balloon being rapidly inflated—a balloon that contained both energy and space. The details of the Big Bang are still a matter of intense debate and are among the most complex issues in science. For our purposes here, suffice it to say that as the newborn universe expanded, it cooled, and matter quickly condensed from energy (Figure 6.1). Within 3 minutes after the beginning, protons and neutrons had formed and had joined to make atomic nuclei, but it took another 100,000 years for electrons to join the nuclei to form atoms. At about the same time, radiation separated from matter and there was light, but for the next 200,000 years the universe was still too dense for that light to travel through it.

By 12 bya, galaxies had begun to form as gravity pulled matter together into huge clusters. These were made up of stars that were mainly hydrogen, the simplest element. As a result of the nuclear reactions in these stars, heavier, more complex elements formed. When these early stars died in tremendous supernova explosions, their elements were scattered into space, some eventually contributing to the formation of new galaxies with all their stars and, in several known cases, planets. (Planets have been discovered orbiting other stars in our galaxy.)

About 5 bya, when the universe was two-thirds its present size, our solar system formed around a medium-sized star in the Milky Way galaxy. Earth, the third of eight existing planets orbiting that star, came into being 500 million years later. Amazingly, in less than a billion years—maybe 3.6 bya—life on earth was established. We know this indirectly from fossils found in Greenland, southern Africa, and Australia (Figure 6.2). In Australia there are also actual fossils, preserved in stone, of single-celled

photosynthesis The process by which plants manufacture their own nutrients from carbon dioxide and water, using chlorophyll as a catalyst and sunlight as an energy source.

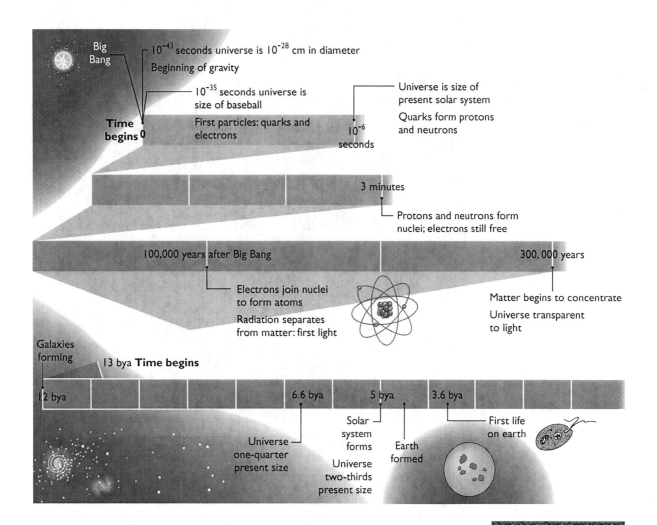

FIGURE 6.1

History of the universe, from the Big Bang to the origin of life on earth. The scale of the timeline changes because some events are condensed into incredibly small periods and others are stretched over unimaginable spans.

organisms from at least 2.7 bya, many of which were probably already capable of **photosynthesis.** This produced oxygen to about modern levels by 2.45 bya.

Just how life came about on the earth is also a matter of debate. For over forty years, scientists have been able to produce carbon-rich **organic** compounds from **inorganic** compounds with a fairly simple

organic Molecules that are part of living organisms. They are based on the chemistry of carbon and contain mostly hydrogen, oxygen, carbon, and nitrogen. Even carbon-based molecules that are not found in living things are sometimes referred to as organic.

inorganic A molecule not containing carbon.

FIGURE 6.2
Stromatolites in Australia, (*top*) are formed when mats of blue-green algae (single-celled organisms) are covered with sand, silt, and mud, which the algae cement down and then grow over. Fossil stromatolites (*bottom*), and thus the organisms that made them, have been dated to 3.5 bya.

laboratory procedure, showing that the process could have occurred quite easily. In fact, they have been able to produce amino acids, which, as you recall, are the building blocks of proteins. But as you also recall, proteins cannot be built without a nucleic acid code. Evidence now suggests that RNA formed very early in earth's history. RNA was able to replicate itself and act as a code for the synthesis of proteins. Later, DNA took over this role (Orgel 1994). It is still, of course, a long way from amino acids and RNA to a living organism, and the details of this path remain unclear.

Whatever happened, it happened fast (about 700 million years from the formation of the earth to life is fast, in the geological time scale), but once established, life at first evolved slowly. The world's first identifiable organisms were simple single cells like bacteria (Figure 6.3). It wasn't until about 2 bya that complex single-celled organisms containing nuclei and organelles evolved (see Figure 3.1). Multicellular organisms first appeared about 1.7 bya. The earliest evidence for simple life on land—bacteria—dates to 1.2 bya.

All these early single-celled organisms reproduced **asexually** by splitting and making copies of themselves. Evolutionary change relied entirely on mutations. Then about 1 bya, some organisms began to reproduce **sexually.** Sexual reproduction may have begun as a mechanism of genetic exchange to replace defective genes. Soon, however, it proved to be an accelerator of evolution. Now, in addition to mutation, fertilization also provided genetic and phenotypic variation, and evolutionary change quickly gained speed. Figure 6.4 summarizes what is known about the timing of important events in the evolution of life on earth.

About 543 mya, in the Cambrian period, complex multicellular organisms burst on the scene. Some even possessed hard parts like shells. So apparently sudden and rapid was this event that it is referred to as the *Cambrian explosion.* In a mere 5 million years, all major body plans of multicellular animals had evolved, including ancestors of the **vertebrates,** animals with backbones (Figure 6.5 on p. 116). So far, there are no agreed-upon explanations for this "explosion," but it is clearly a major event in the history of life, and it set the themes for the subsequent evolution of animals.

By 470 mya, plants and fungi had colonized the land. Fish had evolved and land animals had appeared by 425 mya. Insects appeared about 400 mya; by 350 mya, some of them had evolved wings. Reptiles showed up around 350 mya as well, and the reptilian form that is thought to have

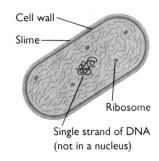

Cell wall

Slime

Ribosome

Single strand of DNA (not in a nucleus)

FIGURE 6.3
This typical bacterium represents some of the earliest forms of life on earth and what are still—in terms of time and numbers—the dominant forms of life today.

asexually Reproducing without sex, by fissioning or budding.

sexually Reproducing by combining genetic material from two individuals.

vertebrates Organisms with backbones and internal skeletons.

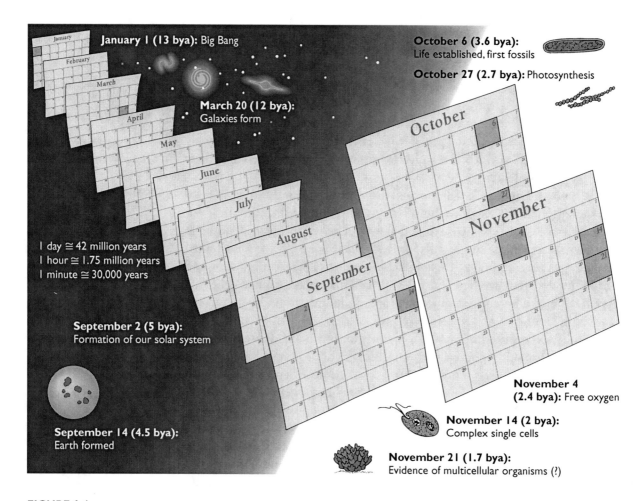

FIGURE 6.4
Astronomer Carl Sagan likened the history of the universe to a single calendar year in his 1975 Pulitzer Prize–winning book, *The Dragons of Eden*. This calendar has been recalculated to show the currently accepted dates for important events.
(Adapted from Sagan, 1977)

given rise to the mammals was found at about 256 mya. Dinosaurs began evolving around 235 mya, with true mammals appearing about 220 mya. Sometime around 150 mya, feathers evolved by a group of dinosaurs signaled the beginning of the evolution of birds (see Figure 5.4). Flowering plants appeared only a little more than 100 mya, and the primates, the group to which humans belong, showed up at least 55 mya and probably earlier.

December

Sexual reproduction (1 bya)

Land fungi and plants (700 mya)

Insects (400 mya)

reptiles (350 mya) Winged insects,

Flowering plants (100 mya)

K/T extinction (65 mya) First definite primates (55 mya)?

First soft-bodied animals (590 mya)

Cambrian explosion (543 mya) First vertebrates (530 mya)

First land plants (470 mya)

Fish, complex land plants, and land animals (425 mya)

Mammal-like reptiles (256 mya)

Dinosaurs (235 mya) True mammals (220 mya)

Birds (150 mya)

1:00 a.m. (40 mya): First monkeys

11:00 a.m. (23 mya): First apes

9:00 p.m. (5–6 mya): First direct human ancestors

10:30 p.m. (2.5 mya): First stone tools

11:22 p.m. (0.5 mya): First use of fire

11:59 p.m. (30,000 ya): Cave paintings

11:59:35 p.m. (12,000 ya): Farming

11:59:55 p.m. (2,000 ya): Common Era begins

11:59:59 p.m. (500 ya): Renaissance

FIGURE 6.4 (Continued)

FIGURE 6.5
Cambrian fauna consisted mostly of arthropods, ancestors of modern-day insects, spiders, and crustaceans. The large creature in the center grew to 3 feet long.

plate tectonics The movement of the plates of the earth's crust, caused by their interaction with the molten rock of the earth's interior. The cause of continental drift.

Pangea The supercontinent that included parts of all present-day landmasses.

DRIFTING CONTINENTS AND MASS EXTINCTIONS: THE PACE OF CHANGE

During all this time, life was not the only thing evolving on earth. The earth itself was also evolving as the continents changed shape and position, a phenomenon known as *continental drift*, which operates through the process of **plate tectonics.** The outer layer of rock on the earth, the *crust*, is in a constant state of change. It is broken into some sixteen *plates* of various sizes that fit together like a huge spherical jigsaw puzzle. The motion of the molten rock, *magma*, below the crust causes the plates to change shape and location. In some areas, magma seeps up between the plates and solidifies, pushing the plates apart. Something has to give, and at other boundaries called *subduction zones*, one plate is pushed under another and plunges deep within the earth, where it melts and adds to the magma. Clearly, then, the continents—those parts of the plates that protrude above sea level—have shifted over time and will continue to do so (Figure 6.6). Plate tectonics accounts for important geological phenomena. Where the plates meet and

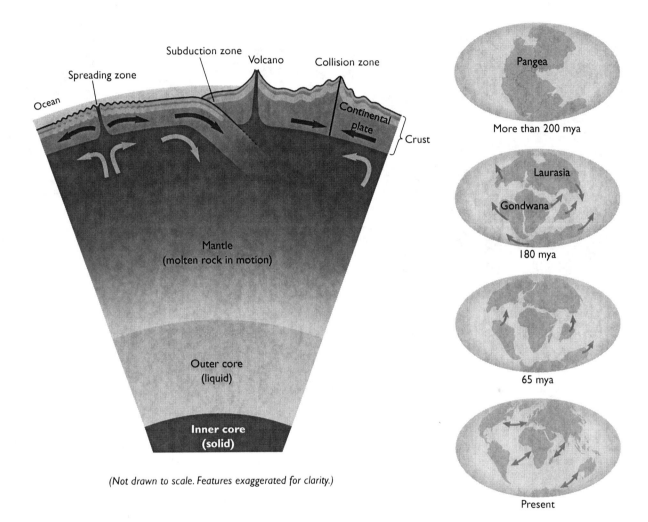

Spreading zone

Subduction zone

Volcano

Collision zone

Ocean

Continental plate

Crust

Mantle
(molten rock in motion)

Outer core
(liquid)

**Inner core
(solid)**

(Not drawn to scale. Features exaggerated for clarity.)

Pangea

More than 200 mya

Laurasia

Gondwana

180 mya

65 mya

Present

move against one another, tremendous forces are produced that result in earthquakes and volcanoes and cause mountains to grow.

By the time the dinosaurs and early mammals appeared, all the continents had drifted together to form a huge supercontinent we call **Pangea,** literally "all lands." This is why, for example, we find fossils of the same type of dinosaur in what are now such widely separated places as China, North America, and Antarctica. Around 200 mya, Pangea began to break up, and the resulting landmasses—the ancestors of our present-day continents—drifted over the globe, producing a diversity of environments and geographic boundaries that has profoundly affected the nature of life on earth as we know it today.

From all we've discussed so far, it would seem that the evolution of the earth and of life—influenced by continental drift and the environmental

FIGURE 6.6

This cross section of the earth shows the process of plate tectonics and the resultant drift of the continents over the past 200 million years. Continental drift, of course, occurred prior to 200 mya and will continue into the future.

FIGURE 6.7

This painting, by Rudolph Zallinger, reflects some now outdated ideas about the appearance and behavior of the dinosaurs. It does show, however, some of the variety of these creatures as they existed over 170 million years of time (*from left to right in the mural*). The dinosaurs once dominated the earth's environments.

changes it brings about—has been a steady process. And basically it has been—relative to the immense amount of time involved. But the fossil record shows that at least five times in the planet's history some change has taken place that was so rapid and extensive that it radically altered the course of biological evolution by causing a mass extinction.

For example, about the time the continents were drifting together to form the supercontinent of Pangea—at the end of the Permian period (250 mya)—over 95 percent of all species of marine and terrestrial organisms suddenly became extinct. Some changes occurred to which none of the variants within all those species were adapted. The cause for this greatest of all mass extinctions is unknown, but a new hypothesis suggests it was the result of massive volcanic eruptions, possibly initiated by a meteor impact in what is now Siberia, that altered the planet's climate. At any rate, such a catastrophe certainly had a major effect on the future course of life's evolution.

Another mass extinction directly affected the evolution of our small section of the evolutionary bush. About 65 mya, the dinosaurs were a dominant form of land animals. There were large reptiles in the seas and close relatives of the dinosaurs in the air (Figure 6.7). Mammals were also around and had been for nearly as long as the dinosaurs and had already begun to diversify into some of the forms known today.

Then one day—literally—an asteroid, thought to measure 6 miles across, crashed through the earth's atmosphere and into the crust where the north coast of the Mexican Yucatán is now. The impact made a crater 200 miles in diameter. The asteroid may have broken apart on impact with the atmosphere, and pieces may have hit in other locations as well.

This collision created a blast like that of a nuclear explosion. Thousands of cubic miles of vaporized rock, water vapor, and small particles and dust were shot into the atmosphere and carried around the world. Heat from the impact caused massive forest fires that created smoke and ash. One hypothesis suggests that the impact produced shock waves that bounced inside the earth and were focused on the opposite side of the planet, causing large-scale volcanic activity in what is now India, which put even more smoke and ash into the air. It has been noted that the Yucatán is rich in sulfur, suggesting that the impact might have produced sulfuric acid in the atmosphere, causing acid rain. All this matter created a blanket that blocked sunlight, cooling the earth and preventing green plants from carrying out photosynthesis.

These extensive environmental changes proved disastrous (a word that means, appropriately, "bad star"). Dinosaurs became extinct, along with every other species of land animal weighing more than about 55 pounds, many plants, and much of the ocean's plankton, the small organisms that provide a great deal of the world's oxygen and that serve a vital role at the base of the food chain. This event is the famous *Cretaceous/Tertiary (K/T) extinction* (Cretaceous is abbreviated K to distinguish it from the earlier Carboniferous).

But many of the mammals survived. By a stroke of luck, they were already adapted to withstand adverse, changing conditions. Now, with the dinosaurs suddenly gone, a whole world of niches was opened to them and to many other creatures that had made it through the catastrophe. This group included some of the birds, thought by many to be the dinosaurs' only living direct descendants (Figure 6.8).

Contemporary Reflections

Are Mass Extinctions a Thing of the Past?

Extinction is part of evolution. For one reason or another, species become extinct all the time. An estimated 90 percent of all species that have ever existed are now extinct.

But the idea of some intense event that can bring about the extinction of up to 95 percent of the earth's living forms over a short period of time seems inconceivable to us. And yet, at least five such events have occurred over the 3.6-billion-year history of life on this planet. The best known of these wiped out the dinosaurs—a long-lived and very successful group of species—65 mya. Surely, we think, these events were part of the earth's "formative" years and could not happen again. Sadly, this view is incorrect—for two reasons.

First, we know that the mass extinction that included the dinosaurs was initiated by the impact of a huge asteroid, and impacts are associated with some of the other mass extinctions as well. Although such impacts were more common in the past, asteroids, comets, and fragments of them are far from used up. Lots of them still orbit through our solar system. Go outside on any clear night, look up long enough, and you're bound to see one of the smaller ones burn up as it hits the earth's atmosphere. These are so-called shooting stars. Bigger ones, parts of which survive the atmosphere, hit the earth regularly (although most are neither seen nor found).

And on occasion we encounter very large ones. A few years ago, an asteroid large enough to do serious damage missed the earth by a mere 250,000 miles—the distance between the earth and the moon, a near miss on the cosmic scale. It was not seen until it had already passed us!

In 1908 a large portion of an asteroid or a fragment of a comet nucleus exploded 6 miles up in the atmosphere over Siberia. The shock waves were heard 600 miles away and flattened trees over 770 square miles. It's altogether possible, then, that our planet will be hit by another large object from space in the future, and if it's big enough, devastating consequences will follow, including the extinction of many species.

But there is a second reason why mass extinctions are not things of the past—a reason even more disturbing since (unlike the situation with asteroids) we *could* do something about it. There is, in fact, a sixth mass extinction in earth's history, and it is happening right now.

Starting about 10,000 ya, species began becoming extinct at a rate faster than usual. At present, species are disappearing at a rate at least as fast as, and probably faster than, during any of the previous five mass extinctions (Eldredge 1991, 1995; Leakey and Lewin 1995). Estimates vary, but the earth may be losing species at a rate of 27,000 a year—that's 3 every hour. Now, one might argue that given what we know of earth's history, extinctions—even mass ones—are "natural." Well, they have been; but this one is different. Unlike the other extinctions, where the conditions causing the problem eventually went away, this situation is unlikely to get better because, as biologist Niles Eldredge says, "the irritant . . . remains on the scene" (1995:128). That "irritant," of course, is us.

Since we figured out how to control natural food sources through farming and animal husbandry some 12,000 ya, our species' population has grown at an ever-increasing rate. Our need for resources, energy, and space has grown along with our numbers. We have pushed other species into marginal areas, destroyed their habitats and resources, and hunted or otherwise exploited them to extinction. We are well into the process of changing the very climate of the earth as our emissions into the atmosphere are causing the world's climate to change.

Although we may or may not experience the catastrophic death and destruction of an asteroid impact, we are—*right now*—in the midst of what may be the biggest and fastest of all mass extinctions. Decidedly *not* a thing of the past.

FIGURE 6.8
The wild turkey shows a striking similarity to bipedal dinosaurs, further evidence of the evolutionary relationship between dinosaurs and birds.

It took a while, but by about 40 mya, all the major types of mammals we know today had appeared—everything from bats to whales to a group of tree-dwelling creatures possessed of acute eyesight, dexterous hands, and large, inquisitive brains. These were the primates, and it is this group that we shall focus on in the next chapters.

SUMMARY

This narrative of the history of the universe has been necessarily brief, but it does point out three themes that are important to remember as we continue.

First, it could be said—by virtue of human numbers (over 6 billion) and our impact on the planet—that we are the dominant species on the earth today. But our evolutionary history makes up a small fraction of the whole history of the universe and even of the earth. We are the new kids on the evolutionary block, and we have not as yet even proved ourselves successful by the criterion of longevity. Cockroaches have been around hundreds of times longer than we have; bacteria have been around since the beginning of the fossil record. By these standards, our species is in its infancy.

Second, as the Bible says, "there is no new thing under the sun." Indeed, although we often speak of the "origin of the earth" or the "origin of life," the only *real* origin is that of the universe itself. All the events subsequent to that have been *rearrangements* of what already existed: matter condensing from energy as it cools; large atomic particles forming from smaller ones; stars coming together from cosmic dust; heavy elements being created from lighter ones in the nuclear furnaces of those stars; the elements of inorganic molecules being rearranged to form the molecules of life; and the shuffling of the genetic code, producing the extraordinary multitude of living things that have inhabited this planet.

Third, and perhaps most humbling, the specific history of the universe, including the earth and its life, could have happened in countless other ways. Each event in our story is contingent on preceding events. Even our evolution is dependent on the specific sequence of events that came before it. If those events had been different, *we* might be different—or we might not be here at all. Imagine if that asteroid had *not* hit the earth 65 mya. In other words, the evolution of humans—or anything else for that matter— was not inevitable. We're lucky we're here.

QUESTIONS FOR FURTHER THOUGHT

1. Consider a question from Chapter 5 from a more specific perspective: We humans may be bringing about the extinction of a large number of other species, but for some of them, what real difference does it make? We hear about such endangered species as the snail darter (a small North American fish), the spotted owl, and the Texas blind salamander. Would it really matter, beyond an ethical or an aesthetic consideration, if any of these became extinct?

2. The astronomer Carl Sagan once referred to human beings as "star stuff." He meant it literally. How so? What does this say about the nature of evolution, both on a biological and a cosmic level?

KEY TERMS

photosynthesis	asexually	plate tectonics
organic	sexually	Pangea
inorganic	vertebrates	

SUGGESTED READINGS

For a good summary of cosmology—the history of the universe—see the February 2000 issue of *Natural History,* especially "Genesis: The Sequel," by Alan Guth. For a good discussion of the science behind our understanding of the history of the universe, I recommend *Coming of Age in the Milky Way*, by Timothy Ferris.

The evolution of life is covered in the lavishly illustrated *The Book of Life*, edited by Stephen Jay Gould. For a good narrative approach, see *Life*, by Richard Fortey, and for a more technical but still readable work, see *History of Life*, second edition, by Richard Cowen. *National Geographic* has a series of articles called "The Rise of Life on Earth" in the March 1998, April 1998, May 1999, February 2000, and September 2000 issues.

The Cambrian explosion is the subject of an article by R. Gore in the October 1993 *National Geographic*: "The Cambrian Period: Explosion of Life." It is also the focus of Stephen Jay Gould's *Wonderful Life* and Simon Conway Morris's *The Crucible of Creation*. These two well-respected authorities disagree on the meaning of the Cambrian fossils and the nature of evolution as a series of contingent events. For a summary of their debate, see "Showdown on the Burgess Shale," by Conway Morris and Gould, in the December 1998/January 1999 *Natural History*.

For a good discussion of the origin of feathers, see "Which Came First, the Feather or the Bird?" by Richard O. Prum and Alan H. Brush in the March 2003 *Scientific American*. And for some of the newest evidence of the dinosaur-bird link, see "Feather Quill Knobs in the Dinosaur *Velociraptor*," by Alan Turner, Peter Makovicky, and Mark Norell in the 21 September 2007 *Science*.

An article on those volcanoes in India, with some impressive pictures, is in the 21 March 2008 *Science*, in "Sulfur and Chlorine in Late Cretaceous Deccan Magmas and Eruptive Gas Release," by Stephen Self et al. Don't let the title put you off; look at the pictures.

New research on the evolution of mammals is in "Transformation and Diversification in Early Mammal Evolution," by Zhe-Xi Luo in the 13 December 2007 *Nature*.

The subject of mass extinctions in general is discussed in Edward O. Wilson's *Diversity of Life* and in an article in the June 1989 *National Geographic*: "Extinctions," by R. Gore.

The link between extraterrestrial collisions and mass extinctions is explored in "Repeated Blows," by Luann Becker, in the March 2002 *Scientific American*.

To see animations of continental drift, go to www.scotese.com/pangeanim .htm. A good site on the geology of North America is http://tapestry .usgs.gov/Default.html. It's called "A Tapestry of Time and Terrain" and features a section called "Rocks of Ages" that discusses the different geological divisions of earth history.

CHAPTER

7

The Primates

> *I confess freely to you, I could never look long upon a monkey, without very mortifying reflections.*
> —William Congreve (1695)

"The proper study of mankind is man," said the poet Alexander Pope. The last few chapters should have convinced you that even biological anthropologists, who by definition focus on the study of humankind, cannot limit their interests to just our own species. The processes that have produced modern *Homo sapiens* are the processes that have produced every single species that has ever inhabited this planet. Additionally, all those species are part of an integrated whole, composed of all environments and all living things in complex interaction with one another across geographical space and through evolutionary time.

Moreover, were we to limit our study just to our species, we would lose a great deal of perspective. We need to compare ourselves with other forms of life to see in what ways we are similar and in what ways we differ. This comparison is made all the more important because we *are* the species we are studying, and so it can be difficult to be objective about ourselves. Thus, primatology is an important part of anthropology.

In this chapter we will address several important questions:

What is our place in nature; that is, where do we fit—from a scientifically objective point of view—in the world of living things?

What are the characteristics of the primates—the group of animals of which we are a part?

In what ways are humans like the other primates? In what ways are we unique?

NAMING THE ANIMALS

Recognition of some relationship among living things is not new. It is probably as old as human intellect itself. But formalizing this recognition was not always seen as important, even to the emerging science of biology at the beginning of the eighteenth century. After all, plants and animals were then thought to be the unchanging products of divine creation, and an understanding of the evolutionary implications of biological relationships was many years in the future.

Linnaean Taxonomy

One eighteenth-century biologist, however, thought that a formalized view of the relationships was important, even though he thought species were specially created and forever fixed. This was the Swedish botanist Carl von Linné (1707–1778), introduced in Chapter 2, known to us by his Latinized name, Carolus Linnaeus. Linnaeus sought to devise a system of names that would reflect the relationships among all the plants and animals on earth. He felt, of course, that he was proposing a way to describe what God had in mind when He created living things. The system he came up with is still used today, and it carries more meaning than Linnaeus dreamed it would.

Linnaeus created a system of nested categories of increasing specificity. The largest category contains gradually smaller categories, ending with the most specific, the species. Such a classification system is known as a **taxonomy,** and Linnaeus proposed his taxonomy for living organisms in his *Systema Naturae*, published in final form in 1758.

Our present taxonomic system, based on Linnaeus's original scheme, uses seven (or more when needed) basic categories: kingdom, phylum (plural, *phyla*), class, order, family, genus (plural, *genera*), and species. Each organism classified is given a name indicating its place within each of these categories and, thus, its relationship to other organisms. Table 7.1 shows a taxonomy of five familiar species.

All these are obviously members of the animal kingdom and share inclusion in phylum Chordata (essentially, animals with internal skeletons, especially backbones) (Table 7.2). All are also obviously mammals, and all are primates (the group we'll describe in detail below). But then, as you can see at a glance, they divide into two intuitive groups: one group comprises humans; the other is made up of the apes, which all share some common phenotypic features. Thus, they separate at the family level. The chimp and bonobo share a genus but differentiate at the species level. So,

taxonomy A classification using nested sets of categories of increasing specificity

TABLE 7.1
Traditional Linnaean Taxonomy of Five Familiar Species

	Human	Chimpanzee	Bonobo	Gorilla	Orangutan
Kingdom	Animalia	Animalia	Animalia	Animalia	Animalia
Phylum	Chordata	Chordata	Chordata	Chordata	Chordata
Class	Mammalia	Mammalia	Mammalia	Mammalia	Mammalia
Order	Primates	Primates	Primates	Primates	Primates
Family	Hominidae	Pongidae	Pongidae	Pongidae	Pongidae
Genus	Homo	Pan	Pan	Gorilla	Pongo
Species	sapiens	troglodytes	paniscus	gorilla	pygmaeus

TABLE 7.2
Traditional Linnaean Taxonomy of Humans (with defining criteria)

Kingdom	**Animalia**
	Ingestion
	Movement
	Sense organs
Phylum	**Chordata**
	Notochord
Class	**Mammalia**
	Hair
	Warm-blooded
	Live birth
	Mammary glands
	Active and intelligent
Order	**Primates**
	Arboreal
	Developed vision
	Grasping hands
	Large brains
Family	**Hominidae**
	Habitual bipeds
Genus	**Homo**
	Toolmaking
	Omnivore
Species	**sapiens**
	Brain size 1,000–2,000 ml*

*Note: This definition is a matter of controversy and will be taken up in Chapters 11 and 12.

even if you didn't know these animals, you could tell how they are related, phenotypically, to one another.

Now, as far as Linnaeus knew, he was describing a static, divinely created system of living things. We now know that a taxonomy also reflects evolutionary relationships, because the degree of similarity between two organisms is a direct result of the amount of time they have been evolutionarily separated. So, although a taxonomy can't tell us specific dates for branchings, we can infer from it the relative times of these evolutionary events.

Figure 7.1 is a tree showing the relative times of branching for the five primates in the table, inferred from their taxonomic categories. Each taxonomic difference is reflected by a branching point on the tree.

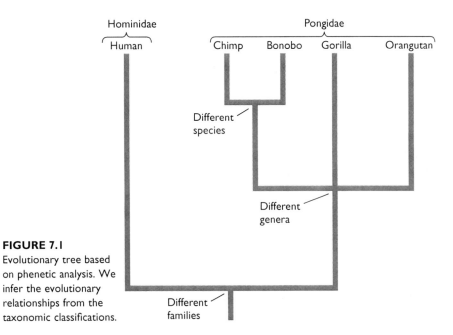

FIGURE 7.1
Evolutionary tree based on phenetic analysis. We infer the evolutionary relationships from the taxonomic classifications.

FIGURE 7.2
Accurate evolutionary tree based on cladistic analysis.

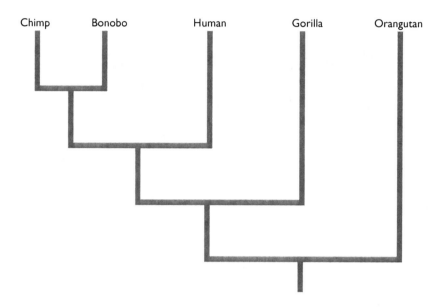

Chimp   Bonobo   Human   Gorilla   Orangutan

Cladistic Taxonomy

There are, however, problems with a Linnaean (or **phenetic**) taxonomy. Because evolution can occur at different rates and in different directions in various evolutionary lines, modern similarities and differences don't always reflect evolutionary branching patterns. Our categories are subjective; we place organisms in the same group based on our judgment of which phenotypic features seem to us most important and diagnostic. As an example (Ridley 1996:373), we easily place lizards and crocodiles in one group and birds in another. This makes intuitive sense. When compared with birds, crocodiles and lizards simply *look* more alike.

But with new genetic technologies (see Chapter 9 for more details) and with increasingly better fossil records, we are able to reconstruct the actual order of branching for existing (and extinct) species, the actual shape of the evolutionary tree. Thus, we now know that birds and crocodiles are more closely related than are crocodiles and lizards. Birds and crocodiles belong to a group that excludes lizards. And for the five species in Table 7.1, Figure 7.2 shows the actual branching order (and we also have a good idea as to the times of the branchings, which we'll discuss in Chapter 10). Notice how it differs from the inferred order of Figure 7.1. And notice, too, that the ape-human distinction no longer holds. There is

phenetics A classification system based on existing phenotypic features and adaptations.

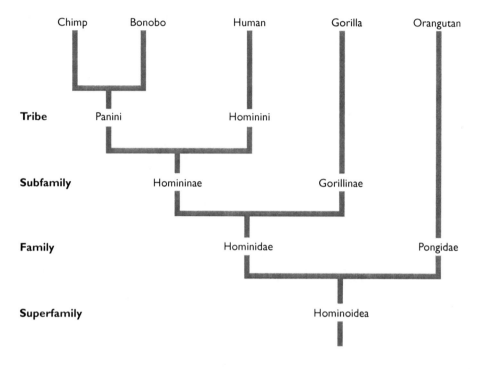

	Chimp	Bonobo	Human	Gorilla	Orangutan

Tribe   Panini   Hominini

Subfamily   Homininae   Gorillinae

Family   Hominidae   Pongidae

Superfamily   Hominoidea

FIGURE 7.3
One possible taxonomic classification based on cladistic analysis. Note that new categories have had to be added.

no group (called a *sister group*) that includes humans but excludes all the apes, no matter what the living species look like.

Now, each branching point (called a *node*) requires a taxonomic name, and so we might find ourselves having to create new levels. Figure 7.3 shows one scheme for classifying these primates based on the order of branching, an approach to taxonomy called **cladistics** (*clade* means "branch"). Under this model, all the *African* apes (the orangutan is native to Asia) and humans are now included in family Hominidae and are thus called **hominids,** a term once applied only to humans (see again Table 7.1). We humans and our direct ancestors are now in tribe Hominini and are called **hominins.**

While there is an ongoing and complex debate about phenetic versus cladistic schemes (see Ridley 1996), I lean toward the more objective cladistic model. It reflects the actual branching pattern and not what we perceive and decide about the end products of those branches. Thus, throughout this book, we will refer to all the African apes *and* humans as *hominids*; the term *hominins,* however, will refer only to humans, both living and extinct.

Now, let's focus on the adaptive strategies and the phenotypic traits that characterize the members of order Primates.

cladistics A classification system based on order of branching rather than on present similarities and differences.

hominids Modern humans and African apes and their direct ancestors. The term previously referred to humans only.

hominins Under a cladistic taxonomy, humans and our direct ancestors.

130   CHAPTER 7 ◆ The Primates

WHAT IS A PRIMATE?

There are about 200 living species of primates. We're not sure how many have existed during the order's evolutionary history of more than 55 million years. Primates range from the very small, such as the mouse lemur of Madagascar, which weighs less than 3 ounces, to the gigantic—*Gigantopithecus*, an extinct ape from China, Vietnam, and India that may have stood 12 feet tall and weighed over half a ton (Figure 7.4). Some primates inhabit small, very specific environmental ranges and spend their lives slowly moving through the trees, eating fruits, leaves, or insects; one species of primate lives in nearly every environment and produces its own food.

Its wide variety makes the primate order a bit difficult to define in a simple sentence. The primates are best defined by looking at the characteristics they have in common and in seeing how these traits facilitate the primate adaptive strategy. We'll look at the primate traits by using the following categories: (1) the senses, (2) movement, (3) reproduction, (4) intelligence, and (5) behavior patterns.

FIGURE 7.4
Here we compare a mouse lemur, the smallest living primate, with a human and with *Gigantopithecus,* now extinct, the largest primate ever (see Chapter 10).

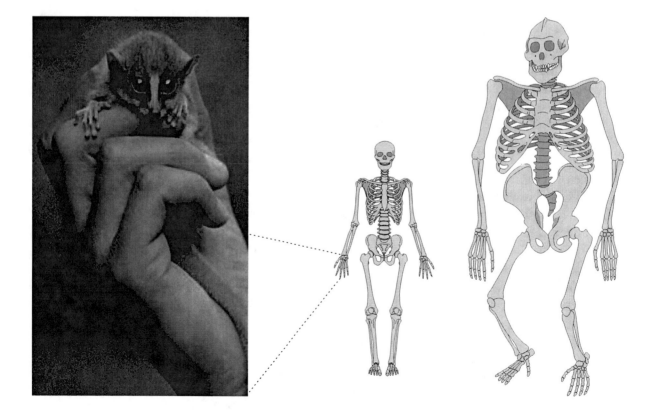

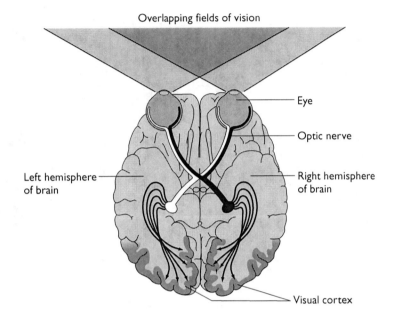

Overlapping fields of vision

Eye

Optic nerve

Left hemisphere of brain

Right hemisphere of brain

Visual cortex

FIGURE 7.5
Stereoscopic vision. The fields of vision overlap, and the optic nerve from each eye travels to both hemispheres of the brain. The result is true depth perception.

The Senses

Bats and dolphins live in worlds of sound. Dogs live in a world of smells. The primates live in a visual world. Vision is the primates' predominant sense.

Most of the so-called higher primates see in color, and all primates see in three dimensions. They have true depth perception (technically called **stereoscopic vision**), which is possible because the eyes face forward and see the same scene from slightly different angles (Figure 7.5). The nerves and muscles of most primate eyes are enclosed within a protective bony socket. Look at your surroundings. What you are able to see is what the majority of primates could see if they were in your place.

Other primate senses are not as acute as in many mammals. Primates lack the auditory (hearing) and olfactory (smelling) sensitivity of such familiar animals as dogs, cats, and cattle. Furthermore, and obviously related to the less acute sense of smell, primates tend to lack a snout and so have a relatively flat face. There is, as you might expect for a group of 200 species, some variation among primates. Many members of one group of primates (the prosimians, which we'll discuss later in this chapter) are nocturnal and lack color vision, but they have better senses of smell and hearing than do monkeys, apes, and humans.

stereoscopic vision Three-dimensional vision; depth perception.

FIGURE 7.6
An orangutan holding its trainer's hand demonstrates the prehensile grip shared by nonhuman and human primates.

Movement

Like most mammals, primates are, with one exception, **quadrupedal.** Although many primates can stand or even walk on two legs for short periods, humans are the only habitually **bipedal** primates. Unlike most mammals, primates have extremely flexible limbs, and their hands (and in many cases their feet) have the ability to grasp objects; that is, they are **prehensile** (Figure 7.6). Primates use this trait for several forms of locomotion. Some primates, called *vertical clingers and leapers,* jump from branch to branch or trunk to trunk using the grasping ability of all four limbs (see Figure 7.13). The apes are *suspensory climbers,* with the ability to hang and climb by the arms (see Figure 7.17). An extreme form of this mode of movement is **brachiation,** swinging arm-over-arm through the trees. When on the ground, most primates use all fours. Asia's orangutans walk on their fists. The African apes have a unique quadrupedalism, supporting themselves on the knuckles of their hands instead of the palms. Primate species may use one or more of these locomotor methods, depending on their anatomy and the situation.

In addition, most primates are able to touch their thumbs to the tips of the other fingers on the same hand, allowing them to pick up and manipulate small objects. This capacity is called **opposability.** Finally, most primates have nails rather than claws on the tips of the fingers and toes. These provide support for the sensitive tactile sense receptors of the fingers. In short, primates have manual dexterity. Some have a great degree of dexterity in the feet as well (see Figure 7.13).

quadrupedal Walking on all four limbs.

bipedal Walking on two legs.

prehensile Having the ability to grasp.

brachiation Locomotion by swinging arm-over-arm.

opposability The ability to touch the thumb to the tips of the other fingers on the same hand.

Reproduction

Most primate species give birth to one offspring at a time. Several primates, such as some of the marmosets from South America and some of the lemurs from Madagascar, normally produce twins or triplets. As is typical of mammals, primate parents take an active role in the protection, nurturing, and socialization of their young. Mostly because of their large, complex brains and because of the importance of learning, young primates are dependent on adults and take a long time to mature. How long, of course, varies according to the size of the primate species. The primates, relative to size, have the longest period of **postnatal dependency** of any mammal.

Intelligence

Intelligence can be defined as the relative ability of an organism's brain to acquire, store, retrieve, and process information. These abilities are related to brain size and brain complexity. A bigger brain has more room for all the complex nerve connections that make it work, just as a very sophisticated computer must necessarily be larger than a simple one. (Brain size variation *within* a species is another matter; in humans, for example, no substantiated correlation has been shown between brain size, within the normal range, and any reasonable measure of intelligence.) But brain size must also be looked at in a relative way: How big is the brain compared to the body it runs? A sperm whale, with its 20-pound brain, has a brain ten times the size of the average human's. A sperm whale's body, however, is over *five hundred* times the size of ours. We have bigger brains than whales have *relative* to the size of our bodies; we run less body with more brain, which is true of the primates in general. Of all land mammals, the primates have the largest relative brain sizes. The human brain, however, is three times the size one would expect for a primate of our body weight.

In addition, the primate brain is complex, especially in the neocortex, that part of the brain where memory, abstract thought, problem solving, and attentiveness take place (Figure 7.7). In short, the primates are smart.

Behavior Patterns

Primates are social animals. Most primate species live in groups. Many other animals do too, but even those few primate species—such as orangutans—that usually remain solitary still interact with other members of their species

postnatal dependency The period after birth during which offspring require the care of adults to survive.

intelligence The relative ability of the brain to acquire, store, retrieve, and process information.

FIGURE 7.7
The human brain and its major parts and functions. The lobes and the motor cortex are all part of the neocortex.

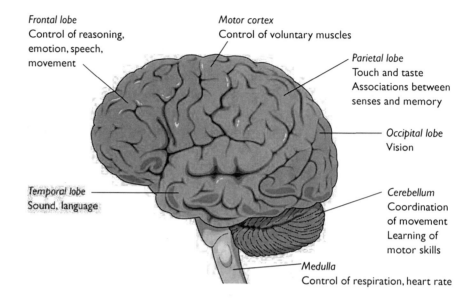

Frontal lobe
Control of reasoning, emotion, speech, movement

Motor cortex
Control of voluntary muscles

Parietal lobe
Touch and taste
Associations between senses and memory

Occipital lobe
Vision

Temporal lobe
Sound, language

Cerebellum
Coordination of movement
Learning of motor skills

Medulla
Control of respiration, heart rate

in far more complex ways than, say, antelopes interact within a herd, or even wolves within a pack. The difference is that primates recognize individuals, and the individual primate holds a particular status relative to others in its group and to the group as a whole. A primate group is made up of the collective relationships among all its individual members. We will see these relationships in action when we examine primate behavior more closely in Chapter 8.

As physical evidence of the importance of these relationships, it may be noted that primates are among the most colorful of mammals, and most of the color patterns of many primates, especially monkeys, are displayed on their faces (Figure 7.8). The attention of one primate to another is drawn to the face, to the primate's identity as an individual.

In some primates—baboons and chimpanzees, for example—each individual may have rather specific status within the group. Some have more social power and influence than others. They are said to be dominant, and the structure of the relative power and influence of a group's individuals is called a **dominance hierarchy.** In addition, most primate species recognize a special status for females with infants, and these mother-child units are well protected by other members of the group, even those that are not directly related to them (Figure 7.9). Among chimpanzees and baboons, we even see lasting relationships that can only be described as friendships.

dominance hierarchy
Individual differences among group members in terms of power, influence, and access to resources and mating.

FIGURE 7.8
We see here some colorful primate faces, including that of one primate that purposely enhances the color. Colorful faces are evidence of the importance of individual recognition within primate societies. Shown here (*clockwise from upper left*) are a Chinese white-handed gibbon, a mandrill, a human, and a bald uakari.

FIGURE 7.9
Male baboon protecting mother and young. The female holding her baby at left was being threatened by the boisterous play of a group of adolescent males, out of the picture to the right. The adult male in the center stepped in and barked at the group, which quickly took its play elsewhere. (These baboons are part of a captive troop.)

Primate social groups are maintained through communication. Primates have large repertoires of vocalizations, facial expressions, and body gestures. Touch is also an important form of communication among primates and often takes the form of **grooming,** an activity that serves not only the practical purpose of removing dirt and parasites but also as a source of reassurance to maintain group harmony and unity (Figure 7.10).

How, then, may we characterize the primate adaptive strategy? It is important to acknowledge the environment that the primates are adapted *to*. The basic primate environment is arboreal. To be sure, several species—gorillas, for instance—spend more time on the ground than in the branches, and we humans are thoroughly terrestrial. But the majority of primates spend most of their time in the trees, and the primate traits in the preceding discussion all evolved in response to an arboreal environment. Even the partially and completely terrestrial primates possess

grooming Here, cleaning the fur of another animal, which promotes social cohesion.

FIGURE 7.10
Primate communication and grooming. (*Top*) A chimp exhibits a *pant-hoot,* a call used when a food source is found, when two groups join together, or to communicate over distances. (*Bottom*) Grooming serves not only to rid these Francois's langurs (monkeys from Southeast Asia) of parasites and dirt but also to maintain group unity and harmony.

features that are variations on the arboreal adaptive theme. So, we can define primates in the following way:

> The primates are mammals adapted to an arboreal environment through well-developed vision, manual dexterity, and large, complex brains; their adaptation relies on learned behavior, which is aided by the birth of few offspring at a time and the direct and extensive care of those offspring during a long period of dependency while they are socialized into groups based on differential relationships among individuals.

Such a complex group of organisms requires a lengthy description.

FIGURE 7.11
A primate taxonomy using cladistic categories. The numbers in parentheses refer to the number of groups in that category.

A SURVEY OF THE LIVING PRIMATES

Figure 7.11 is a cladistic taxonomy of the approximately 200 species of living primates. For the sake of space, some categories are indicated only by the number of groups within them; for instance, there are six families of prosimians.

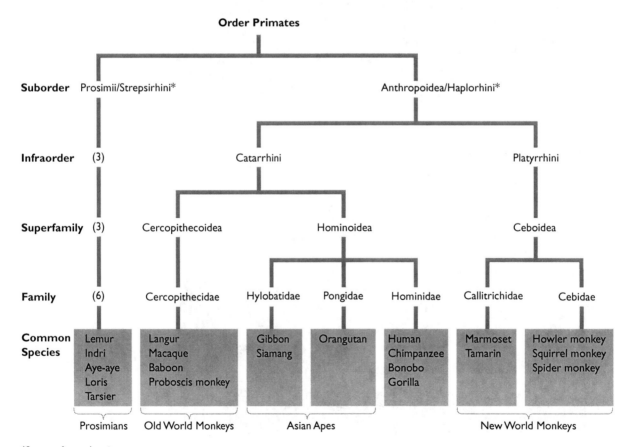

*See text for explanation.

One of the first things you should notice are the new categories here as compared with those shown in Table 7.1. *Suborder, infraorder,* and *superfamily* have been added between the traditional Linnaean categories of *order* and *family.* (A complete taxonomy of insects, for example, a class with over 750,000 *known* species, is, as you can well imagine, incredibly complex.)

Prosimians

The order Primates is traditionally divided into two major suborders, Prosimii and Anthropoidea. Prosimians ("pre-apes") represent the most primitive primates, that is, those that most closely resemble the earliest primates. At first widespread, prosimians were pushed into marginal areas as newer, more adaptively flexible primates evolved. Some modern prosimians live on the mainlands of Africa, India, and Southeast Asia and on the isolated islands of Southeast Asia, but the majority inhabit the island of Madagascar (Figure 7.12).

The forty or so living species of prosimians exhibit a number of differences from the general primate pattern. About half of the prosimian species are nocturnal and so lack color vision. They have large eyes that can gather more light, as well as better than average senses of smell and

FIGURE 7.12
Distribution of living nonhuman primates.

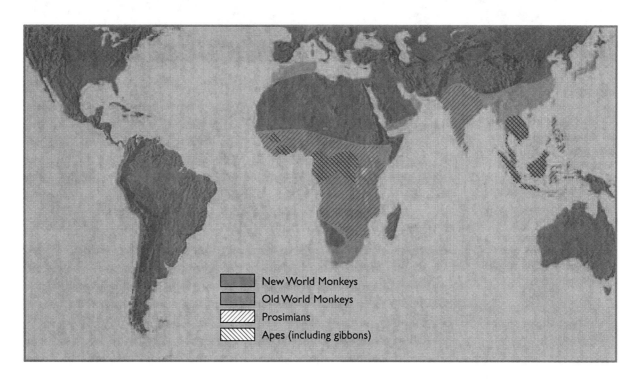

New World Monkeys
Old World Monkeys
Prosimians
Apes (including gibbons)

FIGURE 7.13
Two prosimians. The slender loris of India and Sri Lanka (*left*) has the large eyes and moist, naked nose characteristic of this suborder. Note also the prehensile hands and feet and the grooming claw on one toe of the foot at the top of the picture (*see arrow*). The crowned lemur of Madagascar (*right*) displays a posture that is typical of the locomotor pattern called *vertical clinging and leaping*. All the Madagascar primates are endangered.

hearing (Figure 7.13). To aid their olfactory sense, they have a protruding snout with a large smell receptor area (the mucous membranes within the nose) and a moist, naked outer nose (like that of a dog or cat) to help pick up the molecules that make up olfactory signals. Prosimians do have the stereoscopic vision characteristic of primates, because they need to judge distances in bushes and trees, and their three-dimensional vision helps them catch insects, a favorite food of many prosimian species.

Prosimians have prehensile hands and feet, but the opposability of their thumbs is limited. Many can only touch the thumb with the other four digits together; their digits don't move independently. Some prosimians have claws instead of the typical primate nails on a couple of fingers or toes. These are known as *grooming claws* and are used both for that purpose and to help acquire food.

A few species of lemurs from Madagascar give birth to twins or even triplets on a regular basis. Transporting the infants through the trees,

FIGURE 7.14
Philippine tarsier. Note the huge eyes (each eyeball is as big as the entire brain) for nocturnal vision, the enlarged fingertips and toetips, and the powerfully built legs with elongated ankles.

however, is no problem because an adult male or an older sibling often helps the mother carry and care for her infants. At other times, the infants are kept in a nest.

A particularly interesting primate is the tarsier of Southeast Asia (Figure 7.14). Weighing just 4 to 5 ounces, this little insect eater has powerful hind limbs for jumping, enlarged fingertips and toetips for added friction, and the ability to turn its head 180 degrees in either direction, like an owl. Its name comes from its elongated ankle (or *tarsal*) bones, which make its legs look as if they bend too many times.

The tarsier is another example of the debate within primate taxonomy. Because of its flat face, upright posture when clinging to trunks and branches, lack of the moist, naked nose of other prosimians, and some recent genetic comparisons, some authorities suggest placing the tarsier in the second primate suborder, Anthropoidea. Cladists go further. Focusing on the fact that all prosimians have the moist nose but that no anthropoids do, they suggest dividing order Primates into suborders based on that trait. The former prosimians would thus be in suborder Strepsirhini ("nose with curved nostrils"), and the anthropoids would become suborder Haplorhini ("simple nose"). The latter group would include the tarsier because of its nose, color vision, and other traits.

Anthropoids

The anthropoid ("humanlike") primates include monkeys, apes, and humans. Suborder Anthropoidea is further divided into two infraorders, Platyrrhini and Catarrhini. This division is based on a geographic separation of early primates into a Western Hemisphere (or New World) group and an Eastern Hemisphere (or Old World) group. All the New World platyrrhine primates are monkeys. The Old World catarrhine primates comprise monkeys, apes, and humans. Despite the fact that humans now inhabit the entire globe, we first evolved in the Old World, in Africa.

Several features distinguish New World from Old World primates. The most obvious is the nose. *Platyrrhine* means "broad-nosed," and the noses of the Central and South American monkeys have widely spaced nostrils separated by a broad septum (Figure 7.15). By comparison, *catarrhine* is

FIGURE 7.15
Northern woolly spider monkey, a platyrrhine primate from Brazil. Note the prehensile tail with the bare strip of skin on the inner surface to enhance its grasping ability. Note also the typical platyrrhine nose (see also Figure 7.8 *bottom left*).

translated "hook-nosed." The typical Old World nose has closely spaced nostrils that face downward. Just look in the mirror.

New World and Old World anthropoids also have different dental formulas, that is, the number of each type of tooth in each quadrant of the mouth. Old World anthropoids have two incisors, one canine, two premolars (bicuspids), and three molars. This is written as $\frac{2.1.2.3}{2.1.2.3} \times 2 = 32$. Some of the New World anthropoids have four extra premolars: $\frac{2.1.3.3}{2.1.3.3} \times 2 = 36$. Other New World anthropoids have four extra premolars but four fewer molars: $\frac{2.1.3.2}{2.1.3.2} \times 2 = 32$.

Moreover, because New World monkeys are almost entirely arboreal, they have evolved long limbs, and some have clawlike nails. Several species also have evolved prehensile tails and thus effectively have five grasping limbs. No Old World monkey evolved this adaptation. Finally, two groups of platyrrhines, the marmosets and tamarins, normally give birth to twins.

The Old World primates are divided into two superfamilies. The monkeys of Europe (now limited to Gibraltar), Africa, and Asia make up superfamily Cercopithecoidea. Apes and humans are in superfamily Hominoidea, which is further divided into three families.

There are about 75 species of cercopithecoids (Figure 7.16). They have the nasal shape and tooth number of all Old World primates, and most

FIGURE 7.16
Rhesus monkey, a catarrhine primate from Asia. Note the more closely spaced nostrils as compared to the platyrrhine (New World) monkey in Figure 7.15. (See also Figure 7.8, *top left* and *right* and *bottom right,* and Figure 7.10, *bottom.*) The rhesus has been important in medical and behavioral experimentation. The Rh blood factor was named after it.

have tails. Males tend to be larger than females, a trait not common in New World species. Also unlike the platyrrhines, the Old World monkeys have fully opposable thumbs. The monkeys of the Eastern Hemisphere seem more adaptively flexible than those of the New World. At home in the trees, many cercopithecoids are equally comfortable on the ground. They live everywhere from the deserts of Africa and the Middle East to the mountains of northern Japan.

Superfamily Hominoidea contains the larger, tailless primates. The hominoids—the apes and humans—are generally larger than the monkeys and have larger brains, both relatively and absolutely. Their brains also have larger neocortexes, meaning that the hominoids are more intelligent, as we have defined that term. Finally, a series of traits make the hominoids good suspensory climbers and hangers; they are adapted to an arboreal environment through the ability to climb and hang from branches with their arms. The traits behind this ability are a flexible shoulder joint, a more posterior shoulder blade than in monkeys, and a stronger collarbone (clavicle) for added support. Although modern humans do not display the ability to climb or hang using the arms as often or as well as the apes, we still possess it, as demonstrated by gymnasts on the high bar or rings.

Family Hylobatidae includes the gibbons and siamangs of Southeast Asia and Malaysia. Sometimes referred to as *lesser apes,* they are noted for their brachiating mode of locomotion (Figure 7.17). They also have an unusual social organization for primates. Male and female hylobatids form a monogamous pair, though not neccessarily a permanent one.

There are four species collectively known as the *great apes* (Figure 7.18): the orangutan of Southeast Asia (family Pongidae) and the gorilla (possibly two species), chimpanzee, and bonobo of Africa (along with us, in family Hominidae).

The great apes are large (a male gorilla in the wild may weigh 450 pounds), with heavy, powerful jaws used for eating a wide range of fruits, nuts, and vegetables. Chimps and bonobos also eat meat on occasion. The apes are quadrupeds, although chimps, gorillas, and especially bonobos are fairly good at upright walking for short distances. Orangutans are solitary, but the other apes live in social groups marked by some degree of dominance but otherwise with fairly loose organization and changeable group membership.

The apes have relatively large brains; a large chimp may have a brain half the size of the smallest modern human brain. Apes are intelligent.

FIGURE 7.17
White-handed gibbon from
Southeast Asia. Note the
long, hooklike fingers and the
grasping feet.

They have, for example, an intimate knowledge of a large number of food
sources, many of which ripen seasonally or grow in limited areas.

Some chimpanzees can make simple tools; the best known is their
termite "fishing stick," a modified twig or blade of grass they insert into
a hole in a termite mound and wiggle around to stimulate an attack by
the insects. The termites cling to the "invader," and the chimps draw out
a tasty meal (Figure 7.19). Other chimps have been seen using rocks to
break open hard-shelled nuts. Chimps are also known to cooperatively

FIGURE 7.18
The great apes. Shown here (*clockwise from top left*) are the orangutan of Southeast Asia and the gorilla, bonobo, and chimpanzee of Africa.

FIGURE 7.19

Chimps using tools they have made to extract termites from their mound.

hunt small animals, including other primates, and meat is the one food source that chimps will share with one another (see Chapter 8). And in 2007 it was reported that some chimps in Senegal had been seen sharpening sticks with their teeth to use as spears for stabbing and extracting galagos (also called *bush babies*, small nocturnal primates) from their daytime holes in trees.

Finally, apes have a large repertoire of calls, facial expressions, and body gestures with which they communicate information, mostly about emotional states. Although this form of communication is nothing like human language, some individuals from all the great ape species have been taught to use nonvocal versions of human languages, most notably American Sign Language (Ameslan), developed for the hearing impaired. It is said by some researchers that with this skill they can communicate at the level of a 4- or 5-year-old human.

One branch within family Hominidae is tribe Hominini (see Figure 7.3). This includes all living and extinct species of habitually bipedal primates. Let's now look at the traits of this group.

THE HUMAN PRIMATE

Each of the 200 living primate species has its own unique expression of the primate adaptive strategy. Humans are no exception. Let's describe ourselves by using the same categories with which we characterized primates in general. (See Table 7.3 for a summary.)

The Senses

Our senses are essentially the same as those of the anthropoid monkeys and the apes. There may be some minor differences, but basically all these species hear, smell, feel, and, especially, see the same world.

Movement

Bipedalism is the characteristic that in broad evolutionary perspective defines the hominins. We are the only primate that is habitually bipedal, and we have been for over 4 million years. (Our big brains came along much later.) The bones and muscles of our back, pelvis, legs, and feet are all structured to balance us and hold us upright (see Figure 9.5). Because our legs are the limbs of locomotion, they are longer and more muscular than our arms—just the opposite of the arms and legs of the apes. Completely freed from locomotor functions, our hands have become organs of manipulation. We have the most precise opposability of any of the primates and the relatively longest and strongest primate thumb.

TABLE 7.3
The Features of the Human Primate

Brain	Vision	Face	Hands/Feet	Limbs	Reproduction	Behavior
1,000–2,000 ml	As in anthropoids	Flat	No prehensile feet	Arms most flexible	Longest period of dependency	Culture
3 times expected size			Most dexterous hands	Habitual bipedalism	Differences in sexuality	

FIGURE 7.20
Baboon in estrus. The skin around this female's genital area is swollen, a clear visual sign that she is fertile and sexually receptive. In baboons and other primates, this area may also be brightly colored.

Reproduction

Like most primates, we usually have one offspring at a time. Although we are not the largest living primate (the gorilla is), we have the longest period of postnatal dependency, and we take the longest time to mature. Chimps, for example, reach sexual maturity at about 9 years and physical maturity at about 12. For humans, the averages are 13 and 21. In addition, we are born more helpless than other primates.

Our sexual behavior, too, is different. Most other primates, like most mammals, engage in sexual activity, for the most part, only when it can lead to reproduction. Thus, mating tends to occur when a female has ovulated, that is, when an egg has matured and is ready to be fertilized. She undergoes hormonal changes that make her sexually receptive and lead her to solicit male attention by giving off sexually stimulating signals. During this time, the female is said to be in **estrus** (popularly, "in heat"). In many mammals, the estrus signals are in the form of olfactory stimuli; in some primates, they are also visual (Figure 7.20).

estrus In nonhuman primates, the period of female fertility or the signals indicating this condition.

Contemporary Reflections

What Is the Status of Our Closest Relatives?

In a nutshell, the answer is, not good. The International Union for Conservation of Nature and Natural Resources (www.redlist.org) recognizes 296 species of primates.* Of these, 21 are listed as "critically endangered," 47 as "endangered," 46 as "vulnerable," and 47 as "near threatened." The rest are "lower risk/conservation dependent," "least concern," or "data deficient" (none of which are necessarily good signs).

And it's getting progressively worse, especially in Africa and especially among the great apes. An estimated 80 percent of the world's gorillas and most chimpanzees live in the West African countries of Gabon and the Republic of Congo. In Gabon, the populations of those species have decreased by more than half over the last twenty years. Five thousand gorillas in a sanctuary in Congo died in 2003 and 2004. At its present rate of decline, the bonobo will be extinct in the wild in a decade. In the mountains east of those countries, the population of the rare mountain gorilla (made famous by the book and film *Gorillas in the Mist*) is thought to be down to fewer than 650 individuals. In 2007, seven of these gorillas were murdered, for no apparent reason.

What is causing this disastrous decline? Worldwide we humans threaten the primates, as well as other endangered species, through our overpopulation, depletion of resources, warfare, habitat destruction, pollution, hunting, and other direct exploitation of innumerable species, both plant and animal. In the case of the African apes, the effects of hunting have been recently exacerbated by the "bushmeat" trade, targeting any number of large native animals, including chimpanzees, bonobos, and gorillas. The encroachment of logging and mining into these animals' habitats (particularly in Congo, which is rich in coltan, an ore used in the production of cell phones and laptops) has brought an influx of workers who subsist on the meat of whatever animals are available to hunt, whether endangered or not. Elsewhere, local peoples in need of food in their poverty-stricken countries are also turning to hunting. And most egregiously, and the

---

*There are not that many acknowledged species, so some of these are certainly named subspecies.

Humans, of course, have lost the signals of estrus, a condition best referred to as *nondetectable ovulation* (A. Fuentes, personal communication). Human males don't automatically know when a human female is fertile. This may seem a rather inefficient way to perpetuate the species, but as we are all aware, humans have replaced unconscious, innate sexual signals with sexual consciousness. Sexuality has become part of our conscious thought, tied up with all the other reactions and attitudes and emotions we have toward other members of our species and toward ourselves. You might say we are potentially continually in estrus. Although humans exhibit the most extreme form of this reproductive behavior, we will see it foreshadowed, in the next chapter, in some of our close relatives.

main motivation for hunting, there is a lucrative commercial market for bushmeat in African cities and towns as well as abroad. Some believe that hunting caused the first recorded primate extinction—of the wonderfully named Miss Waldron's red colobus, an African monkey.

Related to the bushmeat trade is a serious threat to humans—the virus that causes Ebola, the hemorrhagic fever whose origin is still unknown (Bermejo et al. 2006; and see Chapter 13). Ebola decimated the gorillas at the sanctuary in Congo and is now spreading toward a national park that has one of the largest, densest ape populations in the world. Outbreaks of the disease in apes coincide with outbreaks in human populations, so it is likely that humans are contracting Ebola from apes, largely as a result of hunting and eating them. It's unclear whether the apes are transmitting the disease to one another or are, because there are more and more humans in the forests, being forced into closer contact with the source of the virus (hypothesized to be bats, mice, or birds). But we do know that outbreaks have occurred among apes in regions remote from human habitation as well.

The debate now centers on what action to take. The status of these western gorillas has been heightened to "critically endangered." Also needed is a "massive investment" in law enforcement to prevent hunting and stem the bushmeat trade. As for Ebola, some have suggested transporting apes to a safe area or otherwise dividing infected groups from noninfected groups. If, however, the apes are continually contracting the disease from its still-unknown source, these measures won't do much. There is an experimental vaccine that works on monkeys, but it still requires testing, and administering it to wild animals would be a difficult task.

The prospects, in other words, don't look good—either for the apes of West Africa or, in the long run, for the world's other primates and all the other endangered species of life. At times, the situation seems hopeless, but various organizations are working tirelessly to prevent the local zoo from ultimately being the *only* place to see the apes and other species. For more information on the crisis, what is being done, and how we can help, see http://pin.primate.wisc.edu and click on "Conservation," under the heading "About the Primates." Also see www.unep.org/grasp for information on the United Nations Great Apes Survival Partnership. To paraphrase Gandhi, whatever we do might be insignificant, but it is very important that we do it.

Intelligence

We are clearly the most intelligent primate, as we have defined that term. We can store, retrieve, and process more information in more complex ways than all the other primates. Our cultural behaviors—our languages, societies, belief systems, norms of behavior, and scientific knowledge—all attest to these abilities. Our intellect is made possible by our large, complex brain, especially our neocortex, the outer layer where abstract thought takes place. Our brains are, in fact, three times the size expected for our body weight as primates (Figure 7.21).

FIGURE 7.21

Relationship between body weight and brain weight in primates. The line indicates the average relationship among various primate species excluding humans. The two dots show expected and observed brain weight for humans. Our brains are three times the weight expected if we followed the typical primate curve.

(Data from Harvey et al. 1987; figure and caption from Relethford 2008.)

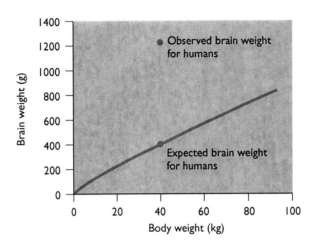

Behavior Patterns

Like most Old World primates, humans live in societies that are based on the collective conscious responses of a group of individuals. The difference is that our groups are structured and maintained by cultural values—ideas, rules, and behavioral norms that we have created and shared through complex **symbolic** communication systems.

SUMMARY

The study of the nonhuman primates has been a traditional aspect of biological anthropology. Humans *are* primates, after all, and the characteristics of our relatively new species have evolved out of the basic primate traits and the adaptive strategy that they facilitate. We can only fully comprehend ourselves as a biological species by understanding where we fit into the natural world.

Taxonomy provides us with a way of naming and categorizing species so as to indicate their biological relationships. It also gives us an idea as to the evolutionary relationships among species. At present, there are two major schools of thought about taxonomy. One (phenetic) names and classifies according to comparisons of phenotypic features and adaptive

symbolic Here, a communication system that uses arbitrary but agreed-upon sounds and signs for meaning.

behaviors. The other (cladistics) uses the actual evolutionary pattern of branching.

The primates are one of nineteen orders of mammals. They may be characterized as being adapted to arboreal environments through manual dexterity, visual acuity, and intelligence. There are about 200 living species of primates, each a unique manifestation of the general primate theme. The human primate's major uniqueness is its form of locomotion; we are the only primate that is habitually bipedal, a trait that evolved more than 4 mya. Since then, our other distinguishing feature has evolved—our big brain, capable of such complex functions that we can create our own adaptive behaviors, expressed as our various cultural systems. It is to the possible precursors of our behaviors that we will turn next.

QUESTIONS FOR FURTHER THOUGHT

1. Birds evolved from a group of small bipedal dinosaurs. Cladistic analysis justifies lumping birds and dinosaurs into the same taxon. Some have taken this to mean that the caged parakeet in your living room is a dinosaur. What do you think of this? Is your dog, then, really a wolf? Are humans apes? How far can we take cladistic taxonomies in our popular nomenclature? Is there some inherent contradiction in cladistic taxonomies, or can you see a resolution?

2. The primates come in a wide variety of shapes and sizes and live in a broad range of environments. It's tempting to attribute this adaptive success to the primates' big brains. But it's more complex than that. Thinking about the processes of evolution, speciation, and adaptive radiation, how would you account for the seeming success of the primate order?

3. Given the problems that now beset the human species on the African continent—AIDS and other diseases, poverty, civil unrest, and warfare—how can we justify expressing so much concern for the plight of the nonhuman primates, much less expending money and time on their behalf? Are these separate concerns that should be considered in order of priority? Or are they actually inextricably linked?

KEY TERMS

taxonomy	quadrupedal	intelligence
phenetics	bipedal	dominance hierarchy
cladistics	prehensile	grooming
hominid	brachiation	estrus
hominin	opposability	symbolic
stereoscopic vision	postnatal dependency	

SUGGESTED READINGS

Noel Rowe's *The Pictorial Guide to the Living Primates* is a beautifully illustrated and informative reference to all living primate species. For a look at the endangered lemurs of Madagascar, see the article in the August 1988 *National Geographic* by primatologist Alison Jolly: "Madagascar's Lemurs: On the Edge of Survival." The National Geographic Society has also produced a beautifully illustrated book on the great apes: *The Great Apes: Between Two Worlds*, by Michael Nichols, Jane Goodall, George Schaller, and Mary Smith, not only discusses the four species of apes but also talks about the scientific studies conducted on them in the wild, as well as the dangers they now face from their close relative.

More on the linguistic abilities of the apes can be found in "Chimpanzee Sign Language Research," by Roger and Debbi Fouts, and in *The Nonhuman Primates*, edited by Phyllis Dolhinow and Agustín Fuentes. A more detailed treatment is Roger Fout's *Next of Kin*.

A comprehensive and readable book comparing humans with other primates is Richard Passingham's *The Human Primate*. For an interesting though somewhat speculative discussion of the evolution of the human brain, try Carl Sagan's Pulitzer Prize–winning *The Dragons of Eden*.

For more on cladistics, see "Evolution by Walking," by Stephen Jay Gould, in the March 1995 *Natural History*, and "Why Cladistics?" by Eugene Gaffney, Lowell Dingus, and Miranda Smith, in the June 1995 issue of the same magazine. For a very detailed discussion of taxonomic models, see Mark Ridley's *Evolution*, second edition, Chapter 14.

The most current information about the Ebola crisis among the apes is "Tracking Ebola's Deadly March Among Wild Apes," by Gretchen Vogel, in the 8 December 2006 *Science*.

For conservation information, try the Web sites listed in this chapter's "Contemporary Reflections" box, as well as www.duke.edu/web/primate.

I'll recommend some more books on the behavior of humans and our fellow primates in the next chapter.

CHAPTER

Primate Behavior and Human Evolution

Often I have gazed into a chimpanzee's eyes and wondered what was going on behind them.
—Jane Goodall (1990)

Just as we look to the anatomy of our close relatives to get some idea about the basic set of phenotypic traits from which we evolved, we may also look to the behavior of the other primates to gain some insight into why we behave the way we do. Because we share common ancestors, some of our behavior patterns—just like some of our physical features—may be variations on the same evolutionary theme.

In this chapter we will look at several particularly relevant nonhuman primates, the several species collectively called baboons (genus *Papio*) and the two species of genus *Pan*, the chimpanzee and the bonobo.

We will address the following questions:

How did behavior evolve, and how do we study it?

What are some of the relevant behaviors of our close relatives?

What do they tell us about the evolution of behavior in the hominins?

BEHAVIORAL EVOLUTION

Studying nonhuman primate behavior to shed light on human behavior is based on the same premise as studying the physical traits of nonhuman primates and comparing them with our own: we share a common heritage with the other primates and so have inherited our shared features from the same source, a common ancestor. It is not a coincidence, for example, that all the primates have prehensile hands. Our common prehensile ability is a **shared derived characteristic,** coming from the same ancient ancestor and, in this case, serving the same basic function. Thus, we gain some perspective on our prehensile hands by fully examining the prehensile appendages of species with whom we share an ancestor that was the source of the trait.

How Does Behavior Evolve?

Just as organisms pass on anatomical and physiological features in their genes, they also pass on behavioral characteristics. In some groups—ants, for example—whole behavioral repertoires are inherited. Ants rely completely on built-in instinct; they don't really think or, in fact, have much of anything to think *with*. So, even though ants live in highly complex societies and act in elaborate ways, all their behaviors are coded in their genes, to be triggered by outside stimuli but with little or no flexibility or variation in their response.

Other organisms with larger and more complex brains can vary their behavior as needed to cope with specific situations. Their behavior is flexible. They have behavioral *potentials* carried in their genetic codes, and they respond to their environments by building on these potentials—taking in information from the outside, remembering it, retrieving stored information, and utilizing it in appropriate circumstances. In other words, they *think*.

The nature of the inborn behavioral potentials in complex organisms is still a matter of debate, especially when humans are the topic. Some have argued that we are born as blank slates or, in a more modern image, as computers with internal hardware but nothing programmed. The extreme opposite view says that our brains come equipped with specific behaviors that are only modified to a small degree by our individual experiences—like a computer with many application programs already in the system.

The reality is no doubt somewhere in the middle. Certainly we come into this world with some basic behavioral responses built in. Facial expressions such as smiling, the newborn's instinct to nurse, the bond between a mother and her offspring, the drives to walk upright and learn language—these are all recognized as universal in our species and as preprogrammed in our biology. But just as certainly, we are not programmed for *particular* ways of expressing these and other behaviors. Language ability, for example, may be instinctive, but the specific language you speak is learned within a specific cultural and individual context.

There is a scientific study that looks for evolutionary explanations for behaviors, especially social behaviors. It is called **sociobiology, evolutionary psychology,** or **behavioral ecology,** and two of its ideas are particularly relevant here. The first, **inclusive fitness,** refers to the fact that your close relatives share many of your genes. As a result, the adaptive fitness of your genes is not just a matter of your own adaptive success (the

shared derived characteristics Phenotypic features shared by two or more taxonomic groups that are derived from a common ancestor and that are not found in other groups.

sociobiology The scientific study that examines evolutionary explanations for social behaviors within species.

evolutionary psychology Another name for sociobiology.

behavioral ecology Another name for sociobiology.

inclusive fitness The idea that fitness is measured by the success of one's genes, whether possessed by the individual or by that individual's relatives.

usual definition of fitness); it also entails the adaptive success of your relatives. Thus, any behavior that has evolved through time that causes you to aid your close relations also serves to help your genes get passed on.

A good example is the case of **altruistic** behavior. If, for instance, I performed some action that saved my sister's life but cost me mine in the process, I could not pass on any more genes, but I would have helped increase the possibility that *some of my genes* would get passed on, because my sister and I share, on average, 50 percent of our genetic endowment.

Of course, humans have moral reasons for altruistic actions, but altruistic behaviors are seen in many other species where there could be no cultural motivation. It may not seem logical that a behavior that might endanger the individual could have evolved by natural selection. But if we look at the genes rather than just the "packages" they come in, we can see how this could be the case. An altruistic behavior was selected for because it helped a group of individuals possessing genes for that behavior to be reproductively successful, even if a few individuals were sacrificed in the process.

The second idea from sociobiology relevant to our discussion concerns **reproductive strategies.** Put simply, individuals have evolved behaviors that maximize their reproductive success. Male and female mammals, however, differ in their contributions to reproduction, so their evolved behaviors may differ as well. Females, of course, carry, nurture, and raise offspring—largely by themselves in most mammalian species, including most primates. Males, on the other hand, contribute sperm. Thus, behaviors have evolved that help females raise healthy offspring and that allow males to try to impregnate as many females as possible.

For the primates, these reproductive strategies are especially important because of our order's emphasis on complex social interactions and social bonds, which in turn facilitate the primates' emphasis on relatively slow development and the focus on learned behavior as an adaptive mechanism. Because most primates give birth to a single offspring at a time, reproductive success in producing and caring for that offspring is vital, and so selection for the most adaptive traits, and the relative reproductive roles of males and females, is crucial.

How Do We Study Behavior?

If it is the case that at least behavioral themes can be inherited, then we can shed light on our behaviors by looking into those of other creatures. In doing so, however, we need to take into account the concept of shared derived characteristics. In comparing the behaviors of humans and chimpanzees or bonobos, it is highly likely that a behavior is shared because it is the *same*

altruistic Benefiting others without regard for one's own needs or safety.

reproductive strategies Behaviors that evolve to maximize an individual's reproductive success.

behavior, derived by all three species from our common ancestor of 6 to 5 mya. Understanding the nature and function of that behavior in chimpanzees or bonobos is likely to provide insight into the behavior in humans.

By contrast, a specific behavior similar in humans and baboons is less likely to be a shared derived characteristic. Our two species have evolved independently for over 20 million years, so there is a greater chance that the behavior evolved separately, under separate environmental circumstances and perhaps for different adaptive reasons. Still, the behavior may be a variation on some *general behavioral pattern* common to the primates and inherited from an early common ancestor.

The chance of two similar behaviors being shared and derived decreases as we compare species that are less and less closely related. Some investigators have compared the behavior of humans with that of social carnivores such as lions, wolves, and African wild dogs (Figure 8.1). There

FIGURE 8.1
African wild dogs are known for their complex social organization, particularly evident when they prepare for and participate in a hunt.

are strikingly "human" behaviors in these species: All three hunt coopera-tively. Lions from the same pride will eat from the same carcass, and moth-ers, of course, will bring food—sometimes still alive—back to their young. Wolves and wild dogs have complex social relationships, they use vocal and gestural signs to maintain these relationships, and both actively feed their young. Wolves, especially, are territorial. These collections of similarities, however, are probably not derived from a common ancestor but have, at most, evolved quite independently from some general mammalian traits of social interaction, care of young, and relatively large, complex brains that allow for flexibility of behavior. What we do learn from the behavior of such species is that one possible route to adaptive success for mammals is through complex social behavior and that this behavior is common in species that eat meat, especially meat from large animals. But it is only one route; other carnivores—the fox and leopard, for example—are solitary hunters. And lions, although they hunt cooperatively, do not share food in the sense that one actively gives a portion of a kill to another.

Comparing such behaviors, then, can be informative and can point out possible clusters of adaptive traits. But such comparisons must be viewed with the understanding that the more evolutionarily distant the species, the less useful the comparison. Ants live in highly complex societ-ies, which investigators often describe in human terms (*slave, caste, queen, nurse, soldier*), but studying the social behavior of ants probably tells us nothing directly about our own societies.

We can now look at the behavior of some other species that have, to varying degrees, been used as models for the origin and evolution of our own behavior. For years, nearly all our information about the behavior of other species came from studies conducted in the artificial environments of zoos and laboratories. It wasn't until the science of **ethology**—studying creatures in the wild, under natural conditions—became popular and possible that we could see how they were *really* adapted. And only then did we begin to learn some of the truly remarkable adaptations that our fellow primates possess.

PRIMATE BEHAVIOR

Baboons

Five distinguishable types of baboon live in the African woodland, desert, and **savanna,** all grouped within genus *Papio.* (Some authorities consider them to be subspecies of a single species because where their ranges overlap,

ethology The study of the natural behavior of animals under natural conditions.

savanna The open grasslands of the tropics.

FIGURE 8.2
Baboons on the African savanna. Our early ancestors might have witnessed scenes like this.

they can and do interbreed and produce fertile offspring. Other taxonomists think that the physical and behavioral differences are sufficient to warrant giving them five different species names.) Although not as closely related to humans as are the apes, these primates have long been of interest to anthropologists because of their complex social organization and their savanna habitat—an important habitat for our early hominin ancestors (Figure 8.2).

Baboon groups range in size from 20 to 200 individuals. One of the most striking aspects of baboon behavior is the aggressive competition for dominance among males, who may be nearly twice the size of females and who are endowed with huge, sharp canine teeth (Figure 8.3). The male who is the largest, strongest, most aggressive, smartest (whatever traits are important to baboons) becomes, for a time, the dominant animal, a position recognized and acknowledged by the whole group. The dominant male is the group's leader and decision maker. He has first rights to food

FIGURE 8.3
Baboon threat. A male baboon shows his long canine teeth and flashes his white eyelids in a "threat gesture," probably directed at a less dominant male.

and often to females. He may produce the most offspring, perpetuating some of those traits that allowed him to achieve dominance. It is also the role of the dominant male and his immediate subordinates to protect the more vulnerable members of the group—the females and infants—from danger (see Figure 7.9).

Males are also, in general, dominant over females. In the hamadryas baboon of Ethiopia, males gather a group of females with whom they have exclusive mating rights. Such a group is referred to as a *harem,* and the proximity of and sexual access to the females in a harem is maintained by male aggression and violence. Many harem females show the scars of such treatment.

Observations of these behaviors led early investigators to depict baboon social organization as almost militaristic—centered around and totally dominated by a hierarchically arranged group of males and maintained through violent (though not always bloody) confrontations. Indeed, baboon groups have traditionally been called *troops.* The female's role was considered to be the bearing and raising of offspring; her individual identity was defined by that role, and her position in baboon society was subordinate to that of all males and specifically determined by the position of the male with whom she mated.

More recent studies have shown, however, that baboon societies are far more complex and variable (Fedigan and Fedigan 1988; Smuts 1985, 1995; Strum 1987). While male baboons do vie for dominance, achieve differential social power and influence, and protect the group from other baboons and from predators—and while hamadryas males do maintain harems through violent coercion—a formal, permanent, tightly structured dominance hierarchy among males does not seem to be at the center of social organization in all cases. Among other types of baboons—for example, the olive baboons of equatorial Africa—social structure is based on "a network of social alliances" (Fedigan and Fedigan 1988:14), including friendships between females and between females and males. These friendships may be so strong that a male will aid his female friends' infants even though he may not be their father. Such friendships, rather than the social position of the males, may be what determines who mates with whom.

Differential social positions exist, but they are based not on those "masculine" traits mentioned previously but more on an individual's "experience, skill, and, . . . ability to manipulate others [and] mobilize allies" (Fedigan and Fedigan 1988:15). If there is any subgroup that is central to a troop and that ties generations together, it is that made up of related females; the males, being more mobile, are a less stable part of the troop than was previously supposed. In fact, the competition that may be most important to the troop is that among females, who compete with one another "over access to the resources necessary to sustain them and their offspring" (Fedigan and Fedigan 1988:5). Finally, it appears that mate choice is more a female prerogative. Males make overtures toward estrous females, but it is the females who decide with whom they will mate.

The behaviors described in the preceding paragraphs are examples of inclusive fitness and reproductive strategies. Male baboons have evolved protective behaviors toward females and offspring in their troop because those offspring *may* be theirs and perhaps because those females may one day bear their offspring. And one study suggests that some male baboons can differentiate their own offspring and "selectively support [them] in agonistic disputes" (Buchan et al. 2003:179). Moreover, they try to keep away males from other troops to enhance their own reproductive success. At the same time, males are more mobile than females and will also try to contribute sperm to females in other troops.

The females, on the other hand, by forming alliances with related females and by selecting the males with whom they will mate, are helping ensure their own reproductive and child-rearing success, as well as the success of their genes via the reproductive success of their close relatives. Keep in mind, however, that baboons don't have these results consciously in mind. The behaviors have evolved over time because they increase the inclusive fitness of the genes of the individuals who perform them. We don't really know what is going on in the minds of baboons—what motivates them to act in these ways.

The earlier interpretation of baboon social organization indicated that to survive on the savanna, the primates needed a tightly organized, male-oriented and dominated, almost militaristic society. The obvious conclusion was that the early hominin savanna dwellers probably had a similar set of behaviors and that our modern social systems are, to one extent or another, variations on this theme.

Again, however, we must remember that we can share with baboons and other nonhominoids only the most general primate traits. Similarities between humans and baboons exist because we have evolved variations of the same basic primate behavioral themes. Our specific expressions of those themes, though, are the results of separate and independent evolutionary histories.

Nevertheless, those separate histories have produced results that are similar in baboons and humans and, as we shall see, in chimpanzees and bonobos: the adaptive focus of a social structure built around a family unit, friendships, mutual aid within the group, defense of the group, and recognition of individuals. This social structure at least tells us that such a focus is one possible adaptive path among primates, and so it is reasonable to assume that something like it was the key to the survival of the early hominins. Given that our closest relatives, the chimpanzees and bonobos, exhibit this cluster of adaptive traits, it seems an even more reasonable assumption.

Chimpanzees

Some of the most remarkable results of ethological observations began with three landmark studies of the great apes: Jane Goodall's study of the chimpanzee, Dian Fossey's of the gorilla, and Biruté Galdikas's of the orangutan. Subsequent studies keep contributing to our understanding of these primates. Each study is interesting in its own right and tells us something of the variations possible on the basic primate pattern of social organization.

The orangutan (*Pongo pygmaeus*) is an Asian ape and is separated from us by 12 million years. The gorilla (*Gorilla gorilla*) is nearly as close to us genetically as the chimp, but while it exhibits many of the same basic social behaviors as the chimpanzee, it is a rather specialized ape. Unlike the chimpanzee, it spends much of its time on the ground, and its almost exclusively vegetarian diet consists largely of ground plants. This species is not known to make or use tools. (Orangutans, however, have recently been observed using simple tools.) The species most relevant to our present subject are the chimpanzee and bonobo.

Much of what we know of the ethology of the chimp (*Pan troglodytes*) comes from nearly fifty years of research led by Jane Goodall (1971, 1986, 1990) at Gombe Stream National Park in Tanzania. Goodall's studies have shown that in addition to physical and physiological traits, we share with chimps a number of behavioral characteristics. These center on aspects of social interaction and are thus instructive for understanding our own behavior.

The bond between mother and infant is strong in chimps, as it is in most mammals. These apes, though, have large, complex brains, and infants have a lot to learn about their world before they can become functioning adults. Thus, the mother-infant bond is particularly long-lived and important, and the nature of that interaction can have a lasting effect on the rest of a chimp's life. Poor treatment by her mother, for example, often makes a chimp a poor mother herself when she bears young. Chimps have been seen helping their mothers with younger siblings, and siblings often remain close into adulthood. Chimps, in other words, *raise* their young, and the family bonds that result may last a lifetime.

The chimps in a group are arranged in a dominance hierarchy. Males are generally dominant over females, but among females a loose hierarchy also exists. Males compete with one another in an attempt to achieve the highest position possible. The rewards are access to feeding places and to females, the latter being another example of male reproductive strategy. Social position, though attained in males through violent-looking but seldom injurious actions (Figure 8.4), is maintained via a series of expressions, gestures, and vocalizations. One of the most important interactions is grooming (see Figure 7.10), which maintains social cohesion and on occasion is a sign of dominance when a subordinate male grooms his superior. Other expressions of social interaction include kissing, hugging, bowing, extending the hand, making sexual gestures, grinning, and vocalizing certain ways— and we can freely use these terms because the meanings of these actions in chimp society seem to be just what they are in human societies.

A chimp society, however, is in no way some sort of dictatorship. Instead, it is marked by cooperation and mutual concern, which is seen mostly within the family unit of mother and offspring (because chimps are sexually promiscuous, a female may mate with a dozen males during estrus and so the biological father is unknown). Throughout their lives, members of this family unit will protect and care for each other, especially in times of illness and injury. Males have even been known to help brothers in their competition for dominance.

Care also extends outside the family unit. Offspring are important to the group as a whole, and adults will come to the aid or protection of a

FIGURE 8.4
A male chimpanzee showing a "full open grin." This expression is a sign of excitement, often used by a high-ranking chimp when in close contact with a subordinate. Compare this with the expression of the baboon in Figure 8.3.

youngster threatened with some harm, possibly risking their own welfare, even if the youngster is not necessarily theirs. Goodall once observed an adolescent male adopt an unrelated youngster who had been orphaned (1990:202). This protectiveness may be another example of inclusive fitness, where genes contributing to a behavior have been selected for because they confer adaptive fitness to individuals, to both the protectors and the protected, who may share genes.

Group membership is somewhat fluid. Chimps, for various reasons, will leave a group, and outsiders will occasionally enter it. Despite this fluidity, there is a sense of group identity and territory. Small bands of males will sometimes patrol the boundaries of their group's range, and when they encounter members of other groups, they react to them as outsiders. This is another case of males performing a behavior that serves to protect their reproductive investment.

With chimps, however, we may reasonably wonder about more conscious motivation for some of these behaviors. In one chilling series of events, for example, males from Goodall's main study group attacked and killed a female and all the males of a group that had broken away to establish their own territory. Goodall thinks the motivation may have been to reclaim the area. Although other examples of similar behavior have been reported, there is still debate over whether it is typical of the species. It has been suggested (Power 1991, for example) that because the researchers at Gombe interfered with the chimps' normal activities by providing food, they may have influenced the apes' behavior, including this event. Others (Sussman 1997) question how convincing the evidence is for similar occurrences.

Among the chimpanzee's wide range of food sources is meat. Chimps from some groups, including those studied by Goodall and associates at Gombe, are hunters (Stanford 1995, 1999). Males, and occasionally females, will hunt and kill small pigs, antelopes, and monkeys, including young baboons (Figure 8.5). The Gombe chimps, sometimes hunting in cooperative groups, kill over 100 red colobus monkeys a year, nearly a fifth of the members of that species within the chimps' range. Meat is the one food that chimps will share, and male chimps are more likely to share with friends than with rivals—they will even withhold meat from rivals. There is evidence, too, that a male will hunt in order to get meat to give as an offering to a female in estrus. And we have mentioned earlier the new observations of chimps making spears with which to hunt small monkeys.

Bonobos

Even more intriguing information has come to light about the third species of African ape, the bonobo (*Pan paniscus*; de Waal 1995; Ingmanson and Kano 1993; Kano 1990; Parker 2007; White 1996). The bonobo lives in the lowland forests of the Democratic Republic of the Congo and has been estimated by genetic studies (see Chapter 9) to have been separate from the chimp for 1 million to 2 million years. The population size of the bonobo is unknown.

Bonobos are sometimes referred to as *pygmy chimpanzees*. But bonobos are not pygmies at all; they are as large as chimps, though more slender

FIGURE 8.5

A chimp in Tanzania eats the carcass of a baboon he has recently hunted and killed. He may share some of his prize with close friends in his group.

and with smaller heads and shoulders. They walk upright more often than chimps (Figure 8.6). Like chimps, bonobos do some hunting (though less frequently) but show no evidence of cooperative hunting; further, females are sometimes the hunters. Also like chimps (see Figure 7.19), bonobos use tools, but never to acquire food. Rather, the bonobos use leaves as rain hats and drag branches to serve the social purposes of initiating and indicating the direction of group movement (Ingmanson 1996).

Bonobos are more peaceful and gregarious than chimps. There is a dominance hierarchy among males, but unlike the case with chimpanzees, the hierarchy is easily established with brief aggressive chases. Female hierarchies appear to be based on seniority. Also unlike chimps, female bonobos may dominate males (de Waal and Lanting 1997), and they hunt more regularly than do female chimps.

FIGURE 8.6
Bonobo standing bipedally.
This bonobo is collecting and
carrying stalks of sugarcane
in his hands, now freed from
locomotor activities.

Bonobos more readily share food with one another, and the food
shared is not limited to luxury items such as meat (Figure 8.7). They have
never been observed killing another of their kind, although violence does
occur (Parker 2007), and their sexual behaviors contribute significantly

to group cohesion. In contrast, sexual coercion, as seen in the hamadryas baboons, has been observed among the chimps of Gombe.

Bonobos, especially when feeding, constantly posture toward one another, rubbing rumps or "presenting" themselves as if initiating sexual activity. When sex does follow, it is usually face-to-face, a behavior uncommon in other primates except humans. Sexual activity is not limited to opposite-sex partners. Females commonly rub genitalia with other females, and males will mount each other.

FIGURE 8.7
Bonobo society is characterized by peaceful relationships, with sexual activity and—as seen here on the left—food sharing as mechanisms to maintain harmony, ease tensions, reassure other members, and show reconciliation.

Contemporary Reflections

Are Some Human Behaviors Genetic?

Since Darwin's time, people have speculated about the possible biological bases of some human behaviors. Over the past thirty years especially, a huge number of books have suggested biological bases for human aggression, social practices such as marriage patterns, altruistic acts, morality, territoriality, and many more. The more extreme versions of such ideas claim that we have a genetic program for such behaviors and that these programs evolved in the past and are maintained today because they confer a reproductive advantage on those who express them. In other words, they have been, and many continue to be, naturally selected for. According to opponents of this idea, a logical—and dangerous—implication of this claim is that variation in the specific expression of a behavior might reflect genetic variation among populations of our species.

Addressing this issue is complicated, but there are a few guiding concepts we may use to think about it. We must remember that genes are instructions for making proteins. It's a long way from the gene to the phenotypic trait, and the more complex the phenotypic trait, the longer the path and the more genes involved. Behaviors are *very* complex phenotypes. In short, just as there is no single "stature gene" that determines my height, there is no "aggression gene," or "marriage gene," or "altruism gene." Even in creatures with less complex nervous systems—ants, for example—whose behaviors *must* be biologically programmed, those behaviors are still complex responses of the whole organism to a whole host of environmental stimuli. There must be very many genes involved.

A behavior's biological program, then, is just a program for a potential or a general theme. Its expression requires some environmental stimulus (that is, something outside the genes themselves) and will vary as the exact nature of the stimulus varies. A biological basis for a human behavior can only be for

Moreover, the signs of fertility, the estrous signals, seem nearly always present in bonobo females. In both chimps and bonobos, the fertile and therefore sexual period is marked by a swelling and coloration of the skin of the genital area, which stimulate sexual interest in males. In chimps, the swelling occurs only when the female has ovulated and is fertile. In bonobos, however, there is some swelling almost all the time, and they seem almost constantly sexually receptive. Sexual activity in this species has become separate from purely reproductive activity and is responded to on a conscious level. The motivation for sex may be as much psychological and social as it is reproductive.

The function of this friendly posturing and sexual receptiveness seems to be the same as that of grooming and as that of some expressions and gestures among chimps: to prevent violence, to ease tension (especially while feeding), to serve as a greeting, to signal reconciliation, or to reassure another group member. Sex or some form of sexual activity, between opposite- or same-sex partners, has even been seen to precede food sharing.

the most general potential. Our cultural environment, which pervades every aspect of our individual and social lives, is immensely complex, and so the expressions of a behavioral potential must be varied indeed. Thus, the variation in a human behavior from society to society (or even from individual to individual) is largely a result of different cultural environments—different systems of belief and knowledge that mark the variety of humans' ways of life.

Language is a perfect—and fairly uncontroversial—example. All normal humans come equipped with the ability to take in raw data—the speech of the people around them and the responses to their attempts to communicate—and turn them into a working knowledge of their native language. Think about it: you spoke your native language fluently before you ever were formally taught all the grammatical rules in school. And you did it by yourself, using some built-in "software" in your nervous system into which data were fed by your senses. The ability to learn language is biological and thus, at its base, genetic. The genetic basis for this ability was selected for during our evolution (see Chapter 11). Linguistic ability conferred a reproductive advantage on our ancestors.

However, *what* language you speak, how well you speak it, what words you know, what accent you have—these particulars are cultural. They vary from society to society and even within societies—not because of genetic differences among populations but because of variation in the cultural contexts of which they are a part.

Similarly, the social system, with its sexual consciousness, that we see in bonobos may represent a common behavioral theme that we humans have translated into various sets of learned cultural norms such as sexual ethics and marriage patterns. Nature has given us behavioral potentials, ultimately coded in our genes, that we inherited from our evolutionary ancestors and that evolved over the course of our species' history. Culture has given rise to our specific expressions of those behaviors. In this way, yes, some of our behaviors may be said to have a genetic basis—but only in this limited way.

CULTURE AND SOCIAL COGNITION

The pioneering work of Goodall and others strongly indicated that humans' closest relatives have behaviors that are flexible, adaptable, and the result of intelligence and reasoning. More recent research substantiates these earlier findings. The following evidence shows that chimp and bonobo behavior, like human culture, varies from group to group.

For example, a chimp group in the forests on the west coast of Africa uses hammerstones to crack open nuts, something the Gombe chimps don't do, though the Gombe chimps are famous for their termite sticks (see Chapter 7). The West African chimps, in fact, use stone tools so regularly that they have left "archaeological sites" of the activity, made up of unintentionally broken stones and nutshells (Mercader et al. 2002). These chimps also have different hunting techniques, relying more on cooperation between hunting males than do the Gombe chimps (Boesch and Boesch-Achermann 1991).

W. C. McGrew (1998) has suggested that this and other observations are evidence of cultural differences. A recent synthesis of data from seven well-established chimpanzee field sites across Africa, comprising an accumulated 151 years of observation, has shown variation in 571 different behavior patterns, not including those for which there are obvious ecological explanations (such as not nesting on the ground where leopards and lions are common). These patterns include tool use, grooming, and courtship behavior, and the nature of the variation points to the chimps' ability to invent new behaviors and pass them on socially—in which case the behaviors might be thought of as "customs" (Cohen 2007; Whiten and Boesch 2001; Whiten et al. 1999). Similar data for orangutans has been described, although on a less complex level than that of the chimpanzees (van Schaik et al. 2003.)

Even more recently, sophisticated experiments using chimps have proposed such complex behaviors and cognitive abilities as the capacity for delayed gratification (Balter 2008); social cooperation that varies in degree according to the strength of social relationships (Miller 2007); and the ability to infer goals and motivations of others (Wood et al. 2007).

Finally, we should mention Kanzi, a male bonobo at the Language Research Center at Georgia State University (Savage-Rumbaugh and Lewin 1994a, 1994b). Kanzi is one of the most successful apes at communicating through a language with the characteristics of human communication. He uses symbols on a computer keyboard; he can even recognize and, using his computer, respond to a large number of spoken English words. In addition to his linguistic skills, he has been taught to make and use simple stone tools. Although not resembling even the earliest known hominin stone tools (see Chapter 10), Kanzi's tools are, nonetheless, true artifacts and so may show us what the *very* earliest stone tools of our lineage might have looked like. Neither of these behaviors—using a humanlike language or stone tool*making*—is seen among wild bonobos, but they do give us an idea as to the cognitive potentials of these apes.

Now, if all the behaviors of the chimp and bonobo sound more than vaguely human, the reason may be simple. We share certain general behavioral patterns because we inherited them from a common ancestor. To be sure, our evolutionary line and that of the chimps and bonobos have been going their separate ways for 5 to 6 million years, and even shared features have had the chance to become modified by all the processes of evolution—to be changed, eliminated, enhanced, and differently adapted to our species' different niches. Chimps and bonobos are not "living fossils" stuck in some 5-million-year-old rut while our ancestors continued to evolve. But because our common ancestor is relatively recent and there is striking similarity between the bodies and behaviors of apes and humans, we can argue that our shared behavioral themes are derived features.

This does *not* mean that humans have specific genes for friendship, food sharing, territoriality, or continual sexuality. These are complex behaviors, and humans and apes are complex species. It does, however, hint that, as with the chimps and bonobos, the focus of the human adaptation—what adapted our earliest hominin ancestors and what has been the adaptive theme of our line—is social interaction based on individual recognition, a strong bond centered around family relationships (generally mothers and their offspring), long-term friendships, sexual consciousness, mutual care within the group, and recognition of and defense of the group. It seems reasonable to assume that our hominin ancestors behaved in similar ways. As Jane Goodall says,

> The concept of early humans poking for insects with twigs and wiping themselves with leaves seems entirely sensible. The thought of those ancestors greeting and reassuring one another with kisses or embraces, cooperating in protecting their territory or in hunting, and sharing food with each other, is appealing. The idea of close affectionate ties within the Stone Age family, of brothers helping one another, of teenage sons hastening to the protection of their old mothers, and of teenage daughters minding the babies, for me brings the fossilized relics of their physical selves dramatically to life. (1990:207)

SUMMARY

As we noted in the previous chapter, one way to guide us as we look at our own species is to understand the context from which our species evolved. This approach works for behavior as well as for physical adaptations. The importance of a well-defined social organization is seen among one savanna primate, the baboon, and is a good hint that an analogous behavior was a key to the survival of early savanna hominins.

More useful to understanding our own behavior is to examine the behavior of close evolutionary relatives, especially the chimpanzee and bonobo. Chimp and bonobo behaviors differ in specifics from ours and have been evolving separately from ours for 5 to 6 million years. All three species have adapted to different niches. The basic patterns for the behavior of all three species, however, are shared derived characteristics. They are the same because we inherited them from a common ancestor. It is highly likely, then, that our remote hominin ancestors also manifested these patterns in some way.

Such studies indicate to us that the early hominins of Africa may very well have been highly social creatures and that their social organization was built around differing interpersonal relationships, a family unit, conscious sexuality, recognition of group membership and territory, and mutual care at both the individual and the group level.

QUESTIONS FOR FURTHER THOUGHT

1. Consider the debate over the biological basis of human behaviors. Much of the debate in both the scientific and popular presses has focused on such things as human aggression, intelligence, and sexual orientation. What are the ramifications of the extreme points of view (e.g., blank slate versus preprogrammed behaviors) of these topics? How might each be seen in terms of an intermediate model, as described in the chapter?

2. In fields as diverse as particle physics and cultural anthropology, it has been noted that the very act of scientific observation affects that which is being observed. Certainly this would also be the case for the ethological observation of nonhuman primates. What are the scientific as well as the ethical implications of this idea? Are some of our scientific ideas potentially inaccurate? Has studying other primates in the wild been in any way detrimental to them? benefical to them?

3. If, as some authorities claim, apes exhibit behaviors that may be classified as cultural, how are we humans different in that regard? Is the difference in cultural behavior one of degree? Or is human culture different in kind? If so, how? While answering this question, keep in mind that although some nonhumans *have* culture, humans *are* cultural.

KEY TERMS

shared derived
  characteristics
sociobiology
evolutionary
  psychology

behavioral ecology
inclusive fitness
altruistic
reproductive
  strategies

ethology
savanna

SUGGESTED READINGS

Descriptions of baboon behavior can be found in Shirley Strum's *Almost Human* and in Barbara Smuts's *Sex and Friendship in Baboons*. Jane Goodall describes her work with the chimps and her experiences studying them in *Through a Window: My Thirty Years with the Chimpanzees of Gombe*.

A good review of the biological basis of human behavior is Robert W. Sussman's *The Biological Basis of Human Behavior: A Critical Review*, second edition.

For more technical information on primate behavior, see *The Evolution of Primate Behavior*, by Alison Jolly; *Patterns of Primate Behavior*, by Claud A. Bramblett; *The Nonhuman Primates*, by Phyllis Dolhinow and Agustín Fuentes; and *Primates in Perspective*, by Christine Campbell et al.

Dian Fossey recounts her study of gorillas in *Gorillas in the Mist*; her own story, in turn, including her murder, is told by Farley Mowat in *Woman in the Mists* and in the 1988 movie *Gorillas in the Mist*. Biruté Galdikas tells about orangutans in *Reflections of Eden: My Years with the Orangutans of Borneo*.

Chimpanzee hunting behavior and the possible influence of meat eating on human evolution are the topic of Craig B. Stanford's *The Hunting Apes: Meat Eating and the Origins of Human Behavior*. His position—that the quest for meat was what helped select for our big brains and gave rise to many human social behaviors—is controversial. For a critique, see the review of Stanford's book "A Theory That's Hard to Digest," by Christophe Boesch in the 17 June 1999 issue of *Nature*.

For information on the cultural customs of chimpanzees, see "The Cultures of Chimpanzees," by Andrew Whiten and Christophe Boesch, in the January 2001 issue of *Scientific American*; "The Second Inheritance System of Chimpanzees and Humans," by Whiten, in the 1 September 2005 issue of *Nature*; and "Why We're Different: Probing the Gap Between Apes and Humans," by Michael Balter, in the 25 January 2008 *Science*.

Bonobos are described in Frans de Waal's *Bonobo: The Forgotten Ape*, which has outstanding photographs by Frans Lanting. For more on the amazing Kanzi and other bonobos, see *Kanzi: The Ape at the Brink of the Human Mind*, by Sue Savage-Rumbaugh and Roger Lewin, and *Apes, Language, and the Human Mind*, by Savage-Rumbaugh et al. A fascinating update on the bonobos is in the 30 July 2007 *New Yorker*: "Swingers," by Ian Parker.

An interesting Web site devoted to primate behavior is www.discoverchimpanzees.org.

CHAPTER

Studying the Human Past

The present contains nothing more than the past, and what is found in the effect was already in the cause.
—Henri Bergson

The study of the human past—our evolutionary history—is a central part of biological anthropology. To understand the human species today, we need to know where, when, how, and from what we evolved. But the past *is* the past. We can't see past events as they were happening. We can't make them happen again. All we have are the present-day results of series of past events, such as the living species of primates we discussed in Chapters 7 and 8. In some cases we have the physical remains of the past, such as the fossils of extinct species, but these have themselves undergone change since they were part of a living creature.

The present, however, can be a powerful tool. Recall from Chapter 2 how Hooke and Steno used fossils and stratigraphy to plot the events of the past and how Hutton and Lyell used the idea of uniformitarianism by observing present-day processes to understand how past events took place.

In this chapter we will address the methods used by bioanthropologists to answer these questions about our past:

What are the features of the primate skeleton, and how can knowledge of them help us identify fossil remains?

How do we locate, recover, and date fossil remains?

How are fossils formed, and what affects the condition of the fossils we find?

What can we learn about our past from new technologies in the study of genetics?

BONES: THE PRIMATE SKELETON

Most of the physical remains we find of the evolutionary past are in the form of preserved bone. Only in rare cases are we lucky enough to discover soft-tissue remains of an ancient organism (see Chapter 15). Therefore, knowledge of the skeletal structure, or **osteology,** is vital. The first thing we need to do, of course, is determine what species the skeletal remains are from. The human skeleton is a variation on the basic mammalian skeletal theme and, more specifically, on the primate skeletal theme. Figure 9.1 compares the skeletons of a modern human, a gorilla, and a domestic cat.

When we look at a skeleton, it's easy to imagine the bones as something separate from the muscles, nerves, blood vessels, and other soft tissues of the body. But, in fact, they all develop together and are adapted to function together. For example, the skull serves to protect the brain; therefore, a skull fossil is a good indicator of the size and shape of the brain it once protected. Muscles are attached to bones, and so the location, size, and shape of the point where the muscle once attached to a bone will provide some indication of the size and shape of the muscle, even though the muscle itself may have decayed long ago. We can tell a lot about a creature from the bones it leaves behind.

One of the more obvious and important things we can tell about a human skeleton is its sex. Humans belong to a species that exhibits **sexual dimorphism,** notable physical differences between the sexes that are not related to reproductive traits. In general, human males tend to be larger and more heavily muscled than females, a fact that also applies to the apes and to extinct hominin species. The skull and, for obvious reasons, the pelvis are the best features for identifying the sex of a skeleton (Figure 9.2).

Age at death may also be determined from skeletal remains. The body, including the bones, goes through many physical changes as it develops, matures, and ages, and many of these changes occur at a fairly predictable rate. By determining on a skeleton which changes have already taken place and which have yet to take place, we may approximate the age at which the individual died (Figure 9.3).

The skeleton acts as a framework for the body, and thus the size and shape of the bones can reveal something of the appearance of the entire living person. We know, for example, from the sheer size and ruggedness of their bones, that a group of humans from ice-age Europe (the Neandertals, whom we will discuss in Chapter 11) were big, brawny, and extremely strong. Several investigators have attempted to reconstruct the faces of our ancestors from the shapes of skulls and facial bones. Using their knowledge

osteology The study of the skeleton.

sexual dimorphism Physical differences between the sexes of a species that are not related to reproductive features.

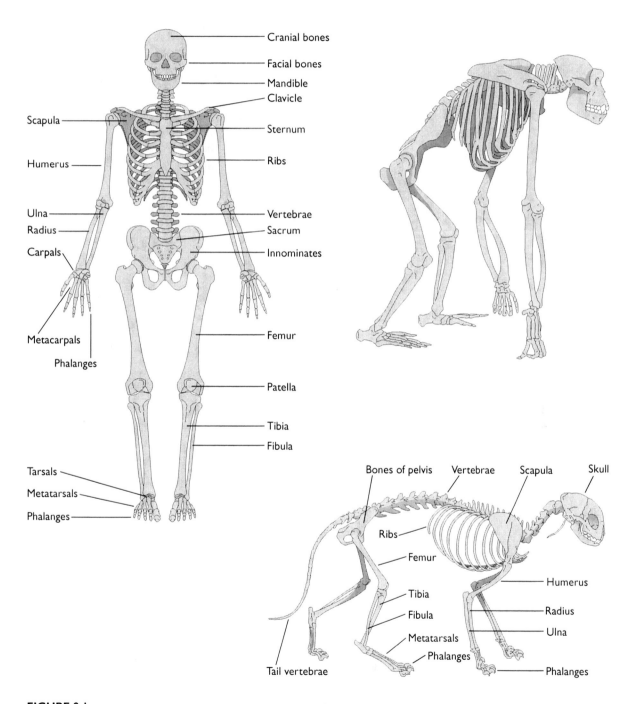

FIGURE 9.1
Skeletons of a modern human, a gorilla, and a domestic cat. (As a learning exercise, label the gorilla skeleton yourself.)

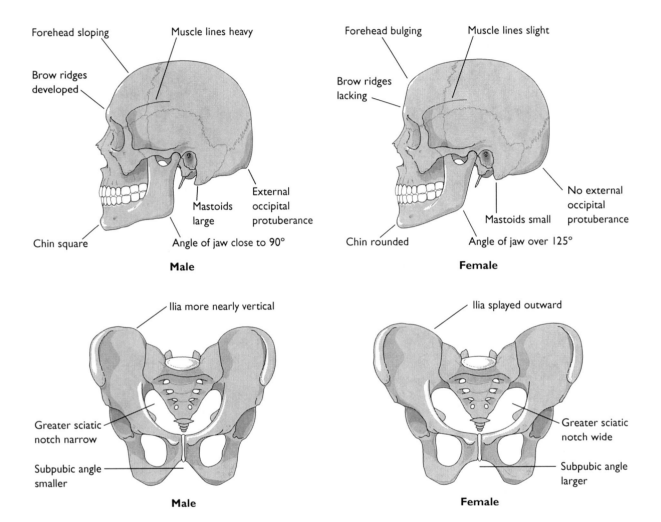

FIGURE 9.2
Major sex differences in the human skull and pelvis.

of human anatomy, they artistically add missing bones, eyes, fatty tissue, cartilage, muscle, and skin to casts of ancient skulls, "fleshing out" our picture of early humans (Figure 9.4; see also Figure 15.2). This technique is also used in law enforcement to try to identify skeletal remains. We will discuss the application of human osteology to legal matters in Chapter 15.

The skeleton can also tell us something about the behavior of the deceased organism. We have mentioned the importance of bipedal locomotion as the first hominin trait to evolve. We know it was first because the nature of the bones of the pelvis and femur, along with the position of the skull atop the spine, suggests posture and movement. Thus, our analysis of the bones of our most ancient ancestors provides clues as to how they walked (Figure 9.5; see also Chapter 10 for the evolution of this behavior).

Average ages for cranial suture closure (years)

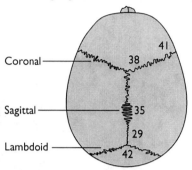

Cranial Suture Closure. The bones of the cranial vault are separate at birth and gradually fuse during a person's lifetime. The numbers indicate the average age (in years) of complete closure at different points along the lines of attachment, the sutures. There are other dates as well, on locations not shown in this view. Because of the great degree of individual variation, this is not a particularly reliable technique, but it is still used.

Eruption dates of deciduous and permanent teeth

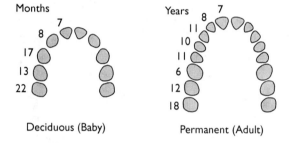

Dental Eruption. Humans have two sets of teeth: deciduous, or "baby" teeth, and permanent, or adult teeth. Each tooth erupts through the gum line at a certain average age. We determine age by seeing which tooth was the last to erupt and which unerupted tooth would have erupted next. We recognize this method in our use of the term "six year molar" for the first adult tooth to erupt. The degree of development of each tooth below the gum line (seen in broken bone or in X-rays) can also be used.

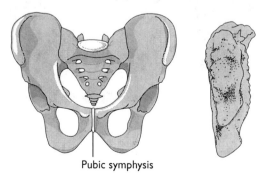

Pubic symphysis

Ages of epiphyseal union (years)

Elbow	14
Hand and foot	15
Ankle	16
Thigh (top)	17
Knee	18
Wrist	19
Shoulder	20
Hip	21
Clavicle	28

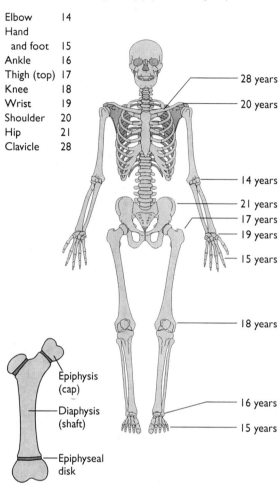

Epiphyseal Union. The bones of the arms, legs, hands, feet, and other body parts grow in sections: a shaft, or diaphysis, and caps, or epiphyses. When growth is complete, the cartilaginous disks between caps and shaft turn to bone and a single bone results. Ages for epiphyseal union are uniform enough to provide a reliable aging method. The ages shown indicate that all the sites at any one location fuse at about the same time. For example, at the elbow, the far (distal) end of the humerus and the near (proximal) ends of the radius and ulna all fuse at approximately 14 years.

Pubic Symphysis. The inner surface of the bones where the pelvis meets in front is called the pubic symphysis. Between the ages of 18 and 50+, the appearance of this surface undergoes characteristic changes. By assessing the phase to which a specimen belongs, we can approximate the age of a specimen at death. The symphyseal face shown is a Phase VIII, giving an age of 40 to 44 years. (Redrawn from Todd 1920.)

FIGURE 9.3 Major techniques used to determine the age of human bones.

FIGURE 9.4
Using a cast of a fossil skull, an anthropologist adds modeling clay to flesh out the face of an ancient human ancestor.

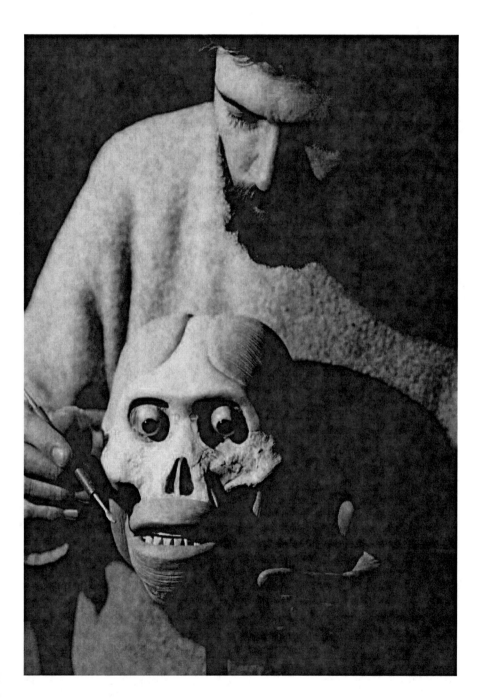

carnivore An organism adapted to a diet of mostly meat.

omnivore An organism with a mixed diet of animal and vegetable foods.

Moreover, we can discern information about a deceased organism's diet from dental and skeletal remains. Look at the dentition of a **carnivore** in your dog or cat and compare it to the teeth of an **omnivore** in your own mouth. The teeth of the dog or cat, although they show some differentiation, are all pointed and sharp, adapted for grasping, piercing, cutting, and

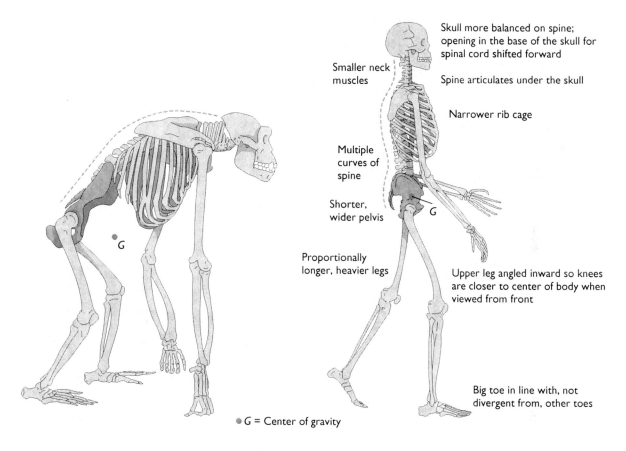

Smaller neck muscles

Skull more balanced on spine; opening in the base of the skull for spinal cord shifted forward

Spine articulates under the skull

Narrower rib cage

Multiple curves of spine

Shorter, wider pelvis

G

Proportionally longer, heavier legs

Upper leg angled inward so knees are closer to center of body when viewed from front

G

Big toe in line with, not divergent from, other toes

● *G* = Center of gravity

FIGURE 9.5

Note the anatomical changes and, thus, the physical evidence associated with bipedalism in the human primate. Compare human features with corresponding ones in the gorilla. *G* represents the center of gravity when standing bipedally. The ape expends much more energy to keep from falling forward when standing upright.

(Modified from John Napier, *The Antiquity of Human Walking*, © 1967 Scientific American. Drawing by Enid Kotschnigo)

crushing meat. Our teeth are adapted for a greater variety of operations and, thus, a greater variety of food types. In addition, certain wear patterns on the teeth, when examined microscopically, can reveal whether the organism's diet consisted of soft foods like fruits, or more abrasive, gritty foods like grains and roots (see Figure 10.18). We can even examine the chemical content of ancient bones for the proportion of strontium, calcium, carbon isotopes, and other elements to determine whether plants or meat made up the bulk of the diet of certain populations.

Finally, we may acquire information about the health status of our ancestors, a field known as **paleopathology.** Many diseases leave characteristic marks on the skeleton. These include such important disorders as arthritis, tumors and other cancers, tuberculosis, leprosy, anemias, syphilis,

paleopathology The study of disease and nutritional deficiency in prehistoric populations, usually through the examination of skeletal material.

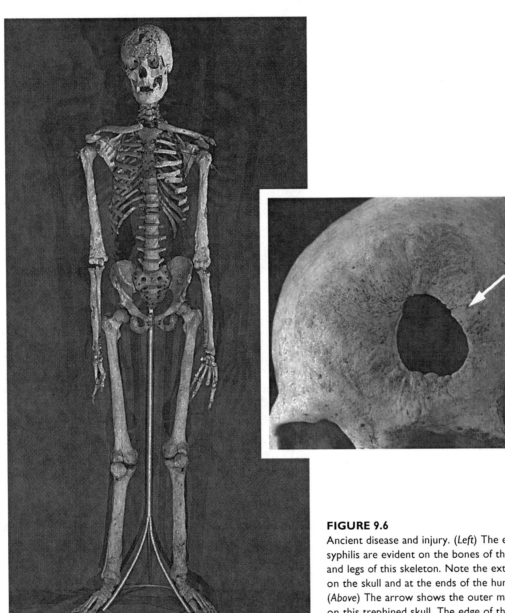

FIGURE 9.6
Ancient disease and injury. (*Left*) The effects of advanced syphilis are evident on the bones of the face, skull, arms, and legs of this skeleton. Note the extensive lesions on the skull and at the ends of the humeri and tibias. (*Above*) The arrow shows the outer margin of the surgery on this trephined skull. The edge of the hole indicates that healing had taken place before the individual died.

osteoporosis, and various infections. Injuries, too, leave their marks, as do other cultural behaviors, including scalping and **trephination,** a surgical procedure that involves cutting a hole in the skull, practiced even in prehistoric times (Figure 9.6).

For some practice on analyzing skeletal remains, go to the "Exercises" in the Online Learning Center Web site.

trephination Cutting a hole in the skull, presumably to treat some illness.

FIGURE 9.7
Olduvai Gorge, Tanzania.
This location is one of the
world's most productive sites
for paleoanthropologists. The
strata represent more than
2 million years of evolution.

OLD BONES: LOCATING, RECOVERING, AND DATING FOSSILS

Finding Fossils

Most creatures that have ever lived, including humans, have left no remains. Fossilization (which we'll discuss shortly) is a rare occurrence. A fossil, therefore, is really a priceless treasure, and finding one is an uncommon event—even in those **sites** that because of their geological history and nature yield many remains. Olduvai Gorge in Tanzania (Figure 9.7)

sites Locations that contain fossil and archaeological evidence of human presence.

has provided us with some of the most important hominin fossils, yet Louis and Mary Leakey lived and worked there for more than twenty years before finding one. How, then, do we even decide where to begin looking?

A lot, of course, depends on just *what* we're looking for. If it's dinosaurs we're interested in, we look in rock strata that date from the time of the dinosaurs. Anthropologists looking for hominin fossils need strata that were deposited in the past 5 to 6 million years.

It helps, too, if those strata are exposed by geological processes. Layers that are far under the surface might contain important fossils, but from a purely practical standpoint, it would be difficult, time-consuming, and expensive to dig them up. A place like Olduvai Gorge is ideal. There, an ancient river cut a canyon 300 feet into the earth, exposing layers of soil and rock that go back about 2 million years. At Omo, in Ethiopia, another important early hominin site, the strata have been tilted by geological forces, so that layers from 1 to 4 mya are all on the surface. Walking back and forth at such sites is like walking through time.

Of course, just because a location *looks* like it might easily yield fossils doesn't mean that the conditions there were always conducive to fossilization. Paleoanthropologists might inquire as to whether fossils of *any* sort have been found in a potential area of investigation in strata from the time period they are interested in. Both Olduvai and Omo already had reputations as rich fossil areas before the search for hominin fossils began there.

Recovering Fossils

Recovering fossils once they are located can be a tricky business. Fossils are old and often very fragile. Many old bones are **petrified**—turned to stone—and so can be hard to distinguish from the stone in which they were found (Figure 9.8). Raymond Dart, the discoverer of one of the most famous hominin fossils (both of whom we shall meet in the next chapter), took seventy-three days to separate the delicate fossil from the limestone in which it was encased (see Figure 10.9). The excavation tools of the paleoanthropologist, then, are not so much the backhoe or even the shovel but rather the mason's trowel, the dentist's pick, and the artist's brush.

A fossil sitting on a shelf in a lab or on display in a museum may be beautiful, intriguing, and provocative, but it is scientifically useless unless we know precisely where it was found, its **provenience.** To keep track of the proveniences of fossils, recovery is carried out with the utmost care directed at detailed and accurate record keeping. After all, a site is destroyed in the process of removing fossils, and we must have records of the relative locations of all the important items contained in that site.

petrified Turned to stone.

provenience Here, the precise location where a fossil or artifact was found.

Many early hominin fossils are simply found on the surface of the ground, exposed by wind and water erosion. Many, however, are dug out of the ground or are found associated with particular strata.

Dating Fossils

Relative Dating Techniques   The depth at which a fossil is found in the natural strata of the soil or rock is, of course, an indication of its relative age. This is the principle of **superposition**—the deeper a layer is, the older

superposition   The principle of stratigraphy that, barring disturbances, more recent layers are superimposed over older ones.

FIGURE 9.9
Hypothetical stratigraphic sequence. The humanlike remains are between two layers of volcanic rock that can be dated using the K/Ar (potassium/argon) method. The remains must be younger than the volcanic deposit below and older than the one above.

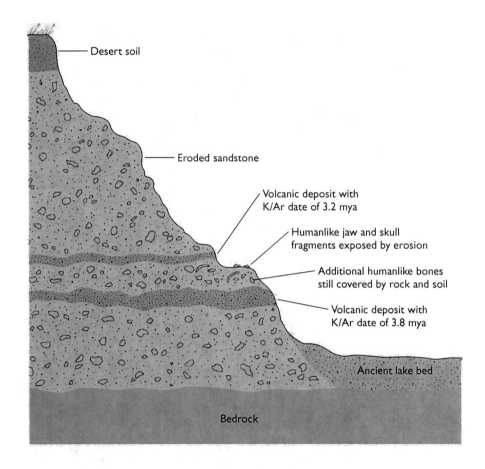

Desert soil

Eroded sandstone

Volcanic deposit with K/Ar date of 3.2 mya

Humanlike jaw and skull fragments exposed by erosion

Additional humanlike bones still covered by rock and soil

Volcanic deposit with K/Ar date of 3.8 mya

Ancient lake bed

Bedrock

it is. It is an important dating method and an example of a **relative dating technique;** that is, it indicates the age of one fossil in comparison with that of another (Figure 9.9). In the absence of any natural stratigraphy, the excavator of fossils must establish one. For example, the investigator may dig down by regular increments, perhaps only centimeters at a time, recording the precise depth of any item of interest.

Fossils can also be dated relative to their stratigraphic correlation with other fossils of known age. This is the principle of **biostratigraphy.** This dating method has been used in some of the early hominin sites in South Africa. Many of these sites are located in limestone caves, which are difficult to date by the techniques discussed in the following paragraphs. But when nonhominin fossils of known age are found in association with hominin fossils, we may infer the age of the hominins.

Similarly, the horizontal location of each fossil is important. Often a paleoanthropologist—like the archaeologist looking for human cultural remains—uses a grid system. A site is divided into squares, or grids, and

relative dating technique
A dating method that indicates the age of one item in comparison to another.

biostratigraphy The study of fossils in their stratigraphic context. Used as a relative dating technique.

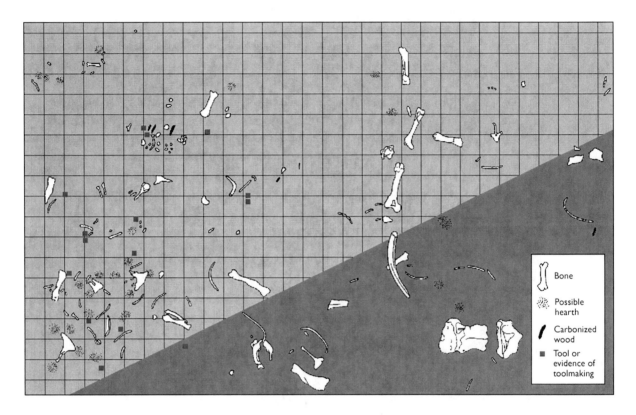

FIGURE 9.10
Grid system diagram from an excavation in Ambrona, Spain, dated at around 350,000 ya (see Chapter 11). The grid helps record the precise location of each bone and artifact. Notice how much less information is conveyed by the part of the drawing that does not show the grid.

each grid is excavated separately (Figure 9.10). The precise location of a fossil, relative to that of others at the same level, is recorded through photographs and maps.

Absolute Dating Techniques   To determine the actual age of a fossil, we use **absolute dating techniques,** or **chronometric techniques.** Among the best known are **radiometric** techniques. They all have essentially the same basic premise: if you know the rate at which some natural process occurs, and if you known how much of that process has already occurred, you can calculate the time at which the process started. There are several radiometric techniques, but two that are particularly useful in paleoanthropology will give you the idea.

Perhaps the best known is **radiocarbon dating,** which can be used to date fossils back to about 40,000 ya and so is relevant to the later period

absolute dating techniques Dating methods that give specific ages, years, or ranges of years for objects or sites.

chronometric techniques Another name for absolute dating techniques.

radiometric Referring to the decay rate of a radioactive substance.

radiocarbon dating A radiometric dating technique using the decay rate of a radioactive form of carbon found in organic remains.

of human evolution. It works as follows: Carbon, in the form of carbon dioxide, is found in all living things, which continuously exchange it with the environment through respiration and metabolism. Nearly all carbon is ^{12}C, indicating that there are twelve particles in the nucleus (six protons and six neutrons). Some carbon, however, is called *carbon 14*, or ^{14}C, because it has two extra neutrons. Carbon 14 is continually being produced in the atmosphere by the impact of high-energy particles (known as *cosmic rays*) emanating from deep space that constantly bombard the earth. We know the proportion of each form (*isotope*) of carbon in a living organism. Once an organism dies, however, it no longer takes in new carbon, and so its ^{14}C—an unstable, or radioactive, isotope—begins to decay back into nitrogen, and it does this at a constant rate called a **half-life.** The half-life of ^{14}C is 5,730 years. In that time, one-half of the ^{14}C will have decayed. In another 5,730 years, half of the remaining half will decay, leaving a quarter of the original. And so on.

Now, if we find some organic remains—bone, for example, or even burnt wood from a campfire—we can test it to see how much ^{14}C is left compared to how much the organism contained when alive. We know how much ^{14}C a living organism should contain, and we test the amount left as we would test any radioactive substance, with a device that measures the amount of radiation emitted. Suppose that our specimen has one-quarter of the living amount. That means that two half-lives have passed, or 5,730 × 2, or 11,460 years.

In fossils older than about 40,000 years, there is not enough ^{14}C left to accurately measure. So how do we date the really old fossils, like those of the early hominins? We could use another important method called **potassium/argon,** or **K/Ar, dating.** Radioactive potassium (^{40}K), found in volcanic rock, decays into stable argon gas over time; its half-life is 1.31 billion years. Organic matter contains ^{40}K as well but loses the argon gas that it decays into. Volcanic rocks, formed during eruptions, trap the argon. Using the same reasoning as for radiocarbon dating, we test volcanic rock for the amount of argon, work backward, and date the eruption. Then, organic remains may be dated relatively: Any fossils found in a layer of volcanic rock are as old as that rock. Fossils found just above are younger; those found just below are older (see again Figure 9.9). Recently, a technique called **argon/argon dating,** which uses the decay of radioactive ^{40}Ar into argon gas (^{39}Ar), has proved more accurate in dating volcanic rock. With the use of lasers, it can be performed on a sample as small as a single crystal.

Other absolute dating techniques exist and are listed in Table 9.1, along with the preceding methods. Several techniques date volcanic rock; others can be used directly on organic remains. In many cases, more than

half-life The time needed for one-half of a given amount of a radioactive substance to decay.

potassium/argon (K/Ar) dating A radiometric dating technique using the rate at which radioactive potassium, found in volcanic rock, decays into stable argon gas.

argon/argon dating A radiometric dating technique that uses the decay of radioactive argon into stable argon gas. Can be used to date smaller samples and volcanic rock with greater accuracy than K/Ar dating.

TABLE 9.1
Absolute Dating Techniques

Dating Method	Age Range	Material Dated	Basis
Accelerator mass spectrometry	70,000–100s BP*	Organic remains	Counts actual number of ^{14}C atoms
Amino (aspartic) acid racemization	1,000,000–2,000 BP	Bone	Measures shift in polarity of amino acids
Electron spin resonance	10 million–100s BP	Teeth, cave deposits	Measures electrons produced by natural radiation that become trapped in crystalline materials at a regular rate
Fission track dating	1,000,000–100,000 BP	Volcanic rock	Measures radioactive decay that leaves microscopic damage "tracks" in rock at a regular rate
Luminescence	To 800,000 BP	Fired clay, pottery, bricks, burnt rock	Measures amount of energy captured in material from the decay of radioactive elements in surrounding soil; amount of energy captured is proportional to age
Obsidian hydration	800,000 BP–present	Obsidian (volcanic glass)	Measures regular buildup of a "hydration layer," caused by the chemical reaction of obsidian to water over time
Paleomagnetism	2,000 BP–present	Material with magnetic minerals	Determines alignment of particles in natural deposits relative to the dated location of the earth's magnetic pole
Potassium/argon and argon/argon	billions–100,000 BP	Volcanic rock	Measures decay of radioactive potassium (or argon isotope) to stable argon gas
Radiocarbon	40,000–100s BP	Organic remains	Measures decay of radioactive carbon isotope to stable nitrogen
Uranium series	350,000–1,000 BP	Calcium carbonate	Measures decay of radioactive uranium to a series of other elements

*BP = "before present."

one of these methods may be applied, and when they agree, we have a well-established date for a geological stratum or a fossil. Most of the dates presented in the following chapters are reasonably well confirmed through the use of one or more of these techniques.

HOW FOSSILS GET TO BE FOSSILS

Most animals and plants that have inhabited the earth have left no fossil remains. There may be whole taxonomic groups unknown to us because we've found no clues to their existence. Why is this so?

The conditions under which an organism, or some of its parts, can be preserved are quite specific. In New England, where I live, the soil is very acidic, due largely to the annual fall of leaves and pine needles. Organic remains tend to disappear very quickly. This is why we were surprised to find the intact skeleton of Henry Opukaha'ia (see Chapter 1). His bones were preserved because he was buried on a hill in sandy soil, so water, with all its related chemical and biological decaying activity, could not accumulate around him; additionally, the cemetery was probably regularly cleared of leaves.

Organic remains tend to be preserved under several conditions. In cases of extreme dryness, even soft tissues—usually eaten by everything from bacteria to insects to scavengers—may mummify. Natural mummies resulted from normal burials in the desert sands of ancient Egypt, even before the Egyptians began artificial mummification. In 1995, near the summit of the 20,760-foot volcano Nevando Ampato in Peru, the naturally mummified remains of a young Inca girl were found (Figure 9.11). Sacrificed to the gods of the mountains some 500 ya, her body was preserved by the cold and dry conditions of the high altitude (Reinhard 1996). More recently, at another and even higher site in the Andes, the bodies of three more children were discovered (Reinhard 1999). (See Chapter 15 for another famous example—the "Ice Man" from the Alps.)

Lack of oxygen also contributes to preservation. Such conditions are found in the thick sediment at the bottom of some lakes and ponds. With no oxygen, there is little bacterial action, and organic remains decay very slowly. Many important fossils have been found in places that were once lake bottoms.

Of course, the longer ago an organism lived, the less likely we are to find its remains, simply because there is more chance that they will have been crushed, dissolved, eaten, washed away, and so on. But in some cases, minerals may crystallize out of water around the bones or shells of a creature. In rare cases, crystals may form around slowly decaying soft tissue and fill in the spaces left by the decay of organic matter. In all these cases, the fossils become petrified. They literally turn to stone and so become harder, more resistant to processes of decay, and no longer edible—although, naturally, some anatomical detail is lost. The dinosaur fossils with which we are so familiar, as well as the remains of the earliest hominins, are all stone. Luckily for us, the creatures that left these remains perished in just the right situations. Most creatures, however, aren't so considerate.

A fossil reveals more than just the type of organism it once belonged to. A fossil also contains clues as to how the animal died and what happened

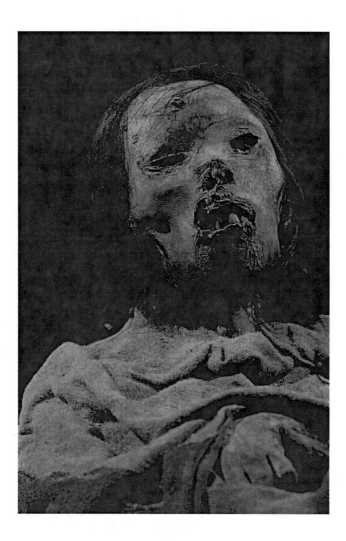

FIGURE 9.11
The Inca "Ice Maiden" is one of several naturally preserved mummies of sacrificial victims found in the Andes.

to it after its death. The study of these factors is called **taphonomy** (from the Greek word *taphos*, "dead"), and it has been important in our understanding of our own evolution.

For example, some early hominin bones have been found in limestone caves in South Africa along with the bones of other mammals. These finds led investigators to believe that our early ancestors inhabited those caves and were hunters who brought their kills back home. More recent taphonomic analysis, however, reveals that the hominins were the hunted, not the hunters. The bones were the leftovers of leopard kills. Here's how scientists believe it happened: Leopards often drag their prey up into a tree, where no other predator or scavenger can

taphonomy The study of how organisms become part of the paleontological record.

FIGURE 9.12
This artist's reconstruction shows a leopard with the remains of an early hominin in a tree above the entrance to a cave. This scenario probably accounts for the accumulation of bones, including bones of our ancestors, in South African caves.

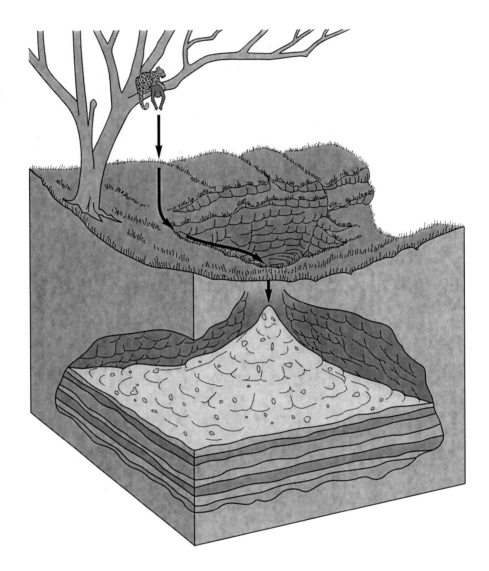

get at it. Although much of South Africa is dry, trees are able to grow around the mouths of limestone caves, which hold moisture. As leopard kills hanging in the trees fell apart—after being eaten over several days or decaying over time—the bones fell into the caves. Those bones were of antelopes, baboons, and other animals leopards eat. Apparently, our ancestors were on the menu as well (Figure 9.12). One early hominin skull shows twin puncture wounds that appear to have been the cause of death. The lower canine teeth of a leopard fit exactly into these punctures, providing evidence for the preceding analysis. Although taphonomy is the study of the dead, it has told us important things about how our distant ancestors *lived*. We will describe another important conclusion from taphonomy in the next chapter, when we see how microscopic scratches on bones and teeth reveal something about the diet of the early hominins.

GENES: NEW WINDOWS TO THE PAST

The "Molecular Clock"

Just as we can reconstruct evolutionary relationships by comparing the anatomical traits of living creatures, we may do the same by making comparisons at the genetic level. In some ways, genetic comparisons are more accurate. Phenotypic traits are normally controlled by a complex interaction of multiple genes, evolutionary processes, and environmental factors. As a result, a trait may look the same in two species, but the expressions of that trait in each species may be based on very different genetics, developmental processes, and environmental interactions. The two traits may also have different adaptive functions.

On the other hand, two species may *look* very different, but their differences may be the result of extensive phenotypic effects of a very small number of genes, and the species may actually be quite close genetically. Humans and chimps are an example.

Comparing genetic differences among individuals, species, and higher taxa (genera, families, and so on) reveals actual biological relationships, no matter what the species look like or how seemingly similar or different some of their traits are. This work was pioneered, in the 1960s, by Vincent Sarich and Allan Wilson of the University of California at Berkeley.

It had been assumed prior to their work that humans and our closest relatives, the great apes, were separated by 12 to 15 million years of evolution. This estimate was based on the degree of phenotypic difference between us and them and on some 12-million-year-old fossils that *appeared* to show the beginnings of hominin traits. Wilson and Sarich's research showed that the blood proteins of humans and chimps are almost identical. In other words, our genes, at least for those traits, are almost the same. Comparing this difference with that between species whose evolutionary divergence time was known, Wilson and Sarich calculated that our two species had branched a mere 5 mya. These 12-million-year-old

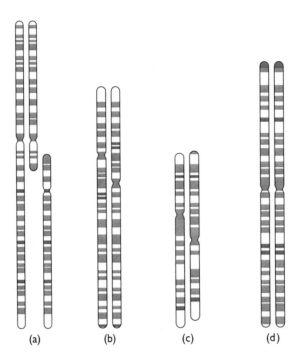

(a)   (b)   (c)   (d)

FIGURE 9.13

Comparison of human and chimpanzee chromosomes. Human chromosomes appear on
the left in each pair and chimpanzee chromosomes on the right. The similarities in banding
pattern (seen after applying a chemical stain) are clear. In pair (a) the pattern of human
chromosome 2 is similar to that of two chimp chromosomes. In pair (d) the patterns are
virtually identical. Banding patterns are the results of different concentrations of the four
bases that make up the genetic code. Light bands are rich in noncoding sequences with mostly
C's (cytosine) and G's (guanine; see Chapter 3). These tend to be associated with areas of
high gene concentration. This is one type of early evidence for the genetic similarity between
our two species.

fossils, they concluded, were not hominins, no matter what they appeared
to be. They were right, as we will see in Chapter 10. Other methods for
making comparisons closer to the genetic level verified this hypothesis
(Figure 9.13).

Today's technologies (see Chapter 3) allow us to look at and compare the most basic genetic components—the sequence of base pairs that
make up the codons, which in turn make up the genes. We can now more
precisely compare the genetic makeup of primate (and other) species,
establishing just how genetically similar or different they are, and, using
the logic described above, estimate how long ago their evolutionary lines
diverged. Scientists have even attempted to reconstruct the ancestral

genome of all living primates (O'Brien and Stanyon 1999). This is one of the bases for determining the order of branching for the cladistic method (see Chapter 7).

The Genetic Differences between Chimps and Humans

A focus of recent studies, of course, is on the genetic comparison of humans with our closest relatives, the chimpanzees and bonobos. A well-known and well-accepted quantitative expression of this comparison says that humans and these apes are 98 percent genetically identical at the nucleotide level. While this does capture the relative degree of our evolutionary closeness—which is no surprise anyway—it doesn't really tell us much. For one thing, since there are only four bases in the genetic code, any two long sequences of DNA from any two species are likely to be at least 25 percent identical (Marks 2002). Second, different sections of DNA evolve at different rates, so some portions of our two species' DNA might be completely identical while others are very different. In addition, while some base sequences of human and chimp and bonobo DNA may be absolutely identical, they may show up in different numbers. For example, the base sequence of the genes for the Rh blood groups is the same in humans and chimps, but humans have two such genes while chimps have three (Marks 2002:27). This phenomenon, called *copy number variation*, shows a 6.4 percent difference between our two species (Cohen 2007). Finally, so-called *indels*, insertions or deletions of one to thousands of base pairs, and duplications of DNA sequences show about 3 percent difference between our species (Li and Saunders 2005). There's more going on than a simple numerical statement indicates.

Far more interesting and useful questions ask *which* genes differ between humans and chimps, *how* those genes differ, and *what* those genes do. Recent research proposes some interesting possibilities. A chemical, for example, that all mammals, including the apes, possess on the surface of all body cells is lacking in humans. This is the result of some differences in a 92–base pair section of a single gene (Gibbons 1998b; Muchmore et al. 1998; Normile 2001). One function of this chemical is cellular communication during brain development and function, so a possible result of the genetic difference could be an influence on the timing and extent of brain growth. This has obvious implications for human evolution. Indeed, there is growing evidence for some major differences in "brain genes" between our species (Balter 2005).

Contemporary Reflections

Who Owns Old Bones?

In 1990 the nearly complete skeleton of a *Tyrannosaurus rex*, nicknamed "Sue," was found in South Dakota and soon became the center of a controversy over ownership. After some complex legal haggling, the owner of the land on which the bones were found was granted permission to sell them. The skeleton went up for public auction in October 1997 and was purchased (with corporate help) by the Field Museum of Natural History in Chicago—for $8.36 million! It will now be available for research and is currently on public display. In this case, everybody won, but scientists worry that this could set a precedent that would remove important evidence of the past from free scientific inquiry.

The issue of ownership and availability to science becomes even more complex when the remains of the past are human. In these cases, ownership may be a matter not only of landholding but also of direct biological or cultural descent. The extreme cases are easy enough to sort out. I don't think anyone would object to the excavation and study of early African hominins, even though they are the ancestors of us all. They are simply too far removed in time, and their potential scientific value is too great. On the other hand, I would object if some anthropologist wanted to dig up my grandparents, examine their bones, and put them in a museum case—and the law would clearly be on my side. Not all situations, however, are as clear-cut.

For years, otherwise well-meaning scientists have enjoyed the freedom to recover, study, and store the skeletal remains of the remote and not-so-remote ancestors of living peoples. In North America, thousands of Native American skeletons have been recovered—many of which were exhumed from the graves into which they had been placed by members of their societies. Although these remains have provided much information about the original inhabitants of this continent, Native American groups have voiced objections, for obvious reasons. In 1990 the Native American Graves Protection and Repatriation Act (NAGPRA) was passed. It says that lineal descendants have a right to the remains of their ancestors housed in institutions or discovered on federal or tribal territory. This legislation has led to the removal of large collections of human remains and associated artifacts from museums and labs and has made new excavations of Native American remains difficult, if not impossible. Indeed, before

Another specific difference is in some genes for enzymes called *proteases*, which are important to the immune system (Check 2004). This could explain why chimps are less severely affected by some diseases such as AIDS and Alzheimer's.

A difference between nonhuman primates and humans has been located on a gene for a protein important in the building of some jaw muscles. Because of a mutation, the human version of the gene is inactivated, resulting in reduced muscle fibers and even a reduced size of some jaw muscles (Stedman "naturally shed" remains were excluded from NAGPRA regulations, two local tribes demanded the return of some 10,000-year-old human hair found at a site in Montana, hair that could provide information on the DNA of early Americans (see Feder 1997 and references therein for a more complete discussion of this and related issues). A well-known example involves the skeletal remains discovered in 1996 in Washington State and commonly known as "Kennewick Man." A coalition of Native American tribes from the area laid claim to the 9,000-year-old bones under the terms of NAGPRA. Despite scientific testimony to the contrary, Secretary of the Interior Bruce Babbitt declared in September 2000 that the remains were culturally affiliated with the coalition and that the bones should be turned over to them. A suit by a group of scientists to gain access to the remains for study was reinstated. On February 4, 2004, a court of appeals ruled that the bones could be studied. But as of this writing, bills opposed to and in support of the study of ancient remains are still being proposed by groups of Native Americans and scientists, respectively.

Is there a compromise between honoring the cultural laws and heritage of indigenous peoples and providing science with important data—data that may even shed light on the history of the people in question? Each case, in the end, must be examined and judged on its own merits. Much evidence of early America is in the form of abandoned and naturally covered-over objects and bones, not intentional burials. Many of these remains cannot be reasonably affiliated with any specific living group and, thus, should be freely open to legitimate scientific investigation. Alternatively, scientists should not go into clearly identified burial areas armed with shovels and trowels. As is most often the case, where ancient bones are uncovered by natural processes or accident (say, during a construction project), the group with which those bones are affiliated might allow scientific information to be gathered before the bones are reburied. This is the situation with the well-known African Burial Ground in New York City. A model example for me is the case of Henry Opukaha'ia (see Chapter 1), where the family kindly allowed us to fully examine Henry's bones before preparing and returning them for burial.

Whatever the individual cases, however, there is one overriding consideration that should guide our actions—no matter how old or from what species, bones were once integral parts of living, breathing, feeling beings. Even when we can use them as scientific specimens, they deserve respectful treatment.

et al. 2004). Moreover, the origin of this mutation has been placed at about 2.4 mya, a date, as we shall see, that is about the time of the first fossils identified as belonging to our genus, *Homo*.

In addition to these specific differences, it has also been established that five chromosomes in our two species show significant differences in the arrangement of the same genes. Some sequences, for example, have been flipped (or inverted) in one species as compared to the other. These changes could lead to different roles for those genes. Identifying their functions is a current goal, as is the establishment of a nonhuman primate genome project to provide a complete sequence of the genomes of our closest relatives (Gibbons 1998b).

In the next three chapters we will outline the story of hominin evolution. All the above scientific techniques have been applied to studying this story and have allowed us to achieve what knowledge we have of our evolutionary history. As we will see, these new technologies have also been applied to the relationships between modern humans and various groups of our ancestors (Chapter 12) and to comparisons among modern human populations (Chapter 14).

SUMMARY

Often when we read a brief article in the popular press about a new fossil find, we get the impression that the scientists conducted some sort of magic to arrive at their stated conclusions. In the 3 October 1994 issue of *Time*, for example, we read that a small fossil tooth and a few other fragmentary bones from Ethiopia had been discovered, heralding "a new chapter in the history of human evolution" (Lemonick 1994). On the basis of these bones, a new species of hominin was established. According to the scientists' description, the individual was probably bipedal, stood about 4 feet tall, was "ravaged by carnivores," and lived 4.4 mya in the forests. That's pretty specific information from a handful of bones turned to stone.

You should now understand that arriving at such conclusions is not magic at all. Although data like these bones are from a creature millions of years old, we may still use scientific methodology to interpret them. We know what modern mammalian skeletons look like and what previous fossil finds look like, so we can compare our new fossils with older ones in order to give them at least a provisional taxonomic assignment. As the fossils were being recovered in Ethiopia, scientists recorded exhaustive data about their provenience, allowing us to generate hypotheses about their environment and, using technologies from physics, when they lived. We understand how fossils are formed and what their specific condition can tell us about how the organism died and became part of the fossil record. We know, for example, what bones that have been "ravaged by carnivores" look like.

Finally, combining the preceding techniques with new methods from genetics, we have been able to piece together a tentative family tree of the hominids and related primates. When a new set of fossils is found, we have a context for comparison and a taxonomic system that can supply it with a name. We will meet this 4.4-million-year-old fossil species and many others in the next chapter, as we see exactly how these fact-finding techniques are applied.

QUESTIONS FOR FURTHER THOUGHT

1. Recently the Parliament of Iceland gave a private company the right to create and maintain a database on the health records, genealogies, and DNA profiles of nearly all living and many deceased Icelanders. The intent is to better understand links between diseases and genes. But there are privacy issues and concerns that the company may sell its information to pharmaceutical and insurance companies. What issues must be taken into account so that we might benefit from such a study while still respecting the rights of individuals?

2. Read the latest information about Kennewick Man on the Web sites listed in this chapter's "Suggested Readings." What do you think about the motives of the scientists who want to use the remains for study, as opposed to those of the Native Americans who want to rebury the bones with no further study? Is a compromise possible? How should we approach remains that have definite cultural affiliations but that might hold important scientific information? How far back into history must we go to find human or archaeological remains that preclude such controversy?

3. Given the phenotypic, behavioral, and, especially, genetic closeness of our species to the chimps and bonobos, should we grant those species special ethical, moral, and even legal consideration? A committee of the Spanish parliament recently approved resolutions to protect apes from harmful experiments and to ban their use in circuses and TV commercials and films. Is this going too far for a nonhuman species? If not, what other nonhumans deserve such consideration? Where do we draw the line between those creatures that do and those that don't deserve such consideration?

KEY TERMS

osteology

sexual dimorphism

carnivore

omnivore

paleopathology

trephination

sites

petrified

provenience

superposition

relative dating
  technique

biostratigraphy

absolute dating
  techniques

chronometric
  techniques

radiometric

radiocarbon dating

half-life

potassium/argon
  (K/Ar) dating

argon/argon dating

taphonomy

SUGGESTED READINGS

A detailed and beautifully photographed book on the human skeleton, with life-sized pictures, is *Human Osteology,* second edition, by Tim White and Pieter Folkens. Analysis of the human skeleton in anthropological context is also covered nicely in *Human Osteology: A Laboratory and Field Manual of the Human Skeleton,* by William Bass; in *Skeleton Keys,* by Jeffrey H. Schwartz; and, for comparative osteology among the primates, in *An Introduction to Human Evolutionary Anatomy,* by Leslie Aiello and Christopher Dean. For a detailed treatment of anatomy and evolution that also includes considerations of soft tissue, see *The Human Strategy: An Evolutionary Perspective on Human Anatomy,* by John H. Langdon.

Techniques of excavation, interpretation, and dating are covered in more detail in Ken Feder and Michael Park's *Human Antiquity,* fifth edition, and in even more detail in Robert Sharer and Wendy Ashmore's *Archaeology: Discovering Our Past* and Brian Fagan's *In the Beginning.*

Taphonomy is covered by Pat Shipman in *Life History of a Fossil: An Introduction to Taphonomy and Paleoecology* and by Lewis Binford in *Bones: Ancient Men and Modern Myths.*

For information on the techniques and discoveries regarding human genetics, see *Genome: The Autobiography of a Species in 23 Chapters,* by Matt Ridley.

More on the Ice Maiden and other mummies uncovered in the Andes can be found in three articles by Johan Reinhard in the June 1996, January 1997, and November 1999 issues of *National Geographic.*

The African Burial Ground is the topic of "Archaeology as Community Service: The African Burial Ground Project in New York City," by Warren Perry and Michael Blakey, in Kenneth Feder's *Lessons from the Past*. For the latest on Kennewick Man, see the following Web sites:
www.nps.gov/archeology/kennewick
www.tri-cityherald.com/kman

The Iceland genetics study is covered in "Decoding Iceland," by Michael Specter, in the 18 January 1999 *New Yorker*.

A thought-provoking book on the genetic similarities between humans and chimps, as well as other major issues in biological anthropology (including Kennewick Man), is Jonathan Marks's *What It Means to Be 98% Chimpanzee: Apes, People, and Their Genes*.

For more on the chimpanzee genome, see the series of articles in the 1 September 2005 issue of *Nature*, especially the lead article by the Chimpanzee Sequencing and Analysis Consortium. See also "Relative Differences: The Myth of 1%," by Jon Cohen, in the 29 June 2007 *Science*.

10
CHAPTER

Evolution of the Early Hominins

*There are no final words. Human origins
will always be enigmatic.*
—Donald Johanson

Paleoanthropologists observe present-day species and the fossilized remnants of other species to try to reconstruct the human past. The study of human evolution is a complicated venture. We have many thousands of individual pieces of data, each observed, measured, dated, and analyzed according to the very latest technologies. But when we try to put them all together, we come up with inconsistencies, contradictions, and often several equally plausible interpretations. This chapter and the two that follow will give you the most current ideas about our evolution, including all the missing pieces and alternative interpretations—at least the ones based on scientific inquiry. We will address the following questions:

What is the evolutionary history of the primates?

When and under what circumstances did the hominins evolve, and why was bipedalism so important?

What is the fossil record of the early hominins?

THE ORIGIN AND EVOLUTION OF THE PRIMATES

We have a large number of fossil specimens of primates, but the fossil record is still spotty. Our identifications of most of the extinct primate species are based on fragmentary remains, mostly pieces of jaws or sometimes just teeth. Although a particular extinct species may be represented by many specimens, fossils of its contemporaries are often lacking, giving us little basis for comparison. There are large gaps in the primate fossil record. Some periods are represented by many fossils, but they all come from just

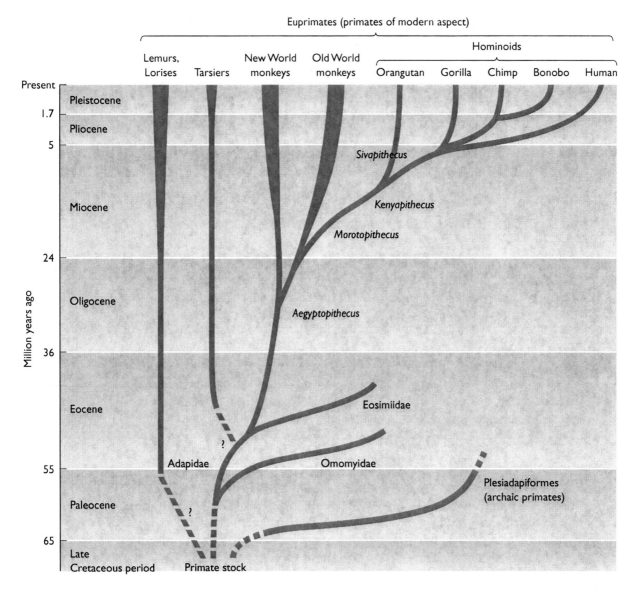

FIGURE 10.1

Simplified evolutionary tree for the primates, with major geological epochs and dates. Question marks and dashed lines indicate insufficient data to establish evolutionary relationships. This tree represents one of several possible interpretations.

a few sites. Still, we can put together a general, if tentative, picture of the course of primate evolution (Figure 10.1).

We have few fossils that tell us about the earliest stages of primate evolution. Some genetic comparisons point to the origin of the primates as far back as 80 to 90 mya, well into the time of the dinosaurs (Gibbons 1998a; Tavaré et al. 2002). In terms of hard evidence, there are a few primatelike teeth from Montana dated at 65 mya and some bones from Wyoming dated at 60 mya that have primate features related to climbing behavior. Remember that at the time, North America and Eurasia were still very close together and possibly still connected in some locations (see Figure 6.6), so the primates probably originated on the large northern landmass called Laurasia.

Undisputed primates appear about 55 mya. The traits that we associate in modern primates with an arboreal environment (see Chapter 7) may not have first evolved specifically to facilitate that adaptation. After all, other mammals that do not possess these traits are also arboreal. Anthropologist Matt Cartmill (1992) suggests that prehensile extremities and stereoscopic vision may have evolved to aid leaping as a means of locomotion in the forest canopy or the shrub-layer undergrowth and to promote fruit eating and "visually directed predation" on insects. Modern mouse lemurs, lorises, and tarsiers, for example, all track insects by sight and seize them by hand. As the primates evolved, these basic traits proved a useful adaptive theme for life in the trees. Some fossil finds from Wyoming (Bloch and Boyer 2002; Sargis 2002)—representing several families of Plesiadapiformes, an extinct branch of archaic primates (as opposed to the euprimates, or primates of modern aspect; see Figure 10.1)—clearly show features related to grasping, indicating that that adaptation evolved early in primate evolution.

The early primates come in three groups, all found in North America, Europe, Asia, and Africa. One group, the Adapidae, are lemurlike and so are thought to be ancestral to modern lemurs and lorises (Figure 10.2). Another group, the Omomyidae, are tarsier-like; they may date back as far as 60 mya and may be ancestral to both tarsiers and anthropoids (Figure 10.3). The Eosimiidae from Asia may represent direct ancestors of monkeys and hominoids. Important evolutionary shifts that marked the origin of the anthropoids included changes to (1) a diurnal lifestyle from a nocturnal one, (2) less leaping and more climbing through the trees with all fours, and (3) a more herbivorous diet with less emphasis on insects.

By the time the omomyids were moving into Asia, the Eastern and Western Hemispheres were completely separate. We know that all modern New World primates are monkeys, but there are very few monkey fossils from the New World, mostly because the jungle environment leads to quick and complete scavenging or decay of dead animals. Thus, we don't know for sure how the evolution of the primates proceeded in the Western Hemisphere. There are two views on the subject. The first is that the early New World prosimians moved into Central and South America when those areas joined together with North America and that the prosimians subsequently evolved into modern platyrrhines, the New World monkeys.

FIGURE 10.2

Skeleton and reconstruction of early adapid, *Smilodectes*. The form was similar to that of some modern prosimians. (Compare with Figure 7.13.)

The second view is that early monkeys from the Old World "rafted" over to the Americas, literally floating on logs and branches, "island-hopping" over a chain of volcanic islands when the two hemispheres were closer together. These early monkeys replaced any prosimians that still inhabited the New World, and they eventually evolved into the modern New World monkey species. Although there are some distinct differences (see Chapter 7), the basic similarity between the Old World and New World monkeys argues for a single origin and thus for the second scenario. In addition, although most of the fossils from the New World are incomplete and therefore hard to evaluate, a find of a 25- to 27-million-year-old

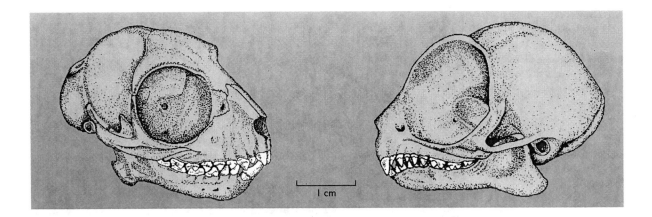

1 cm

FIGURE 10.3
Fossil omomyid, *Necrolemur* (*left*), compared with modern tarsier. (See also Figure 7.14.)

monkey from Bolivia (Takai et al. 2000), whose teeth are very similar to an older fossil form from Egypt, suggests that the New World monkeys originated and diversified first in Africa. That this scenario is plausible was shown by a report (Yoon 1998) of fifteen iguana lizards floating on a huge raft of trees 200 miles from their native Caribbean island of Guadeloupe to the island of Anguilla, where they had not previously been found. They are established and reproducing in their new habitat.

We are most interested in primate evolution in the Old World. A great deal of the history of the Old World anthropoids comes from a single site, the depression formed by an ancient lake in the desert southwest of Cairo, Egypt, called the Fayum. In the early 1960s, paleontologist Elwyn Simons began extensive investigations there that continue today (Simons and Rasmussen 1994). From this valuable site come a number of monkeylike forms dated from 40 to 25 mya. The most important, perhaps, is *Aegyptopithecus*, from about 34 mya (Figure 10.4). This 10-pound primate shows anthropoid traits, as well as several features of the teeth, braincase, and skull that resemble later hominoids (apes and hominins). It may be ancestral, then, to all the modern Old World anthropoids.

As the early anthropoids expanded, they outcompeted the prosimians and pushed those more primitive primates into marginal areas. Most prosimians now live—as endangered species—on the island of Madagascar, which they probably reached by rafting, possibly aided by a land bridge. No other primates invaded Madagascar until humans got there.

Apes appear in the fossil record about 23 mya. We refer to these earliest apes as *dental apes* because it is their teeth, rather than their overall anatomy, that resemble those of modern apes. Especially important is a feature of the molar teeth found only in hominoids and no other primates. It is called the *Y-5 cusp pattern* (Figure 10.5).

FIGURE 10.4
Skull of *Aegyptopithecus* from the Fayum in Egypt. This fossil is considered an early monkeylike form that may be ancestral to later Old World anthropoids.

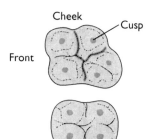

FIGURE 10.5
The Y-5 cusp pattern is found only in hominoids, and the four-cusp pattern is found in *all* anthropoids. The chewing surface is shown here. Look in the mirror, and you will probably see a Y-5 tooth, but note that not all hominid molars show this feature.

Between 23 and 5 mya, there were an estimated thirty or more different types of apes—larger-bodied, tailless, larger-brained primates. Only one lineage, however, gave rise to the modern apes and hominins. Evidence is scanty, but fossil finds point to African forms as candidates for the earliest hominoid. One form shows similarities to the modern chimpanzee in the arm and ankle bones that allow for the ability to hang in trees and to rotate the foot. Another form from 20 mya shows a mobile shoulder joint that would have aided in hanging from trees by the arms, as chimps and orangutans do, and vertebrae that suggest a short, stiff spine, a feature of modern apes that allows them occasional upright posture (Gebo et al. 1997).

Starting about 12 mya, we find fossils of more ground-dwelling, open-country apes, whose larger back teeth with thicker enamel point to a more mixed vegetable diet that included harder foods such as nuts. Fossils of these apes have been found in Africa, India, Pakistan, China, Turkey, Hungary, and Greece. One group from India and Pakistan, *Sivapithecus*, shares features with the modern orangutan and so is most likely an ancestor of that species (Figure 10.6). A new find from Ethiopia (Suwa et al. 2007) is said to be of a 10-million-year-old ancestor of modern gorillas.

Another form, *Ouranopithecus*, so far found only in Greece and dated at 10 to 9 mya, shares some features with hominins. Although clearly an

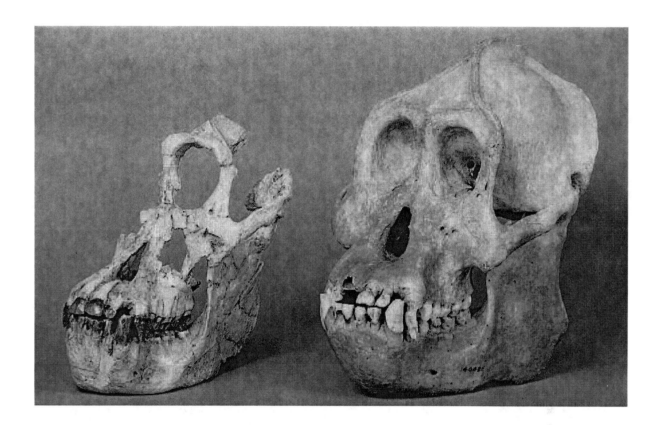

FIGURE 10.6
Skull of *Sivapithecus* (*left*) compared to that of a modern orangutan. They are essentially identical.

ape, about the size of a female gorilla, it is thought by some to be a good candidate for a member of the ape line that eventually led to the hominins (Begun 2003; De Bonis and Koufos 1994).*

We can't leave this discussion without noting perhaps the most famous and the biggest sivapithecid—indeed, the biggest primate ever. This giant ape, whose fossils have been found in China, northern India, and Vietnam, is called, appropriately, *Gigantopithecus* (see Figure 7.4). So far, only jaws and teeth have been found, but estimates from these indicate that this primate may have been 10 to 12 feet tall when standing upright and may have weighed from 700 to 1,200 pounds. Evidence from the teeth indicates that it was, like the gorilla, a vegetarian and linked to the sivapithecid group. *Gigantopithecus* lived from about 7 mya to perhaps

---

*This is probably a good place to refresh your memory regarding the taxonomic terms *hominid* and *hominin*. With reference to Figure 7.3, remember that, as the terms are used in this book, hominids are members of family Hominidae, which includes humans and the African apes. Hominins are members of tribe Hominini, which includes only humans and our habitually bipedal ancestors.

as recently as 300,000 ya, recently enough to have possibly encountered modern humans. (One can't help but wonder if these creatures, or at least their bones, may have given rise to legends of the famous abominable snowman, or yeti, from the Himalayas. In any case, there is absolutely no indication that this primate still exists.)

Current evidence indicates that apes evolved in Africa and Europe about 20 mya and diverged subsequently into a number of evolutionary lines all over the Old World. Gradually these lines decreased, leaving relatively few forms to evolve into the modern hominoids. An African form gave rise to the line leading to modern African apes and to the hominins, traditionally, the "bipedal primates."

BIPEDALISM

The Benefits of Bipedalism

What's the benefit of standing upright, an adaptation that involved major realignments of much of the body of a quadrupedal animal? Under what circumstances might it have been selected for in the earliest members of our lineage?

Not many creatures use full bipedal locomotion. Birds do—and many dinosaurs did—but they also use their tails for balance and support. Birds have, essentially, prehensile feet; they can even sleep perched on a branch. Human bipedalism, although it obviously works quite well, involves a large number of individual physical features and evolutionary changes (see Figure 9.5) and remarkable acts of coordination. When we stand and walk, with our trunk erect and knees straight, we have to balance our bodies vertically on two relatively small points of contact with the ground. We can't run particularly fast, and we aren't very stable on rough or slippery surfaces. So what could be the benefit of such a mode of locomotion, and under what environmental circumstances was it adaptive enough to confer a reproductive advantage and so become established in our evolutionary line?

Compare the map of early hominin sites (Figure 10.7) with the map of Africa's climatic and vegetation zones (Figure 10.8). Note that the sites are located in savannas or tropical deciduous forests (open grasslands or woodlands more open than the rain forest and with trees that undergo seasonal cycles of growth). Where these zones meet, an area called an **ecotone,** there is a mix of forest and open areas, as one zone grades into another. And as we will see, our earliest ancestors exhibited traits associated

ecotone An area where one ecosystem overlaps and grades into another; a mixed ecosystem.

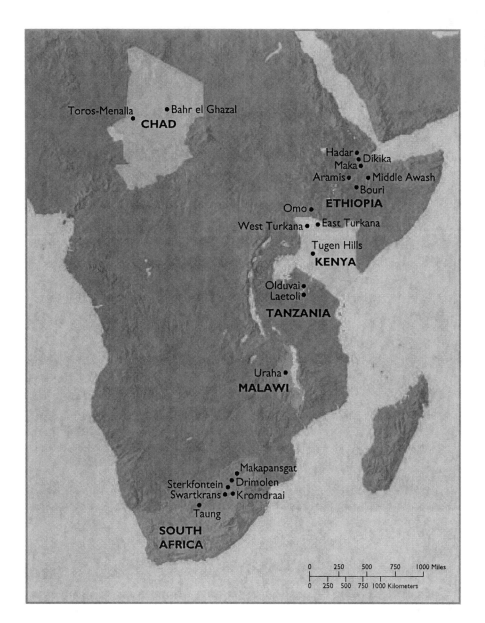

FIGURE 10.7
Map of major early fossil hominin sites.

with both bipedalism *and* an arboreal adaptation: relatively long arms; heavy shoulder girdles, arm bones, and arm muscles; and curved finger and toe bones. Perhaps in the earliest stages of our lineage, our ancestors were adapted to both a tree-climbing *and* a terrestrial, open-area way of life.

So, we may ask how bipedalism could have been a benefit in such a mix of environments, where open space intermingled with the typically arboreal environment of the primates. Several different models have been

FIGURE 10.8
General climatic and vegetation zones of Africa today. Except for the large deserts in the north and south, the zones are much the same as when our evolutionary story began some 5 mya, although specific local conditions may have differed. Moreover, where zones meet, the conditions grade into one another, producing an area of mixed vegetation and other conditions.

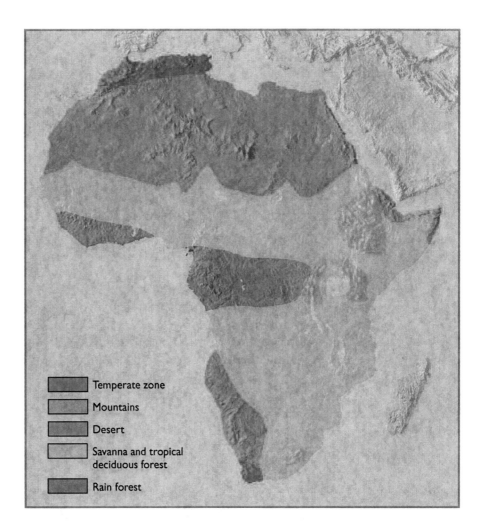

Temperate zone

Mountains

Desert

Savanna and tropical deciduous forest

Rain forest

proposed to account for the evolution of bipedalism under the environmental conditions just described.

1. **Carrying model.** Bipedalism could have allowed our early ancestors to search for and collect food in greater safety and with greater efficiency. Freeing the arms and hands from a role in locomotion would have meant that our ancestors could transport food from open areas to safer locations, such as a grove of trees or perhaps the foot of a steep hill. This would have been especially important if the food were part of an animal carcass, since other meat eaters would also have found it attractive. Moreover, bipedalism would have allowed mothers to carry children in their arms while walking in search of food. Perhaps our ancestors carried sticks and rocks to throw in defense against predators

or to scare scavengers away from a kill. (Chimps will occasionally hurl rocks and sticks, though not particularly accurately.) Under experimental conditions (Videan and McGrew 2000), it has been shown that having something to carry is a major stimulus for bipedal locomotion in chimpanzees and bonobos (see Figure 8.6).

2. **Vigilance model.** It has been proposed that bipedalism, by elevating the head, helped our ancestors locate potential sources of food and danger. Observe, for example, how squirrels sit upright to better look around. Videan and McGrew's (2000) experiment, just noted, showed this to be an important factor in the use of bipedalism, at least in their controlled studies among captive apes. In fact, it was the most frequent context of upright posture. It should be noted here, however, that this model only addresses upright posture, not necessarily upright locomotion.

3. **Heat dissipation model.** According to another view, the vertical orientation of bipedalism helps cool the body by presenting a smaller target to the intense equatorial rays of the sun and by placing more of the body above the ground to catch any cooling air currents. Open spaces in Africa can be hot, and the heat built up by long periods of walking in search of food needs to be dissipated. (This factor may also explain the adaptive significance of the relatively hairless bodies of modern hominins. Having no hair allows sweat to evaporate more quickly and cool the body more efficiently.)

4. **Energy efficiency model.** Data indicate that although bipedalism is an energy-inefficient way of running fast, compared to quadrupedalism, it is *more* efficient for walking. For example, a 154-pound man uses 140 more joules of energy per meter walking than standing still and 260 more joules running than standing still. A 154-pound quadrupedal mammal uses 200 more joules of energy per meter both walking and running (Alexander 1995). Long periods of steady bipedal walking in search of food, then, would seem to require less energy. Remember, however, that the first hominins may not have walked bipedally quite like later members of our family, and they may not have been any more efficient at walking upright than are chimpanzees. Moreover, it is not certain that what makes our walking more efficient is simply our upright stance. Body mass and other anatomical features may be related as well. So, as Steudel (1996) maintains, efficiency may not have been the *initial* key factor in selection for bipedal locomotion. It may be that bipedalism had, at first, other advantages and that once it was established, further anatomical changes made it more energy efficient.

5. ***Foraging/bipedal harvesting model.*** This idea refers to the benefits of standing upright to reach sources of food on bushes and trees, particularly those difficult or impossible to climb. The introduction of raised feeding structures in Videan and McGrew's experiment stimulated bipedal posture in chimps.

6. ***Display model.*** Jablonski and Chaplin (2000) propose that the important factor of bipedalism was an upright display posture like that seen in chimps during dominance confrontations and, to a lesser extent, in male bonobos (who sometimes also stand erect, in both senses, as a sexual display). Among these primates, an upright display posture conveys meaning because it makes the individual seem larger; it is also directly related to mating success.

7. ***Walking in the trees.*** This benefit of bipedalism actually refers to an arboreal adaptation. Modern orangutans, the most arboreal of apes, use hand-assisted bipedalism when walking along branches too flexible to support their weight. They reach up and grab onto branches overhead, with their lower limbs extended. If this was true of earlier apes, it could extend bipedalism well before the hominins and redefine hominin bipedalism as "less an innovation than an exploitation of a locomotor behavior retained from the common great ape ancestor" (Thorpe et al. 2007:1328).

Each of these models has logic and evidence in its support. It seems reasonable, at the moment, to provisionally suppose that *all* these factors, acting together, could have played an adaptive role in the emergence of the hominin lineage and its characteristic mode of locomotion. But do these models explain why bipedalism would have made some individuals, and eventually some groups, more reproductively successful? *Remember that reproductive success under a given set of environmental circumstances is the measure of natural selection. Individual survival and longevity are only part of it.*

The Evolution of Bipedalism

There are two types of evidence that need to be considered here: the environments in which the relevant fossils were found and the fossils themselves.

The past 6 million years mark a period of increasing environmental fluctuation that produced great oscillations in moisture and vegetation in Africa (Potts 1996, 1998). So we can picture the boundaries of the climatic zones in Figure 10.8 as overlapping and moving as the continent got alternately wetter and drier.

Our early ancestors and some of their primate contemporaries thus encountered a variety of environments—the forest/open-space ecotone already discussed, as well as changes through time—and so underwent selection for the ability to deal with a mixed environment of increasing variability. Richard Potts calls this "variability selection"—adaptations that result in "flexible, novel responses to . . . diversity" and that "buffer" a species against "episodic change" (1998:86). The retention of arboreal features accompanied by the enhancement of bipedal locomotion seems a perfect example of this kind of adaptation. As we will see in detail, the fossils themselves, during the period we're considering, show such a combination, to varying degrees.

In fact—again, as we will detail—there are so many fossils with demonstrated or potential bipedal abilities that bipedalism was probably "not a characteristic exclusive to the human ancestral line, but a locomotor capacity . . . found amongst some ground dwelling apes from at least 4.4 to as much as 7 million years ago" (Wells and Stock 2007).

Let's look at the specific evidence from the fossil record, and then we will return to these points at the end of the chapter.

THE EARLY HOMININS

The first evidence from the dawn of hominin evolution came in 1925. South African anatomist Raymond Dart was given a fossil found in a limestone quarry at a site called Taung (Figure 10.9). It took Dart seventy-three days to separate the fossil from the limestone around it. When freed, it revealed the face, braincase, and partial natural brain cast of a young primate, apelike but for two important differences. First, the canine teeth—which are long and large in apes, with gaps to let the jaws shut—were no bigger than those of a human child. Second was the position of the **foramen magnum.** This is the hole in the base of the skull through which the spinal cord extends from the brain and around the outside of which the top vertebra articulates. In the Taung specimen, this hole was well underneath the skull rather than toward the back, as in apes, indicating an upright, bipedal posture rather than a quadrupedal one (Figure 10.10). Dart hypothesized that the "Taung Baby," as it came to be known, was an intermediate between apes and humans. Nevertheless, he named it *Australopithecus africanus*, the "southern ape of Africa"; because of its many apelike traits, he wasn't ready to formally classify it in the human family. After all, for a quarter century or more, the expectation was that our earliest ancestors would have big brains with apelike bodies,

foramen magnum The hole in the base of the skull through which the spinal cord emerges and around the outside of which the top vertebra articulates.

FIGURE 10.9
The "Taung Baby," the first specimen of *Australopithecus*. Note the naturally formed cast of the brain toward the back of the skull. (See also Figure 11.17.)

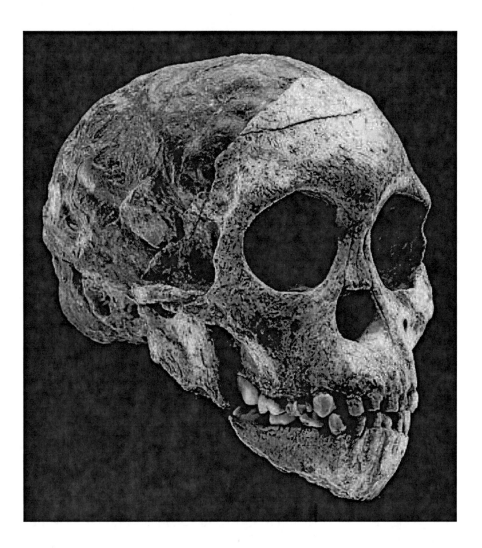

not apelike bodies that were bipedal (see the "Contemporary Reflections" box for this chapter).

Further finds in Africa in the following decades substantiated Dart's assessment of the anatomy of his fossil and his opinion that it represented a new type of primate. Those finds also made it clear that *Australopithecus,* rather than being an intermediary, was in fact a hominin, a bipedal primate by definition. (The rules of scientific nomenclature, or taxonomic names, however, require that first-used names stick, even if they later prove to be descriptively inaccurate. Thus, these hominins are still named "southern apes.")

The story that the early hominin fossils tell is by no means clear or agreed upon by everyone. But we can begin with some reasonably well-established fossil forms and dates, which will provide a basis for understanding this period of human evolution. Then, in the following section

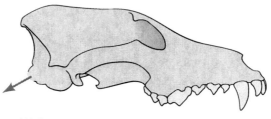

Wolf

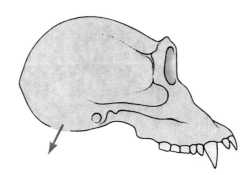

Chimpanzee

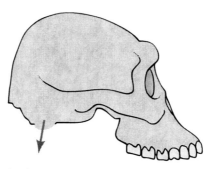

Australopithecus

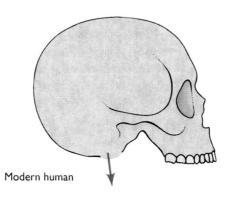

Modern human

FIGURE 10.10
Comparison of the placement of the foramen magnum and orientation of the spinal column relative to the skull in a nonprimate quadruped and three primates. The wolf, with equally long fore and hind limbs, has a foramen magnum toward the back of the skull with an almost horizontal orientation of the spine. The chimp, still a quadruped but with longer arms than legs, has a more forward placement with the spine extending at an angle. In the bipedal hominins we see a trend toward a more forward placement and a vertical orientation of the spine.

we can examine some of the newer and more controversial fossils and consider some of the ways to put all these data together.

First, a general orientation: All the fossils discussed here belong to family Hominidae, subfamily Homininae, and tribe Hominini (see Chapter 7 for the discussion of these taxonomic categories). Within tribe Hominini, anthropologists can agree on three well-established genera. Only *Homo* still exists; the others are extinct. These taxa may be defined by the following criteria, on which I'll elaborate as we continue in the chapter:

Tribe Hominini: The Habitually Bipedal Primates (the Hominins)

Genus *Australopithecus*: small-brained; more "gracile" (graceful, slender) in the cranial features; a mixed fruit/vegetable diet; mixed bipedal-arboreal morphology

Genus *Paranthropus*: small-brained; more robust cranial features, possibly for seasonal or "fallback" use of grassland plant foods; mixed bipedal-arboreal morphology

Genus *Homo*: large-brained; omnivorous; fully bipedal; increasing reliance on culture, including tools and symbolic communication

It should be noted that authorities are about evenly divided on whether *Paranthropus* is a separate genus or is part of *Australopithecus*. I will consider them separate genera. In part, using a different name simply helps organize our discussion of evolutionary trends during this period. But, more importantly, while determining species identity in the past is difficult if not impossible, and thus can be very controversial (as we will see in this and the coming chapters), a genus can be more easily defined as a "group of species . . . that share a common adaptation—variations on a single theme" (Marks 2005:51). It is, then, in the words of famed biologist G. G. Simpson, "a more usable and reliable unit" (1961:199). Thus, from *Australopithecus*, who "successfully used a bipedal habit," *Paranthropus* later took the "dental route" and *Homo* the "mental route" (Marks 2005:52). We will name and discuss some common species of the early hominins, but our examination of this remote period of human ancestry will focus on "sort[ing] things out at the genus level" (Marks 2005:51).

Table 10.1 summarizes information about some commonly accepted species of *Australopithecus* and *Paranthropus*. Refer to Figure 10.7 for the locations of the sites.

Australopithecus

In August 1995 the earliest commonly accepted hominin species was announced (Leakey and Lewin 1995; C. Ward et al. 1999). Called

TABLE 10.1

Summary of Well-Accepted Early Fossil Hominin Species of *Australopithecus* and *Paranthropus*

	A. anamensis	*A. afarensis*	*A. africanus*	*P. robustus*	*P. boisei*
Dates	4.2–3.8 mya	3.9–3 mya	3–2.3 mya	2.2–1.5 mya (?)	2.2–1 mya
Sites	Lake Turkana Middle Awash	Hadar Omo Laetoli Maka Lake Turkana Dikika	Taung Sterkfontein Makapansgat Lake Turkana (?) Omo (?)	Kromdraai Swartkrans Drimolen	Olduvai Lake Turkana Omo
Cranial capacity (in ml)	(no data)	380–500 mean = 440	370–515 mean = 440	520 (based on one specimen)	500–530 mean = 515
Estimated size (average, in lb)	114	110	100	105	101
Skull	Canines large, but hominin-like canine roots More apelike chin than A. afarensis Tooth rows parallel as in apes	Very prognathous Receding chin Large teeth Pointed canine with gap Shape of tooth row between ape and human Hint of sagittal crest	Less prognathous than A. afarensis Jaw more rounded Large back teeth Canines smaller than P. robustus, larger than A. afarensis No sagittal crest	Heavy jaws Small canines and front teeth Large back teeth Definite sagittal crest	Very large jaws Very large back teeth Large sagittal crest
Postcranial skeleton	Bipedal knee and ankle joints Fibula intermediate between ape and hominin	Long arms Short thumb Curved fingers and toes Bipedal	Similar to A. afarensis but possibly with longer arms and shorter legs	Hands and feet more like modern humans Retention of long arms	Similar to P. robustus

Australopithecus anamensis, it consists of specimens from the Lake Turkana region of Kenya (*anam* means "lake"), including jaws, teeth, a skull fragment, a tibia, and a humerus (Figure 10.11). The specimens are dated at 4.2 to 3.8 mya. Although they exhibit apelike features such as large canine teeth and parallel tooth rows (Figure 10.12), the root of the canine is vertical as in later hominins rather than angled as in apes, and the tooth enamel is thicker than in apes and more like that in later hominins. Most notably, the leg bones are clearly those of a biped.

FIGURE 10.11
Mandible (*left*) and maxilla of *Australopithecus anamensis*. The chinless jaw is apelike, but the vertical root of the canine is clearly a hominin trait (the canine roots of apes are angled).

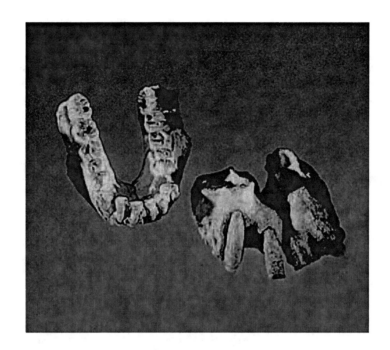

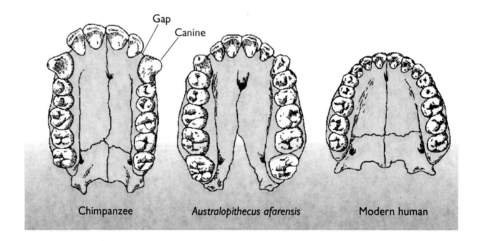

FIGURE 10.12
Comparison of upper jaws and tooth rows of chimpanzee, *Australopithecus afarensis*, and modern human. Note the parallel postcanine teeth in the chimp, the slightly divergent tooth row in the early hominin, and the divergent row in the modern human. Note also the large canines and the large gap (*diastema*) in the chimp, the lack of these in the modern human, and the intermediate state in the early hominin. *Australopithecus anamensis* had slightly larger canines than the later *A. afarensis* and tooth rows more like the ape (see Figure 10.11).

The next species is also commonly accepted, and its nature is generally agreed upon. The species is *Australopithecus afarensis*, and its first and most famous specimen is the 3.2-million-year-old skeleton from Ethiopia known as "Lucy" (Figure 10.13), found in 1974 by Donald Johanson and his team. Lucy is remarkable because, as old as she is, nearly 40 percent of her skeleton was preserved, and all parts of her body were well represented except the cranium, the remains of which are fragmentary. We know—based on the kind of osteological analysis described in Chapter 9—that she was a female and that she stood about 3 feet 8 inches and weighed about 65 pounds. Although there is some disagreement about details, there is no doubt that Lucy and her kind were bipeds.

Other fragmentary specimens, including a portion of a skull dated at 3.9 mya, were unearthed in Ethiopia and Tanzania and assigned to this species. Based on this evidence, a reconstruction of the head of A. *afarensis* was attempted, but a single complete fossil skull was not found until 1992. In February of that year, Donald Johanson and his team discovered 200 skull fragments, again in Ethiopia. Once reconstructed, the skull closely resembled the previously discovered fragments, except that it was large and rugged, probably the skull of a male. It was dated at about 3 mya (Figure 10.14).

In 2006 researchers announced the discovery in Ethiopia of a 3-year-old female A. *afarensis* dated at 3.3 mya (Alemseged et al. 2006). The well-preserved skull and some postcranial bones show diagnostic features

FIGURE 10.13
Skeleton of "Lucy," the first specimen of *A. afarensis.*

FIGURE 10.14
Side view of cranium of *Australopithecus afarensis.* Spaces between missing bones have been filled in using information from other specimens and knowledge of related species.

even at that young age. The lower limbs and feet indicate bipedalism, while the scapula is gorilla-like and the curved finger bone like that of a chimpanzee. The hyoid bone, a horseshoe-shaped bone in the throat, is apelike, as are the semicircular canals of the inner ear, important in maintaining balance. Again, this specimen shows a mix of arboreal and bipedal adaptations.

The evidence so far—over 300 specimens—indicates that there was a well-established hominin species, A. *afarensis,* that lived from 3.9 to 3 mya. The variation in size of the specimens fits the pattern of sexual dimorphism of apes and other early hominins. We are looking at the remains of both males (for example, the skull found in 1992) and females (for example, Lucy) of one species.

However, in 1995 a French team found the remains of a partial hominin jaw in Chad, in north-central Africa, dated at 3.5 to 3 mya. The team announced that this find represents a second species of hominin living during that time (Simons 1996). The species has been named *Australopithecus bahrelghazalia* (after an Arabic name for a nearby riverbed), and it suggests that early hominins were more widely spread on the continent than previously thought. Full acceptance of this classification and the implications of the fossil await further study.

What did Lucy and her kin look like? They might be described as "bipedal apes." Their average brain size was about 440 ml (a can of soda holds 355 ml), close to the average for chimpanzees and with the same maximum size of about 500 ml. A. *afarensis* had the **prognathism** (projection of the lower face and jaws), the pointy canine teeth, and the gaps in the tooth rows characteristic of apes, though the canine teeth and gaps were not as pronounced as in apes. There was a hint of a **sagittal crest,** a ridge of bone along the top of the skull for the attachment of major chewing muscles. Gorillas have pronounced crests (Figure 10.15). In modern humans, these muscles are attached on the sides of the head. (Put your hand on your head, about 2 inches above one ear, and then clench and unclench your teeth. You'll feel the muscle called the *temporalis.*)

At first there was some disagreement as to just how bipedal A. *afarensis* was, especially considering the apelike nature of much of the rest of its anatomy. (Disagreements continue; see Stern 2000 for a summary.) All the interpretations, after all, were based on fossilized bones; no one, obviously, had ever actually seen one walk. But in 1976 Mary Leakey recovered the next best thing at a site in Tanzania called Laetoli—a set of footprints made in a fresh layer of volcanic ash that quickly hardened and preserved for us a striking picture of an event that took place 3.7 mya. Two

prognathism The jutting forward of the lower face and jaw area.

sagittal crest A ridge of bone, running from front to back along the top of the skull, for the attachment of chewing muscles.

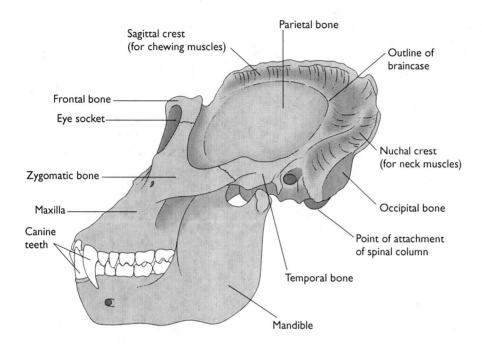

Sagittal crest
(for chewing muscles)

Parietal bone

Outline of
braincase

Frontal bone

Eye socket

Nuchal crest
(for neck muscles)

Zygomatic bone

Maxilla

Occipital bone

Canine
teeth

Point of attachment
of spinal column

Temporal bone

Mandible

FIGURE 10.15
Skull of a male gorilla.
Compare the sagittal crest
with those in Figures 10.19,
10.20, and 10.21.

hominins, one large, one small, had walked side-by-side through the ash shortly after an eruption. The hominins' footprints show an anatomy and stride no different from ours today (Figure 10.16).

The basic set of early hominin features represented by Lucy and her kin continued for another three-quarters of a million years. Although little changed from *Australopithecus afarensis*, the fossils representing the next period are normally called by their original name, A. *africanus* (Dart's "southern ape of Africa"). The remains of this group have been found mostly in South Africa, but there are some fossils from Kenya and Ethiopia as well. They have the same body size and shape and the same brain size as A. *afarensis*. There are a few differences, however (Figure 10.17). Their faces are a bit less prognathous, and they lack a sagittal crest. Their canine teeth are smaller, there are no gaps in the tooth row, and the tooth row is more rounded, as in a human rather than an ape (see Figure 10.12).

The relative size and shape of the teeth of both A. *afarensis* and A. *africanus*, on the whole larger than those of modern humans, indicate a mostly mixed vegetable diet of fruits and leaves. This is confirmed by analysis of microscopic scratches and wear patterns on the teeth (Figure 10.18). There is no direct evidence of meat eating, but a study (Sponheimer and Lee-Thorp 1999) of a carbon isotope (^{13}C) in the tooth enamel of a sample of A. *africanus* hinted that they may have either hunted small animals or scavenged the carcasses of larger ones. There is also evidence that early

FIGURE 10.16
The larger photograph shows the Laetoli footprints from Tanzania. The inset shows a reconstruction from the American Museum of Natural History in New York City of male and female A. *afarensis*, who are thought to have made these footprints.

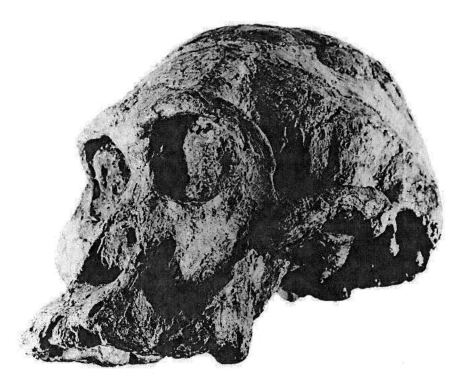

FIGURE 10.17
Skull of *Australopithecus africanus* (female?) from Sterkfontein, South Africa. Note the general similarity to *A. afarensis* (see Figure 10.14).

FIGURE 10.18
Scanning electron microscope pictures of teeth surfaces of early hominins. The enamel of the teeth of *Australopithecus africanus* (left) is polished and scratched, while that of *Paranthropus* (right) is pitted and very rough. This is evidence of the hard, tough, gritty foods eaten by the latter. (See the text for more on this topic.)

hominins dug up rootstocks (Ragir 2000) and opened termite mounds (Holden 2001a).

The essential similarity of *A. afarensis* and *A. africanus* and the overlap in time suggest a plausible, and simple, interpretation: that *A. africanus* is a continuation of *A. afarensis*, more widely distributed in southern and possibly eastern Africa and showing some evolutionary changes. But this interpretation is not agreed upon by all investigators and remains hypothetical. Moreover, this simple linear relationship is confounded by the

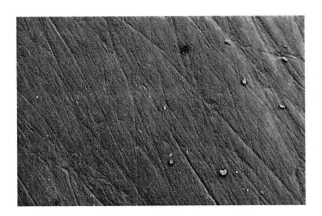

suggestion of some older dates for A. *africanus* (Patridge et al. 2003). So A. *africanus* and A. *afarensis* may be contemporaries and thus either the same species or different species living at the same time.

Some evidence lends support to the meat-eating interpretation and to the definition of another new hominin species. The site of Bouri in Ethiopia, dated at 2.5 mya, has revealed (in separate locations) hominin cranial and postcranial bones, as well as the bones of antelopes, horses, and other animals that exhibit cut marks made by stone tools (Asfaw et al. 1999; Culotta 1999a; de Heinzelin et al. 1999). The cranial bones indicate a brain size of 450 ml, and the prognathous jaw is similar to that of A. *afarensis*. Several features of the teeth resemble those of early *Homo*, but the molars are unusually large, even larger than those of the southern African robust hominins called *Paranthropus* (to be discussed next). This set of traits led investigators to designate these bones as a new species, *Australopithecus garhi* (*garhi* means "surprise" in a local language). The postcranial remains from Bouri, not clearly from the same species as the cranial specimens, show the relative lengths of the upper arm and upper leg to be humanlike, while the lower arm remains long, as in apes. This may indicate that in the evolution of human limb proportions, the leg elongated first and the arm shortened later. Finally, the stone-tool cut marks on the animal bones show that whatever hominin (not necessarily A. *garhi*) made them was butchering animals for meat and smashing bones to get at the fat-rich marrow.

The evolutionary relationship of A. *garhi* to other hominins is still a matter of debate. Its discoverers (Asfaw et al. 1999) feel it is descended from A. *afarensis* and is a direct ancestor of *Homo*. Others disagree (Strait and Grine 1999; and see Culotta 1999b). Clearly, more evidence is needed to interpret these specimens more precisely, but they do show the extent of the variation among hominins during this period.

Paranthropus

Between 3 and 2 mya, two new genera of hominins appear in the fossil record: *Paranthropus* and our genus, *Homo*. *Paranthropus* retains the chimpanzee-sized brains and small bodies of *Australopithecus* but has evolved a notable robusticity in the areas of the skull involved with chewing.

The fossils representing the beginning of this genus are a single skull from Lake Turkana, Kenya—dubbed the "Black Skull" because of its dark color resulting from minerals in the ground (Figure 10.19)—and some fragmentary fossils from Ethiopia. These fossils are commonly grouped into

FIGURE 10.19
The "Black Skull,"
Paranthropus aethiopicus,
is a possible ancestor of
P. robustus and *P. boisei.*
It shows a great degree
of prognathism and the
largest hominin sagittal
crest.

a separate species, *Paranthropus aethiopicus,* and are dated at between 2.8 and 2.2 mya.

The Black Skull is striking for several reasons. First, at only 410 ml, its brain is the smallest adult brain ever found in any well-established hominin. Also, it has the largest sagittal crest of any hominin, the most prognathous face, and an extremely large area in the back of the mouth for the molar teeth. Although no teeth were found, its molars appear to have been four or five times the size of a modern human's.

The Black Skull represents the beginning of the "robust" hominins. Although they were pretty much the same as *Australopithecus* in brain and body size, the members of genus *Paranthropus* were considerably more robust in all those features involved with chewing. The sagittal crest, broad dished-out face, large cheekbones, huge mandible, back teeth that are much larger relative to the front teeth, and wear-pattern analysis (see Figure 10.18) indicate a variable diet with hard items such as seeds, nuts, and

FIGURE 10.20
Paranthropus robustus from Swartkrans, South Africa. Note the remnant of a sagittal crest.

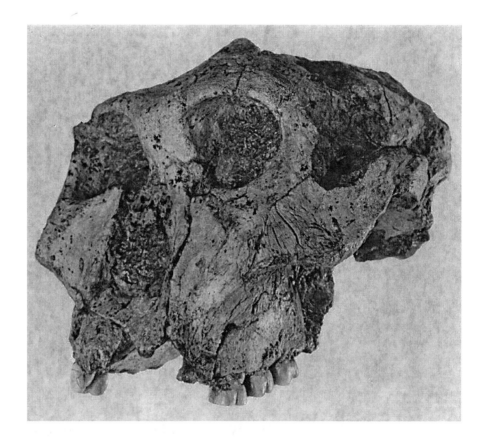

tubers being a "fallback" diet seasonally or during hard times. In fact, it appears that from *A. afarensis* to *A. africanus* to *P. robustus*, dietary variability increased (Sponheimer et al. 2006; Unger and Scott 2008).

A little over 2 mya, two more types of robust hominins appear. One species, *Paranthropus robustus*, was found in South Africa and dates between 2.2 and 1.5 mya or even later (Figure 10.20). It retains the body size of *Australopithecus*, but there is a slight increase in average brain capacity to about 520 ml. The jaws are heavy, the back teeth are large, and there is a sagittal crest—all indications of a variable vegetable diet. The crania, though, are obviously not as robust as in *P. aethiopicus*.

The second robust species continues the extreme ruggedness of *P. aethiopicus*, though it is not quite as pronounced. Found in Tanzania, Kenya, and Ethiopia and existing from 2.2 to 1 mya, *Paranthropus boisei* shows features that, along with those of *P. aethiopicus*, are sometimes referred to as "hyperrobust" (Figure 10.21). The specimen that defined the species is the famous "Zinjanthropus," found by Mary and Louis Leakey in 1959. Dubbed "Nutcracker Man," this specimen has extremely large jaws

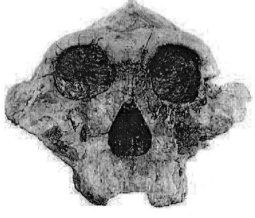

FIGURE 10.21
These three views of *Paranthropus boisei* from Lake Turkana, Kenya, reveal a similarity to the first specimen of the species, originally called "Zinjanthropus."

and back teeth and a large sagittal crest. Otherwise, *P. boisei* has the body and brain size of the southern African robust hominins.

A recent *P. boisei* fossil from Ethiopia (Suwa et al. 1997) consists of the first cranium of this species with an associated mandible. The largest-known skull of the species, it comes from a new site that extends the species' known range in Africa and is clearly associated with a dry grassland environment. It also shows some physical differences from existing *P. boisei* fossils that indicate a considerable range of phenotypic variation.

Thus, fossils assigned to the species of genera *Australopithecus* and *Paranthropus* are generally agreed to represent an important early stage in the establishment of the hominin tribe, with *Australopithecus* usually considered our more direct ancestor. But older fossils have also been discovered, and while they certainly will shed more light on hominin origins, they are, at the moment, muddying the waters even more.

THE SEARCH FOR THE FIRST HOMININS

There are four early fossil forms that have been touted by their discoverers and others to be major steps in the evolution of the hominins in general or of genus *Homo* in particular. These claims, not surprisingly, are surrounded by disagreement and controversy.

In 1992 and 1993 in Ethiopia, seventeen fossil fragments were discovered, including some arm bones, two skull bases, a child's mandible, and some teeth (Figure 10.22). The fossils were said to be different enough from any found previously to warrant creating a fourth hominin genus and a new species, *Ardipithecus ramidus* (the genus name means "ground ape" and the species name "root" in the Afar language). The fossils were dated at 4.4 mya. In 1994 more fossil bones were recovered in Ethiopia, close

FIGURE 10.22
Fossil tooth and portion of jaw from *Ardipithecus ramidus*.

to the first site. These consisted of ninety fragments representing about 45 percent of a skeleton.

Some consider *Ardipithecus ramidus* to be a hominin—dating close to the time of the split between humans and apes—because the foramen magnum is more forward than in apes (hinting at bipedalism) and because of some detailed features of the elbow joint and teeth. At the same time, it is "the most apelike hominid ancestor known" (White et al. 1994, using the old sense of the term *hominid*).

In March 2004 a new subspecies of *Ardipithecus* was announced (Haile-Selassie et al. 2004), *Ardipithecus kadabba* (*kadabba* means "base family ancestor" in the Afar language). Found in the same Ethiopian location as *Ard. ramidus*, these fossils are older, 5.8 to 5.2 mya, and comprise a mandible, teeth, partial clavicle, hand bones, and, most important, a toe bone. The latter is said to show an angle at the joint that indicates a "toe-off" stride, as in modern human walking—in other words, evidence of habitual bipedalism at an early date. The interpretation, of course, is not without controversy; some authorities even claim these fossils represent chimpanzee ancestors (see discussion by Gee 2001).

In March 2001 Meave Leakey, daughter of Louis and Mary Leakey, announced a new hominin genus (Leakey et al. 2001). It is based on a fairly complete, although distorted cranium and mandible, found in 1998 and 1999 in Kenya and reliably dated at 3.5 mya (Figure 10.23). The fossils

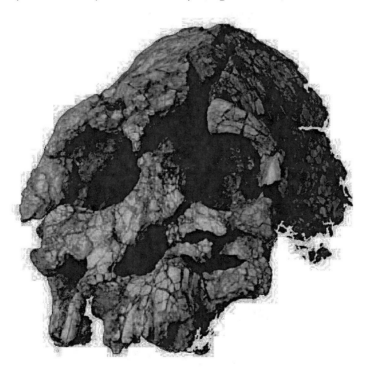

FIGURE 10.23
Three-quarter view of skull of *Kenyanthropus platyops*.

are said to show a combination of features unlike that of any other forms. The brain size, some dental features, and details of the nasal region are like those of genus *Australopithecus*. But its face appears flat, it has a tall, vertically oriented cheek area, and shows no depression behind the brow ridges. In these ways, it bears a resemblance to a later hominin form from East Africa (see Figure 11.4). This set of traits in a fossil contemporaneous with A. *afarensis* led its discoverers to give it not only a new species name but a new genus name as well—*Kenyanthropus platyops* ("flat-faced hominin from Kenya"). Some authorities have suggested that this new form may be a better common ancestor for *Homo* than any species of *Australopithecus*. More evidence, however, is needed to even establish that these fossils do represent a whole new taxon; more examples with the same set of features—with less distortion—would have to be found (White 2003).

In October 2000 an even older possible hominin ancestor was proposed by French paleoanthropologists (Balter 2001b), based on thirteen fossil fragments from the Tugen Hills in northwestern Kenya. The dating of these fossils—femurs, teeth, portions of a mandible—is agreed upon; they are about 5.6 to 6.2 million years old. Their identity, however, is a matter of debate. The discoverers claim that the fossils represent the real ancestor of modern humans and that the other early hominins, the species of *Australopithecus*, are side branches. *Ardipithecus kadabba*, they say, is a chimp ancestor. They base their claim on their assessment that this hominin—placed by them into a new genus and species, *Orrorin tugenensis* (*orrorin* means "original man" in the local dialect)—was bipedal and exhibited expressions of certain traits that were more modern than those of other early hominins. Features of the head of the femur and grooves for muscle and ligament attachments are said to point to bipedalism. This has recently been confirmed (Richmond and Jungers 2008). Other authorities disagree with this analysis, and some question whether this form even *is* a hominin (Haile-Selassie 2001).

The most recent candidate for "first hominin" is a find from the Toros-Menalla site in northern Chad consisting of a cranium, jaw fragment, and several teeth and dated from 7 to 6 mya (Figure 10.24; Brunet et al. 2002, 2005; Zollikofer 2005). It has been placed in a new genus and species, *Sahelanthropus tchadensis* (after the Sahel region of Africa that borders the southern Sahara) and is known popularly as "Toumaï" ("hope of life" in the local Goran language). This form is described as having a "mosaic" of features. It is very apelike in its brain size (estimated at 320 to 380 ml), widely spaced eye orbits, and other details of its morphology, but according to its discoverers it has a number of striking features characteristic of later hominins. These include small canines of a hominin size, shape, and wear pattern; a face with reduced prognathism; and a continuous brow ridge. The forward position of the foramen magnum, while not enough

FIGURE 10.24
The cranium of
Sahelanthropus tchadensis.

evidence to reliably infer habitual bipedalism, still makes such an infer-
ence "not . . . unreasonable" (Brunet et al. 2002:150). The primary investigators thus claim that this form represents "the oldest and most primitive
known member of the hominid clade, close to the divergence of hominids
[hominins, using the terminology of this book] and chimpanzees" (151).

   This view, of course, has its detractors. One group (Wolpoff et al.
2002) claims that this form was not bipedal and, indeed, "was an ape"
(582). (See Brunet 2002 for a counterargument.)

PUTTING IT ALL TOGETHER

Connecting the Dots

Figure 10.25 shows the dates of all the established and proposed early
hominin fossils discussed in this chapter (with *Homo* added for perspective and a preview of what's to come). A number of different specific

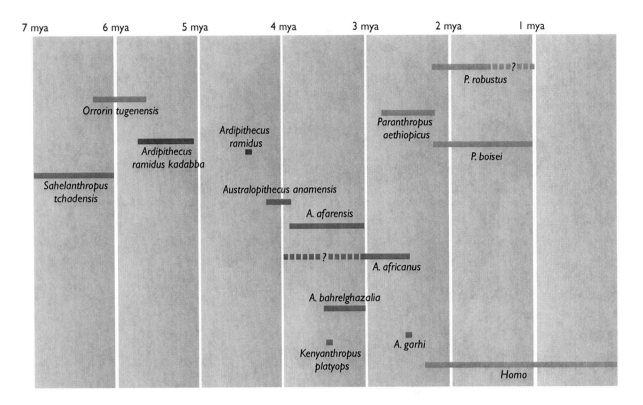

FIGURE 10.25
The fossils discussed in this chapter with their currently accepted time ranges. The dashed lines indicate possible extensions of those ranges.

models have been proposed for connecting all these fossils into an evolutionary tree. Most authorities generally agree that the hominins from about 4 mya on can be grouped into two natural categories, *Australopithecus* and *Paranthropus*. I've grouped them in the timeline to reflect this. There is also general agreement that it was some member of the gracile hominins that gave rise to *Homo*. A simple tree, then, would look like this:

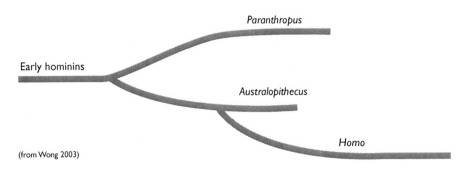

(from Wong 2003)

There is a difference of opinion as to *which* australopithecine, if there are several species, is the direct ancestor of *Homo,* and authorities have different favorite candidates. But there is even more debate over the newest fossil finds: *Ardipithecus kadabba, Orrorin tugenensis,* and *Sahelanthropus tchadensis.* With relatively scanty evidence so far, and with different body parts represented by the existing fossils, comparison and analysis are necessarily very tentative. At one extreme (see Wong 2003) is the idea that those three are lineal descendants, all on the line to *Homo:*

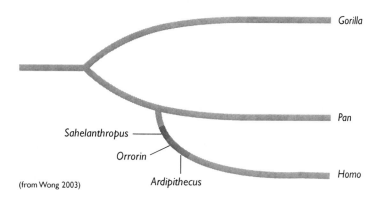

(from Wong 2003)

The opposite extreme has the three representing ancestors of three different genera:

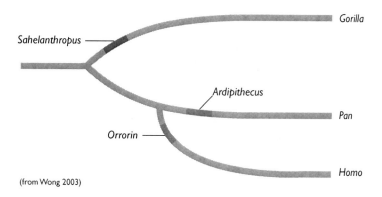

(from Wong 2003)

Note, however, that the second and third models illustrated above—and, indeed, all existing models—assume that the basic tree is formed by connecting the three *living* genera—*Gorilla, Pan,* and *Homo.* We then place all new fossil species on the resulting lines, or maybe connect them as branches from those lines. But perhaps the fossils in Figure 10.25 are related in a more complex fashion.

FIGURE 10.26
Hypothetical tree of hominid evolution. *A* through *F* represent extinct forms. Perhaps, say, *B, D, E,* and *F* show evidence of bipedalism, but note that *B* and *F* are not connected to the hominin line. Thus, bipedalism does not necessarily place a fossil in our tribe.

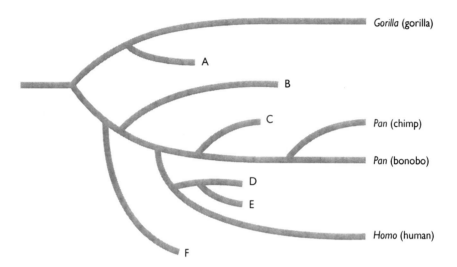

Perhaps some of these fossils, even if they were bipedal, were, literally, bipedal apes; the phrase is more than a physical description of some of our early ancestors. It might be taxonomically accurate. In other words, bipedalism might have evolved more than once and in evolutionary lines that are not directly connected to the hominins. Put another way, bipedalism—while a distinction of humans *at present*—might not be the defining characteristic of the beginning of our line (Figure 10.26). What are my reasons for proposing this? There are three.

There Is an Increasing Number of Distinct Fossil Forms   These are distributed over much of Africa and over millions of years (see Figure 10.25). It would seem reasonable that there were more evolutionary lines in the past than are represented by the four living species in question. Perhaps some of these now-extinct lines exhibited phenotypic combinations not seen in living species, including bipedalism in groups more closely related to living apes than to us.

Bipedalism Is Not Unknown in the Apes   All the African great apes are capable of bipedal standing and walking, and a recent study (Stanford 2006) has shown that postural (as opposed to locomotor) bipedalism is common in chimpanzees as they stand to forage in and from trees. The same is true for orangutans. The precursor of locomotor bipedalism, in other words, is exhibited by apes and could have evolved to a more refined state in some ape lines, for all the adaptive reasons we have hypothesized for that evolution in humans.

Bipedalism Differs between Genera *Homo* and *Australopithecus*
Homo, it seems, is built not only for bipedal walking but for bipedal endurance running as well, a trait that would also be potentially useful on the African plains and elsewhere (Bramble and Lieberman 2004; Summers 2005).

The attachment point of our Achilles tendon and the full arch of our feet, both different in chimps and *Australopithecus,* aid in a bouncing gait, a more energy-efficient way to run long distances. Our large gluteus maximus (butt) muscles help stabilize our hips while running; chimps and *Australopithecus* show more stable shoulders than hips. And *Homo* has muscle attachments, lacking in chimps and the australopithecines, that keep our heads steady while running, as well as modifications of the semicircular canals in the ears that keep us balanced by telling us, essentially, which way is up.

Put in evolutionary terms, then, these adaptations for endurance running are derived characteristics of *Homo* and are seen in early *Homo erectus* (the first undisputed member of our genus) and perhaps in even earlier *Homo habilis* (see Chapter 11; Bramble and Lieberman 2004:351). Thus, *Homo* is characterized not only by habitual bipedalism but also by a *kind* of bipedalism *different from* that of earlier hominins. So our current mantra— "If it's a biped, it must be human or a human ancestor"—might not be true, and perhaps the only sure sign of a fossil on our evolutionary line might be the body plan associated with *Homo* (including our *type* of bipedalism) and the beginnings of an enlargement of the brain. Connecting the fossils as shown in Figure 10.25 is, then, currently premature, because we simply don't have enough evidence.

The Ecological Context

What might have caused the branching that founded the new genera of *Paranthropus* and *Homo*? What caused the extinction, around the same time, of genus *Australopithecus*? Finally, what might have caused the extinction of the *Paranthropus* species about 1 mya?

We can't answer these questions with certainty, but recall Richard Potts's evidence for a sharp increase in environmental variability in Africa starting about 6 mya and continuing—and further increasing—through time (1996, 1998). There is also evidence for a major and abrupt change about 2.8 mya—an intensification of cycles that produced a shift toward grasslands (Kerr 2001). Increased environmental variability resulting in a series of newly emerging, complex, and diverse habitats may have initially promoted different adaptations among hominid populations,

Contemporary Reflections

Is There a "Missing Link"?

A headline in the 19 December 1912 issue of the *New York Times* proclaimed, "Paleolithic Skull Is a Missing Link." The skull referred to was the now-infamous "Piltdown Man," discovered in England, named *Eoanthropus* (the "dawn man")—and forty years later shown to be a fraud (see Feder 2008 for details). At the time, however, it was touted as the "missing link" because it possessed traits that were a perfect mix between those of human and ape. Its cranium was the shape and size of a modern human's, and its mandible was decidedly apelike. (In fact, the cranium *was* of a modern human and the jaw *was* of a modern orangutan—modified by the still-unidentified perpetrator to appear ancient.)

For much of the history of evolutionary thought, evolution was conceived of as a ladder or a chain, progressing from primitive to modern, with living forms representing points on that chain. Even when it was generally acknowledged that humans had descended from apes, this evolution was thought of as unilinear—a single line of progress from ape to man. Thus, as we go back into the fossil record, we should eventually find something that is intermediate—half ape and half human. Since modern apes were thought of as the remnants of primitive forms that had never evolved further, the missing link (notice the chain metaphor) was conceived of as a mix of the traits of *modern* humans and *modern* apes. In our hubris, we were sure it was our big brains that separated us from the apes and that had evolved first, so the combination fabricated to concoct the Piltdown skull fit the bill perfectly. It had that big-brain hallmark of humanity, perched on top of an otherwise apelike jaw.

Indeed, even when evolution was recognized as being a branching tree rather than a ladder or chain, the idea of fossil forms that were intermediates between modern species still held. Famed anatomist Sir Arthur Keith wrote that "to unravel man's pedigree, we have to thread our way, not along the links of a chain, but through the meshes of a complicated network" (1927:8). Then, on the next page, he accepted the Piltdown find as authentic.

We recognize today that living species are not leftover primitive links on an evolutionary chain but are, themselves, the products of evolution. A missing link in the traditional sense—between modern humans and modern apes—simply does not exist. What *does* exist is a common ancestor of humans and our closest relatives, the chimpanzees and bonobos—and it did not look exactly like any of those modern species. Granted, we have reason to think that the common ancestor resembled a bonobo or chimp more than a modern human, but this is just because evolution happened to take place at a more rapid pace in hominins than in the apes. The apes are still modern species.

So what we *can* look for is that common ancestor. It is a "link" not in the sense of a chain, but in the sense of being that point where our two evolutionary lines converge. At the moment, that form is still missing.

What will it look like? It should have characteristics shared by both modern hominins and apes, but it will look, on the whole, like neither. It could be one of the forms we know about (see Figure 10.25), or it could be a form yet to be discovered.

as seen in the branching that gave rise to the robust hominins and to *Homo*. But if the degree of the fluctuations continued to increase, this may have put such pressure on the hominin adaptive responses that those groups less able to cope eventually became extinct. Unable to survive well enough to perpetuate themselves in the face of decreasing resources, these now-extinct hominins were possibly outcompeted for space and resources by the better adapted, a phenomenon known as **competitive exclusion.** In this case, only the adaptive response that included the ability for endurance running and an increase in brain size, with its concomitant increase in ability to understand and manipulate the environment, proved successful in the long run. We turn to the story of these adaptive responses next.

SUMMARY

The primates are one of the earliest of the existing mammal groups to evolve. They appear to have evolved first in what are now North America and Europe, but the success of their adaptations allowed them to radiate over the Old World and into the New World.

About 23 mya, the hominoids appear in the form of primitive apes. This successful group has left fossils all over Africa, Europe, and Asia. It is from one of the African apes that our tribe, Hominini, branched off probably 6 to 5 mya.

The evolution of habitual bipedalism is thought to mark the beginnings of our tribe and was the major distinguishing characteristic of this tribe for the first half of its time on earth. Bipedalism may have begun as part of one group's adaptation to the forests. We still see this trait—along with food sharing and sexual consciousness—in today's bonobos. However, these adaptations would also prove useful in Africa's increasingly variable environment, and the hominins soon were well established and radiated into three distinct groups, best classified as separate genera: *Australopithecus, Paranthropus,* and *Homo.*

The first two genera, *Australopithecus* and *Paranthropus,* with their chimp-sized brains, remained largely vegetarian and persisted until nearly 1 mya. They eventually lost out to a combination of environmental change and competition from the third hominin genus, *Homo,* with its bigger brain and ability to manipulate its environment. Our genus is the subject of the next chapter.

competitive exclusion
What occurs when one species outcompetes others for the resources of a particular area.

QUESTIONS FOR FURTHER THOUGHT

1. People often ask this logical question: If humans are descended from apes, then how come there are still apes? How would you respond to this?

2. Looking at the fossil record of the hominins, we see that the hominin line that survived after about 1 mya was the one with the big brain. From our perspective, this makes it seem as if our evolution was inevitable. Is this the case? Would the big-brained species have been successful in all circumstances? Once the evolution of hominins got started, were *we* a predictable result?

KEY TERMS

ecotone	prognathism	competitive exclusion
foramen magnum	sagittal crest	

SUGGESTED READINGS

The primates and their evolution are covered in John G. Fleagle's *Primate Adaptation and Evolution*. The intriguing story of *Gigantopithecus* is told in *Other Origins: The Search for the Giant Ape in Human Prehistory*, by Russell Ciochon, John Olsen, and Jamie James.

The story of the study of the human fossil record and of some of the major recent discoveries is told in *Lucy: The Beginnings of Humankind*, by Donald Johanson and Maitland Edey, and in a sequel, *Lucy's Child: The Discovery of a Human Ancestor*, by Donald Johanson and James Shreeve. Both of these books are somewhat outdated but still convey the excitement of paleoanthropology. A slightly different perspective on much of the same material is found in Richard Leakey and Roger Lewin's *Origins Reconsidered: In Search of What Makes Us Human*. For some history of the study, try *Debating Humankind's Place in Nature, 1860–2000: The Nature of Paleoanthropology*, by Richard G. Delisle.

A *National Geographic* series, "The Dawn of Humans," covering the 6 million years of our evolution, appears in the following issues: September 1995; January and March 1996; February, May, July, and

September 1997; August 1998; and May, July, and December 2000. The photographs and graphics are, as usual, superb. And see the October 2001 issue for photos of *Kenyanthropus*.

For two nice popular accounts of the human evolution story, see *How Do We Know the Nature of Human Origins,* by Dale Anderson, and *The Complete Idiot's Guide to Human Prehistory,* by Robert J. Meier. A more technical treatment is by Camilo J. Cela-Conde and Francisco J. Ayala, titled *Human Evolution: Trails from the Past.*

For more on the early apes and possible hominin ancestors, see David R. Begun's "Planet of the Apes" in the August 2003 *Scientific American.* And for a nice article on the juvenile fossil of *A. afarensis,* see "Lucy's Baby," by Kate Wong, in the December 2006 *Scientific American.*

You might be interested in seeing what a primary report on an important fossil looks like. A good example is the first report on the discovery of *Sahelanthropus* by Brunet et al. in the 11 July 2002 issue of *Nature,* "A New Hominid from the Upper Miocene of Chad, Central Africa." And for a piece on all the new finds, see "An Ancestor to Call Our Own," by Kate Wong, in the January 2003 *Scientific American.*

For a nice summary of the different views on the possible climate-change influences on human evolution, see "Sunset on the Savanna," by James Shreeve, in the July 1996 issue of *Discover.* A nicely illustrated explanation of the Great Rift Valley, by Yves Coppens, appears in the May 1994 *Scientific American:* "East Side Story: The Origin of Humankind."

A review of two books on the bipedalism question and a nice discussion of the topic in and of itself is Ian Tattersall's "Stand and Deliver" in the November 2003 *Natural History.* And for more on human endurance running, see "Born to Run," by Adam Summers, in the April 2005 *Natural History.*

11

CHAPTER

The Evolution of Genus Homo

The great tragedy of Science—the slaying of a beautiful hypothesis by an ugly fact.
—Thomas Henry Huxley

As we saw in the last chapter, it is hard for us to agree on the fossils that represent the first 2.5 million years of the hominin record. It gets worse when we address the latest 2.5 million years. The reason is simple: this is the time during which our genus, *Homo*, evolved. The data from these fossils matter to us because they will tell us just who we are and where we came from.

There are widely different interpretations of the nature, dates, and taxonomic affiliations of the hominin fossils from this period, and there are several divergent schools of thought regarding just what the family tree of our genus looks like. At stake in these discussions is the very identity of the species to which we all belong. In this chapter, we will address the following questions:

How can we best go about describing and organizing the fossil evidence for the evolution of genus *Homo*?

What do we know about the dates, the distribution, and the physical appearance of the various groups of fossils assigned to genus *Homo*?

What can we say about their lives, particularly about their cultural behaviors?

LUMPERS AND SPLITTERS: AN ORGANIZING PLAN

Recall from Chapter 10 that there is disagreement over whether the early, small-brained hominins all belong to one genus, *Australopithecus*, or to two genera, *Australopithecus* and *Paranthropus*. In this debate, those who support a single genus are "lumpers," and those who advocate two genera are "splitters."

Splitters tend to focus on differences among fossils and express those differences by assigning the fossils in question to different taxonomic categories—different species if the distinctions are small, different genera if they are more pronounced and related to distinct adaptations. Lumpers, emphasizing the extent of diversity present in living species and genera, consider differences among some fossil groups to reflect a similar degree of diversity. They believe that the "default" course is to lump fossils into the same category unless there is clear evidence that they should be split.

Both these approaches are, of course, provisional starting points. All good scientists understand that hypotheses are open to testing and that new data may require new models—sometimes radically new ones. Time and again, someone's "beautiful hypothesis" is slayed by some new "ugly fact." Moreover, no researcher is always a splitter or a lumper. One scientist's approach can vary from group to group. I favor the two-genera classification of the early hominins (*Australopithecus* and *Paranthropus*), but as you will see, I favor a lumping model with regard to genus *Homo*.

The lumping and splitting factions are very much at odds regarding the evolution of genus *Homo*. At one extreme is the viewpoint that all members of *Homo* since the earliest fossils assigned to that genus (which we will discuss in the next section) belong to a single species, *Homo sapiens*. The other extreme claims six or more species within genus *Homo* over that 2-million-year period. There are also versions of the splitter point of view that recognize two to five *Homo* species. Each model has evidence in its support, and each has opposition based on reasonable counterarguments. These models are the topic of Chapter 12.

How, then, to begin discussing the fossil evidence for the evolution of our genus if authorities cannot even agree on the names? The simplest scheme would, of course, be the one that lumps nearly all the fossils into *Homo sapiens*—that would certainly cut down on the taxonomic categories. But such an approach would make it difficult to describe and discuss differences among groups of fossils that some authorities feel are enough to merit species distinction. And when these species names are used—regardless of one's point of view on the debate—there is usually no misunderstanding about which fossils are being referred to.

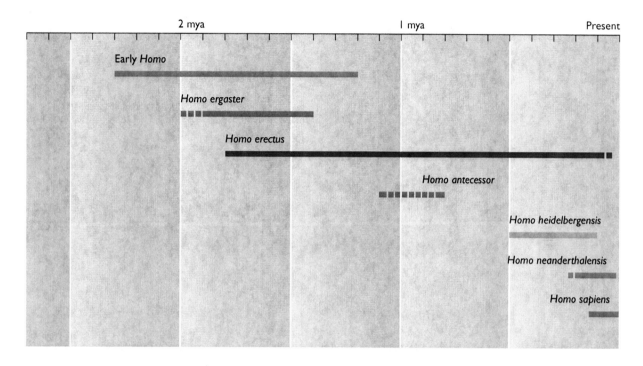

FIGURE 11.1

Timeline of species within genus *Homo* according to an extreme splitter model. Dashes indicate that some evidence exists for extending the time range of that species as shown. Each species, of course, may be extended in time either way as more fossil evidence is recovered. This model does not necessarily reflect the author's views but is used to clearly sort the fossils into named groups recognized by some authorities as separate species. (The so-called Hobbits from Indonesia, *Homo floresiensis*, dated at 74,000 to 12,000 ya, are still controversial and, thus, not included in this timeline. They will be discussed in the "Contemporary Reflections" box at the end of this chapter.)

Thus, let's begin with a moderate splitter model that divides all later *Homo* into six species (Figure 11.1). We will describe and discuss these species in terms of their phenotypic features, dates, geographic distributions, and behaviors. Then, in Chapter 12, we will discuss the various hypotheses for just how many species these groups represent and, most important, how they are related evolutionarily. *Understand that I am not necessarily advocating this model.* I just feel that organizing our discussion in this order will allow us to easily consider both points of view.

THE FIRST MEMBERS OF GENUS *HOMO*

The First Stone Tools

When the Leakeys found Zinjanthropus (*Paranthropus boisei*) in 1959, they uncovered some simple stone tools at the same level of Olduvai Gorge (Figure 11.2). At first they thought Zinjanthropus had made the tools, but they began to feel that "Zinj" was too primitive to have made something so sophisticated.

FIGURE 11.2
A sample of Oldowan tools. The two at the lower right are flake tools. The others are core tools.

These tools, called **Oldowan** after Olduvai Gorge (see Figure 9.7), seem very simple to us. Also called *pebble tools*, they are nothing more than water-smoothed cobbles 3 to 4 inches across, modified by knocking off a few chips from one or two faces to make a sharp edge. But unlike the termite sticks of the chimpanzees, there is nothing in the raw material—the unmodified stone—that immediately suggests the tools that can be made from it or the method of manufacture. A stone tool requires that the maker be able to imagine within the stone the intended tool and to picture the process needed to make it. Making even a simple Oldowan tool is also a far more complex technological feat than stripping the leaves off a branch to make it narrow enough to fit down the hole of a termite mound (Figure 11.3). (I can attest to the difficulty.) This leap of the imagination and increase in technological skill are what make the first evidence of stone toolmaking so important.

Authorities originally thought that the Oldowan tools were all **core tools** and that the flakes were the waste products of their manufacture. However, it has been shown that though some flaked cores were used as tools, the majority were the raw materials for the manufacture of **flake tools,** which were used for a variety of tasks, such as cutting meat and plant material, scraping meat off a bone, and sawing wood or bone (Schick and Toth 1993; Toth 1985). Under microscopic analysis, the edges of these flakes show a polish that is characteristic of these activities.

It also appears that the makers of the Oldowan tools may have traveled some distance to find a source of stone known to be superior for the production of sharp, durable tools. The cores themselves were probably carried around to wherever flakes were needed; it is common to find flakes at a site

Oldowan A toolmaking tradition from Africa associated with early *Homo.*

core tools Tools made by taking flakes off a stone nucleus.

flake tools Tools made from the flakes removed from a stone core.

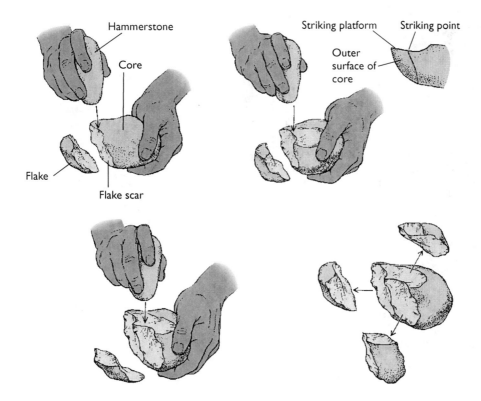

FIGURE 11.3
Process of removing flakes from a stone core in the Oldowan tradition. A hard stone was struck in just the right locations to remove sharp, thin flakes.

but not the cores from which they were struck. All this shows a high level of planning (Schick and Toth 1993), and although there is some evidence for bone-tool manufacture among the earlier hominins (Holden 2001a), no evidence of stone-tool manufacture has yet been found.

The Fossils

It appeared in 1959, and still does, that Zinjanthropus was not a good candidate for having been the maker of the pebble tools. Then in 1961 the Leakeys found a second hominin from the same time period. Actually, they had found fragmentary fossils of this form in the same year that they found Zinjanthropus, but they had not fully recognized them as something different. They named the new form *Homo habilis* ("handy man"; Figure 11.4).

The reasons for including these fossils in genus *Homo* are twofold. First, *H. habilis* shows a notable increase in brain size, from the average of about 480 ml for *Australopithecus* and *Paranthropus* to an average of 680 ml, with a possible maximum of 800 ml. (The range for modern humans is 1,000–2,000 ml.) Second, the presence of the stone tools indicates that those larger brains were capable of a complexity of thought not seen in the

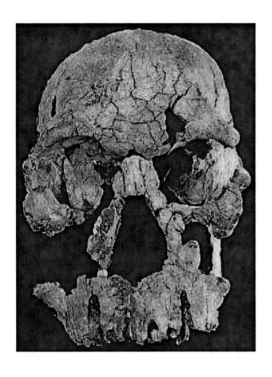

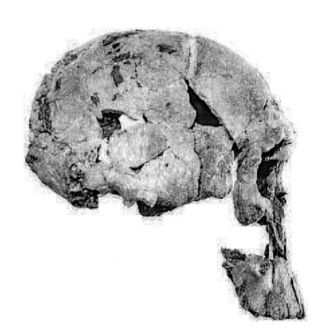

FIGURE 11.4
The well-known skull 1470 from Lake Turkana, Kenya, front and side views. Note the flatter face, smoother contours, lack of a sagittal crest, and more rounded braincase as compared with *Australopithecus* and *Paranthropus*. This fossil was first classified as *Homo habilis* and still is by some authorities. Others consider it a separate species, *Homo rudolfensis*.

record of the other two hominin genera. Thus, *H. habilis* seems to mark the beginning of a new trend in hominin evolution—toward bigger brains and greater intelligence and changes in bipedalism. Fossils of *H. habilis* have now been found in Tanzania, Kenya, Ethiopia, and perhaps southern Africa and have been dated at 2.3 to 1.44 mya.

The exact taxonomic affiliations of this group of fossils, however, are far from agreed upon. The specimens from East Turkana, Kenya, are considered different enough by some to be placed in a new species, *Homo rudolfensis*. The specimen pictured in Figure 11.4 is an example. Differences include a larger body and brain size than in *H. habilis* and the lack of a continuous brow ridge over the eyes. (See Tattersall 1992 for a review of this argument.) Others (Blumenschine et al. 2003) believe that all these specimens belong in *H. habilis*. Still others (Wood and Collard 1999) feel that the fossils labeled *H. habilis* and *H. rudolfensis* are in important ways closer to *Australopithecus* than to *Homo* and should thus be lumped into the former genus. This assessment is based on similar body proportions, evidence of continued arboreal ability, and similarity of brain size *relative to body size* (rather than absolute differences in brain size). Still others (Sherwood 2000) agree that while *H. habilis* might be lumped into *Australopithecus*, *H. rudolfensis* should remain in *Homo*. For the remainder of this discussion, we will use the term "early *Homo*," in keeping with what is, at the moment, the majority view, and we will also consider all the fossils together. As more fossils that cover a broader span of time are found, the picture of hominin evolution during this period may become clearer.

A New Adaptation

What is it about the stone tools that may have given early *Homo* an edge? Paleoanthropologist Richard Leakey, the son of Louis and Mary, suggests that sharp stone tools allowed these hominins to more quickly cut meat and bones off a carcass, making the addition of meat to the diet through scavenging safer and more efficient. There is evidence for this suggestion.

Ten Olduvai sites from the early *Homo* period contain Oldowan tools, flakes, and animal bones. These are "stone cache" sites (Potts 1984) where hominins left supplies of stones and to which they took scavenged animal remains for quick, safe processing and eating. Analysis indicates that these sites were used for short periods, but repeatedly, as one would expect of such places.

Archaeologist Lewis Binford (1985) has analyzed the animal bones from these sites and found that they are mostly the lower leg bones of antelopes. These bones carry little meat and, along with the skull, are about the only parts left after a large carnivore has finished eating. However, such bones are rich in marrow, so a major activity at the sites in question may have been to cut off what little meat remained on these bones and then to break them open for the nutritious marrow inside.

Finally, Pat Shipman has studied the taphonomy of these and other bones with a scanning electron microscope (1984, 1986). She found that cut marks left by stone tools were usually on the shafts of the bones as if pieces of meat were cut off, not near the joints as if an entire carcass had been butchered (Figure 11.5). Also, the hominin tool marks sometimes overlapped carnivore tooth marks, showing that the carnivores had gotten there first.

We may envision early *Homo* in small cooperative groups, maybe family groups, foraging in a mixed grassland/woodland area (Blumenschine et al. 2003) for plant foods and always on the lookout for the telltale signs of a carnivore kill—a group of scavengers gathered on the ground or a flock of vultures circling overhead. Their big brains allowed them to better understand their environment and to manipulate it, making imaginative and technologically advanced tools from stone. With these tools they may have cut apart the carcasses they found and taken the pieces back to a safe place, maybe where they had stored more tools.

FIGURE 11.5
This micrograph of a fossil bone from Olduvai Gorge shows tool marks (the horizontal lines and the diagonal line beginning at the top of the photo) and a carnivore tooth mark (beginning on the right side and angled toward the center). In this case, the tooth mark overlaps the tool mark, indicating that the hominins sliced meat off this part of the bone *before* a scavenger began eating.

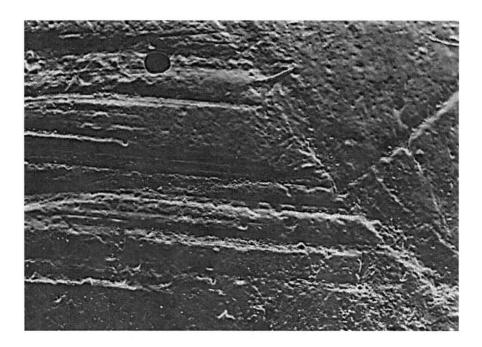

There they cut the remaining meat off the bones and, using large hammerstones, smashed open the bones for marrow. It was no doubt a harsh life, but it was successful. The adaptive themes of bipedalism, large brains, social organization, and tool technology set the stage for the rest of hominin evolution.

Fossils indicate that forms with the characteristics of early *Homo* were around for about two million years. Before they disappeared from the fossil record, a new hominin species came on the scene—one that continued and enhanced the trends of big brains and tool technology, adaptations that soon carried this hominin all over the Old World.

TO NEW LANDS

The First Fossils

Most of the fossils at the beginning of genus *Homo* (subsequent to the still-debated fossils of early *Homo*) are included in species *Homo erectus*. Some authorities split the African fossils of this group into a second species, *Homo ergaster* (Table 11.1 and Figure 11.6).

The Dutch physician Eugene Dubois made the first finds ever of *H. erectus* in Java in 1891. Dubois chose Java to look for hominin fossils

TABLE 11.1

Major Fossils of *Homo ergaster* and *Homo erectus*

Country	Locality	Fossils	Age (million years)	Est. Brain Size (ml)
Homo ergaster				
Kenya	East Turkana	Cranial and postcranial fragments	1.78	850
		including mandibles and pelvis and	1.57	800
		long bone fragments		
		Cranial fragments	1.55	691
	West Turkana	Nearly complete juvenile individual	1.6	880
Homo erectus				
Algeria	Ternifine	3 mandibles and a skull	0.5–0.7	—
China	Hexian (Lontandong)	Partial skull	0.25–0.5	1,000
	Lantian (Gongwangling)	Cranial fragments and mandible	>1	800
	Longgupo	Mandible fragments	1.8	—
	Yunxian	2 crania	>0.35	—
	Zhoukoudian	Cranial and postcranial remains	0.77	1,030
		of 40 individuals	0.77	915
			0.77	850
			0.77	1,225
			0.77	1,015
			0.77	1,030
			0.77	—
	Tangshan Cave	Fragments	0.58–0.62	—
Ethiopia	Bouri	Cranial and postcranial fragments	1.0	995
Georgia	Dmanisi	3 mandibles,	1.77	780
		16 teeth,	1.77	650
		3 crania, postcranial bones	1.77	600
Israel	'Ubeidiya	Fragments	<1	—
Italy	Ceprano	Cranium	0.8–0.9	—
Java	Modjokerto	Child's cranium	1.8	—
	Ngandong	Cranial and postcranial fragments	<0.1	1,170
		from >12 individuals	<0.1	1,250
			<0.1	1,230
			<0.1	1,090
	Sambungmachan	Large cranial fragment	<0.1	1,000
	Sangiran	Cranial and postcranial fragments	1.6	800
		from ~40 individuals	1.6	900
			1.6	850
			1.6	1,050
			1.6	1,000
			1.1–1.4	856
	Trinil	Skullcap and femur	<1	940

(continued)

TABLE 11.1 (Continued)

Country	Locality	Fossils	Age (million years)	Est. Brain Size (ml)
Homo erectus (continued)				
Kenya	Olorgesailie	Cranial fragments	0.90–0.97	<800
	Ileret	Cranial fragment	1.55	—
Morocco	Salé	Cranium	0.4	880
	Sidi Abderrahman	2 mandible fragments	—	—
	Thomas Quarry	Mandible and skull fragments	0.5	—
Tanzania	Olduvai	Cranial and postcranial fragments, including mandibles and pelvis and long bone fragments	1.4 0.6–0.8	1,060 700–800
Turkey	Kocabaş	Cranial fragments	0.51–0.49	—
			Mean	**984.79**

largely because he was already stationed there with the military. But the choice was also a logical one for the time, since most people thought that humans had first evolved in Asia, despite Darwin's clear suggestion that Africa was the human homeland. The idea that our evolutionary line was originally African apparently did not sit well with many Europeans.

When Dubois found a skullcap and a diseased femur at the site of Trinil (Figure 11.7), he thought they represented the "missing link" between apes and humans, and he dubbed the specimens "Pithecanthropus erectus" (the "upright ape-man"), popularly known as "Java Man." Since Dubois's work, numerous other fossils have been located in Java (see Table 11.1) and are now recognized as fully hominin and assigned to our genus, *Homo*. The fossils found in Java are similar in phenotype to the African and other Asian specimens, although their average brain size is larger than in some of the earlier fossils, and many are over 1,000 ml.

Perhaps the most famous *H. erectus* fossils are those from Zhoukoudian, a cave outside of Beijing, China. Starting in the 1920s, six nearly complete skulls, a couple dozen cranial and mandible fragments, over a hundred teeth, and a few postcranial pieces were recovered from the cave. Stone tools and animal bones, including those of horses and hyenas, were also recovered. The hominin remains are clearly similar to other specimens of *H. erectus*. Dating indicates that the cave was first occupied about 770,000 ya and was used until about 230,000 ya, although new evidence (Boaz and Ciochon 2001) suggests that most of the *H. erectus* bones in the cave were the remains of hyenas' meals.

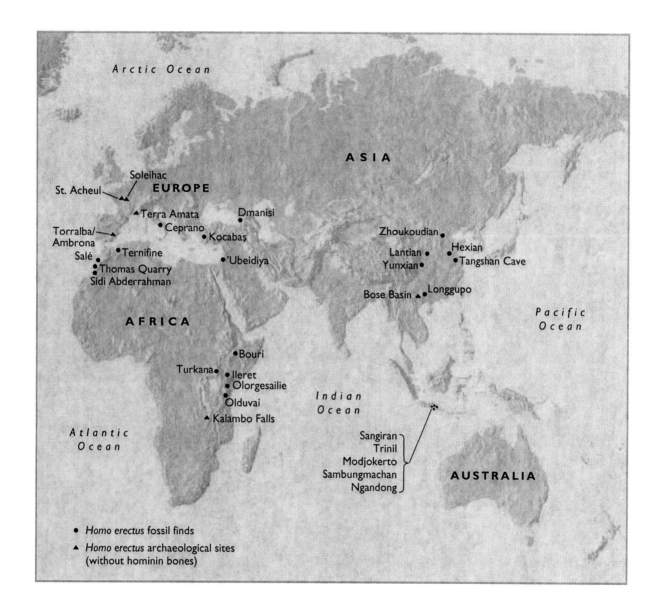

Arctic Ocean

ASIA

Soleihac
St. Acheul
EUROPE
Terra Amata   Dmanisi
Ceprano
Torralba/   Kocabaş
Ambrona
Salé   Ternifine
Thomas Quarry   'Ubeidiya
Sidi Abderrahman

Zhoukoudian
Lantian   Hexian
Yunxian   Tangshan Cave

Bose Basin   Longgupo

Pacific
Ocean

AFRICA

Bouri
Turkana   Ileret
Olorgesailie
Olduvai
Kalambo Falls

Indian
Ocean

Atlantic
Ocean

Sangiran
Trinil
Modjokerto
Sambungmachan
Ngandong

AUSTRALIA

• *Homo erectus* fossil finds
▲ *Homo erectus* archaeological sites
(without hominin bones)

FIGURE 11.6

Map of major *Homo erectus/ ergaster* sites.

The fame of the Zhoukoudian fossils, called "Peking Man" (from the old spelling of Beijing), lies mostly in the fact that they are missing. When Japan invaded China in 1937, U.S. Marines attempting to get the fossils out of the country were captured by Japanese troops. The fossils were never seen again. Their whereabouts remain one of the great mysteries in anthropology. Fortunately, extensive measurements had already been taken of the bones, and accurate casts had been made (Figure 11.8).

Since then, numerous fossils classified as *H. erectus* have been recovered, and we are filling in—although not without controversy—our

FIGURE 11.7
Skullcap and femur of "Java Man" *Homo erectus*. The growth near the neck of the femur is the result of a pathological condition.

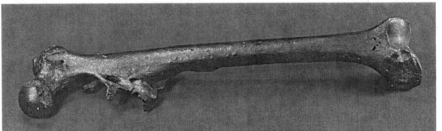

FIGURE 11.8
Cast of one of the missing "Peking Man" skulls.

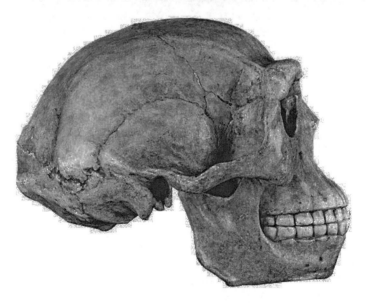

knowledge of this important period in hominin evolution. Among the oldest fossils of this group are those that some authorities (see, for example, Tattersall 1997) place in a separate species, *H. ergaster* ("work man," a reference to stone tools found in association with the fossils). The oldest

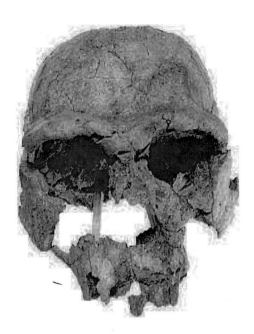

FIGURE 11.9
The *Homo erectus* (or *Homo ergaster*) skull of KNM-ER 3733 from Lake Turkana, Kenya, is fairly typical of this group.

well-established find, from East Turkana in Kenya, is dated at 1.78 mya (Figure 11.9). In some ways it is typical of *H. erectus* crania. It has heavy brow ridges, a prognathous face, a sloping forehead, an elongated profile, a **sagittal keel,** a sharply angled occipital bone with a pronounced **torus,** and a cranial capacity of 850 ml (Figure 11.10). (The sagittal keel should not be confused with the sagittal crest. The crest is a ridge of bone for the attachment of chewing muscles [see Figure 10.15]. The keel is an aspect of the skull's shape.) The average cranial capacity for this hominin group is about 980 ml, just slightly under the modern human minimum of 1,000 ml, but a considerable jump from the 680 ml average for early *Homo*. Some *H. erectus* fossils have cranial capacities within the modern human range (see Table 11.1).

In other ways, however, the Turkana skull differs from others labeled as *H. erectus*. It is thinner and higher in profile, with smaller facial bones. These modern-looking features are what have led to its placement in a separate species. The cranium is thought to have belonged to a female. A similar skull from East Turkana dated at 1.57 mya is more ruggedly constructed. It is thought to have belonged to a male.

From the neck up, then, *H. erectus/ergaster* is quite distinct from early *Homo* in overall size, ruggedness, and especially brain size. The skull still retains primitive features that distinguish it from modern *H. sapiens*. From the neck down, however, *H. erectus/ergaster* is essentially modern and apparently was so from its beginnings.

sagittal keel A sloping of the sides of the skull toward the top, as viewed from the front.

torus A bony ridge at the back of the skull, where the neck muscles attach.

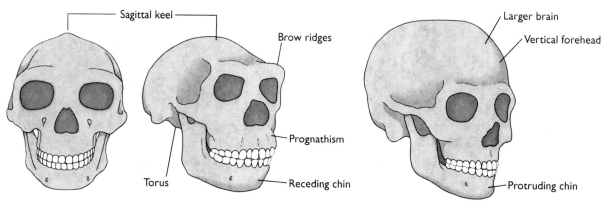

Sagittal keel

Brow ridges

Prognathism

Torus

Receding chin

Larger brain

Vertical forehead

Protruding chin

Homo erectus/ergaster

Modern *Homo sapiens*

FIGURE 11.10
Cranial features of *Homo erectus/ergaster* (side and front views) compared with those of modern *Homo sapiens*.

We know this because one of the oldest fossils of the group—also included in *H. ergaster*—is also the most complete. It is a nearly whole skeleton found at West Turkana in Kenya and is dated at 1.6 mya (Figure 11.11). The shape of the pelvis indicates that it was a male. Based on dental eruption and lack of any epiphyseal union, it is estimated that he was 12 years old when he died. "Turkana Boy," as he is commonly known, was about 5½ feet tall; he might have been 150 pounds and 6 feet tall had he lived to adulthood.

All other fossils from this group are assigned to *Homo erectus*. Most of the *H. erectus* fossils from Africa are younger, from 400,000 to 800,000 years old. This means that *H. erectus* spread throughout the African continent and that populations of the species remained there for about a million years.

Migration and the Ice Ages

H. erectus, however, did not remain only in Africa. According to recent data, members of the species had reached China and Southeast Asia by almost 2 mya. What prompted them to leave the savannas to which they were apparently so well adapted?

We can't know the answer for sure, but a good guess is that the spread of *H. erectus* was simply an outcome of their reproductive success. Their big brains enabled them to exploit the savannas to a greater extent than had the other hominins to date. They had better and more varied tools (which we'll discuss later), the ability to learn more about their environment and to reason out the problems that their habitat presented, and, no doubt, a more complex social organization. With these adaptations, *H. erectus* would have rapidly increased in population size.

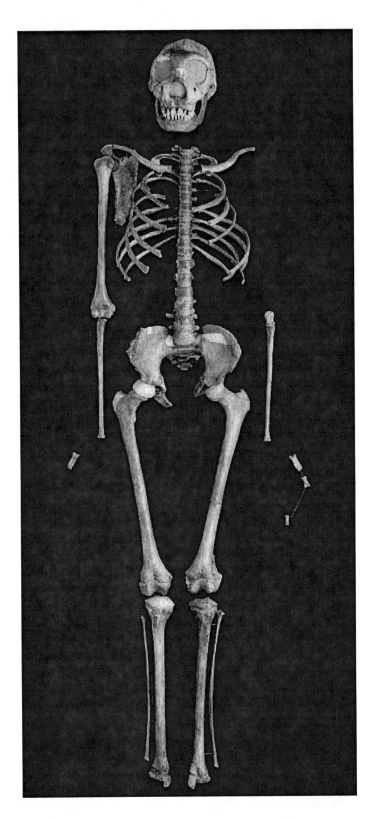

FIGURE 11.11
The "Turkana Boy," *Homo ergaster* fossil KNM-WT 15000, is one of the most complete early hominin fossils ever found. The pelvis is clearly that of a male, and the epiphyses at the top of his left femur are obviously not fused (see Figure 9.3).

Population increase, however, puts pressure on resources and, perhaps, on social harmony. So groups of *H. erectus* probably fissioned and moved outside of familiar areas in search of less competition over food, space, and two other resources that may have been even more important—water and shelter. Water can be scarce on the savannas, as can shelter. With bodies the same as ours, they were no longer good tree climbers and so had to seek shelter on the ground, in groves of trees, or, if they could locate one, in a cave or rock shelter. They may also have been following migrations of animal herds that had become important sources of food.

In search of food, water, shelter, and perhaps space and social harmony, *H. erectus* wandered the Old World. At first, their travels would have been made easier because, at the time, the savannas stretched from western Africa, across southern Asia, and all the way to northern China (Dennell and Roebroeks 2005). Those wanderings eventually carried them as far from their African homeland as what is now Beijing, China, and the Indonesian island of Java, and perhaps to Europe. Not only did these journeys take them to new climates, but the travels also brought them into contact with the changeable environments of the ice ages, known technically as the **Pleistocene.**

Beginning about 1.6 mya and ending 10,000 ya, the Pleistocene was a complex series of extremely cold periods separated by warm phases, some warmer than today. There may have been as many as eighteen cold episodes during the Pleistocene, some lasting tens of thousands of years. We still don't know what caused these cold periods. Suggestions range from increased volcanic activity, with dust and ash blocking the sun's rays, to changes in the earth's orbit.

When the average world temperature drops, ice and snow accumulate over the years at the poles and in higher elevations. The pressure of this accumulation forces the movement of great sheets and rivers of ice known as **glaciers** (Figure 11.12). During periods of glacial advances, much of North America, Europe, and Asia were covered by ice, sometimes nearly a mile thick (Figure 11.13). Parts of the world not covered by the glaciers were nonetheless affected, having cooler summers and wetter winters. The advance of the glaciers also had the effect of condensing the world's climatic zones into smaller spaces. Several times during the Pleistocene, the temperate oak and pine forests of Connecticut, where I now live, were like the arctic **tundra** of Alaska and northern Canada. Moreover, with so much of the earth's water tied up in the great ice sheets, sea levels dropped as much as 400 feet, exposing large areas of land formerly under water. This allowed humans to migrate to areas previously inaccessible; for instance, modern *Homo sapiens* migrated to North America.

Pleistocene The geological time period, from 1.6 mya to 10,000 ya, characterized by a series of glacial advances and retreats.

glaciers Massive sheets of ice that expand and move.

tundra A treeless area with low-growing vegetation and permanently frozen ground.

FIGURE 11.12
A veritable river of ice, the Moreno Glacier is located in Patagonia, a region of Argentina.

The Evolution of *Homo erectus*

The world of the Pleistocene was the world through which *H. erectus* was able to migrate and establish themselves, and we find their remains in some of the far corners of the Old World. They undoubtedly also inhabited the areas in between, but we have yet to uncover fossils in these areas.

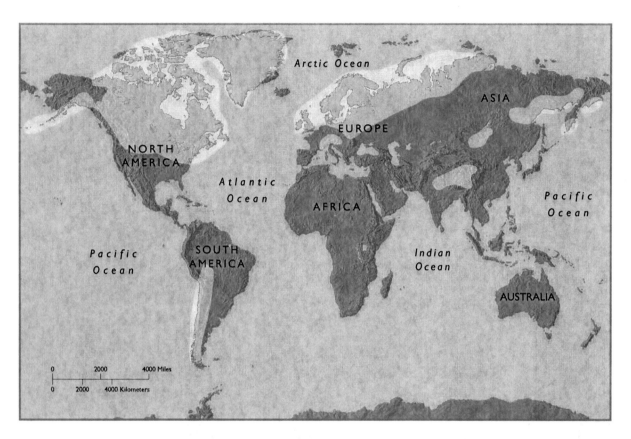

FIGURE 11.13
Maximum worldwide glacial expansion during the Pleistocene. The Antarctic ice cover, not shown here, also expanded during this epoch.

Redating of early finds from Java has posed interesting questions regarding the spread of H. *erectus* around the Old World. Using new versions of the potassium/argon dating technique, researchers have redated the Sangiran *erectus* fossils to 1.6 mya and the Modjokerto remains to 1.8 mya—twice as old as previously thought and at least as old as the oldest African *erectus/ergaster* fossil. This could mean that H. *erectus* evolved somewhere other than Africa. But all previous hominin fossils come only from Africa, so it's unlikely that *erectus* evolved anywhere but there.

That leaves two plausible explanations. Perhaps H. *erectus* (or *ergaster*) actually first evolved in Africa earlier than any of the fossils we have—remember how rare fossilization is—and then spread. The other possibility is simply that their expansion began very shortly after they first evolved and was rapid. Science writer James Shreeve (1994:86) notes that Java is 10,000 to 15,000 miles from Africa, depending on the route, and that parts of Indonesia were connected to Asia at the time due to lower sea levels during the Pleistocene. If *erectus* walked just a mile a year, it would have taken only about 15,000 years to reach Java. That's still pretty fast, considering that they did not necessarily move 1 mile every year *in the right direction*. I think that if the Java dates are correct, they probably mean that *H. erectus/ergaster* is both older than we now assume based on existing fossils *and* that the species' expansion began early on.

Evidence for this interpretation comes from the Republic of Georgia and from Kenya. In 2002, a new cranium from the Dmanisi site was discovered (Vekua et al. 2002). Dated at 1.77 mya, as were the previous Dmanisi fossils, this one was distinct in that it was smaller (an estimated 600 ml cranial capacity) and more "primitive" than the others, so much so that although it is provisionally assigned to *Homo erectus,* it has some features that resemble early *Homo* (Figure 11.14). In other words, hominins may have ventured out of Africa sooner and at an earlier evolutionary stage than we had previously assumed (Balter and Gibbons 2002; Dennell and Roebroeks 2005).

In 2007 even newer fossils were announced from the Dmanisi site, some associated with previously discovered crania. These were postcranial bones of three adults and a teen (Lordkipanidze et al. 2007). They showed a mix of

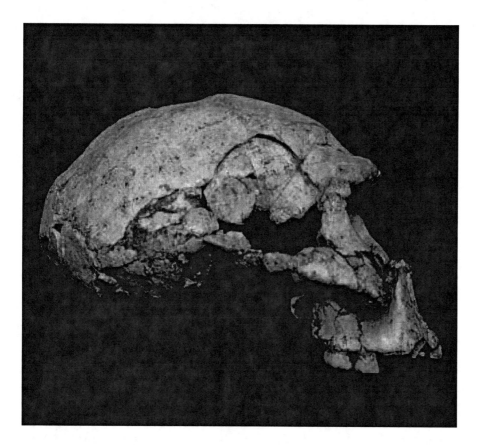

FIGURE 11.14
One of the previously discovered crania from Dmanisi, Georgia, dated 1.77 mya and provisionally assigned to *Homo erectus.* The skulls from this site show a remarkable degree of variation, and some have traits that resemble early *Homo* from Africa.

modern and primitive traits, among the latter some features of the shoulders and arms, short statures (four feet nine inches to five feet five inches), and small body mass (88 to 110 pounds). These fossils are much smaller than the "Turkana Boy," who lived at close to the same time.

Compare this information with that from a skull found in Kenya (Leakey et al. 2003), dated at 1.55 mya, that bears a resemblance to the Dmanisi skull in its size and some detailed features. The skull is assigned to *H. erectus*, but like the Dmanisi skull, it shows that early *H. erectus* had a transitional or intermediary stage—as compared with early *Homo*—and it was at this stage that the species first left Africa.

Moreover, new dating on a site in northern China shows the stone tools there to be 1.36 million years old, by far the oldest evidence of human presence in that region (Zhu et al. 2001). This is further evidence for an earlier initial migration of some populations from Africa than previously thought.

Another important date concerns the Java site of Ngandong. There is evidence that some *erectus* fossils there may be younger than 100,000 years— perhaps as young as 27,000 to 53,000 years old. If so, there were populations of *erectus* still around well after modern *Homo sapiens* had evolved. (We'll discuss the meanings of this in the next chapter.)

It should be noted that with the exception of the Ceprano find in Italy (see Table 11.1), the European evidence of *H. erectus* comes in the form of cultural artifacts dated at times that have been associated with that species from other locations. At the site of Soleihac in France are tools and animal remains dated at 800,000 ya. Another French site, Terra Amata, on the Riviera, has been proposed as a site where *H. erectus* built shelters around 400,000 ya. In Spain, at two adjacent sites called Torralba and Ambrona, dated at 400,000 ya, are the remains of some large mammals, including elephants, along with some stone tools that suggest a hunting or, more probably, a scavenging site. Until, however, we locate definite fossils of *H. erectus* from Europe—other than the cranium from Ceprano, Italy—we can only conclude that the species was there but was not widespread or, perhaps, that these sites are associated with another hominin species.

The Life of *Homo erectus*

Acheulian technique
A toolmaking tradition associated with *Homo erectus* in Africa and Europe.

Tools   Like early *Homo*, early *H. ergaster* made stone tools by taking a few flakes off a core, just enough to make the "business end." They also, of course, used the flakes as tools. But beginning about 1.4 mya, *H. erectus* elaborated on this stone toolmaking technique by flaking the entire stone, controlling the shape of the whole core tool. This toolmaking tradition is called the **Acheulian technique,** after the site in France where it was first

identified. The core tool produced by the Acheulian technique is the **hand axe.** It is symmetrical, edged and pointed, and **bifacial** (flaked on both sides; Figure 11.15). It was the all-purpose tool of its time, used for any number of tasks, from butchering to cutting wood.

In addition to hand axes, *H. erectus* also made tools with straight, sharp edges called *cleavers.* Moreover, making a hand axe or cleaver produces a great many flakes—as many as fifty usable ones by one estimate—and *H. erectus* also made flake tools, used either unmodified or further worked to produce a desired shape.

Hand axes appeared in Africa about 1.4 mya and lasted for over a million years. They spread throughout Africa and into Europe. They are, however, rarely found in Asia. Instead, Asian *erectus* populations, like those at Zhoukoudian, made what are called *choppers,* with flakes removed from one side, and a few other tools with flakes removed from both sides (Figure 11.16). But these tool types, unlike the Acheulian hand axe, were asymmetrical and not flaked over the whole surface.

On the subject of hand axes, some new evidence from Tanzania (Schuster 2001) includes hand axes dated at 1.5 mya that bear traces of acacia wood on their blades. One interpretation suggests that the toolmakers used these stone tools for woodworking. No actual wooden artifacts were recovered, however.

Fire   Perhaps the most striking behavioral advance associated with *Homo erectus* is the purposeful use of fire. There is some evidence, though it is disputed, for the use of fire in Africa at 1.5 mya and France at 750,000 ya.

FIGURE 11.15
Bifacially flaked hand axes became one of history's most popular tools and were found in a variety of sizes showing varying degrees of quality. The hand axe on the far right is from the French site of St. Acheul, which lent its name to this toolmaking tradition.

hand axe   A bifacial, all-purpose stone tool, shaped somewhat like an axe head.

bifacial   Refers to a stone tool that has been worked on both sides.

FIGURE 11.16
Flake and chopper tools associated with *Homo erectus* from the cave at Zhoukoudian. Although the functions of these tools are uncertain, some are named for inferred use. Burins may have been used to etch out thin slivers of antler or bone, which were then further modified into awls or needles. Points may have served as cutting tools for fine work. Scrapers may have helped remove flesh from animal hides. And choppers chopped wood and perhaps broke open bones to extract marrow.

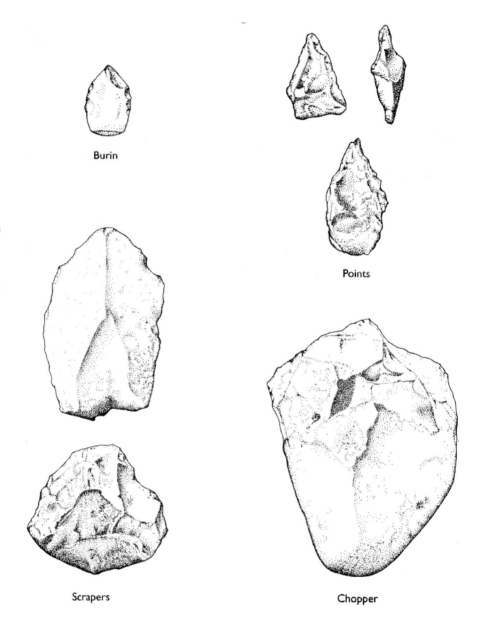

Burin

Points

Scrapers

Chopper

A rock shelter in Thailand has yielded evidence of fire dated at 700,000 ya. The earliest well-accepted date (although even it is not without its skeptics) is from the cave at Zhoukoudian sometime after 500,000 ya (Binford and Chuan 1985; Binford and Stone 1986).

Fire, of course, provides heat, and so it is not surprising that some of the earliest evidence of fire comes from cold northern areas. Fire also provides protection from animals and can be used for cooking, making meat easier to chew and digest. But in the long run, perhaps its most important use is as a source of light. Science writer John Pfeiffer (1966) suggests that fire could extend the hours of activity into the night and provide a social focus for group interaction. Sitting around the campfire at night was when people experimented, created, talked, and socialized. Fire serves these functions in human cultures today. Moreover, the use of fire may well have given people a psychological advantage—a sense of mastery and control over a force of nature—and a source of energy. As Pfeiffer says in the title of his article, "When *Homo erectus* Tamed Fire, He Tamed Himself."

Food   Was *Homo erectus* a hunter of big game, as often portrayed, or did they continue to scavenge for most of the meat in their diet? At the 400,000-year-old Spanish sites of Torralba and Ambrona, located on two hills on either side of a mountain pass, scientists found the remains of fifty elephants and over sixty other game animals (see Figure 9.10). The traditional interpretation is a rather elaborate reconstruction of a cooperative hunt, indeed, of several seasons of cooperative hunting. In this scenario the animals were stampeded, possibly with the use of fire, into a bog where they were killed and butchered. The pieces of the carcasses were then taken to a campsite where they were further cut up, cooked, and eaten. There are also some tools at the sites.

Is there evidence for this interpretation? A taphonomic analysis of 3,000 bones from these sites found that 95 percent of them were so damaged that the search for specific evidence of human activity was impossible (Shipman and Rose 1983). Scratches on many of the bones, once thought to be stone-tool cut marks, turn out on examination under a scanning electron microscope to be merely the results of soil abrasion and root growth. Of the fifty-five bones that could be analyzed, the microscope showed only sixteen cut marks on fourteen bones. The pattern of the marks does not indicate systematic butchering. There is even little evidence of carnivore tooth marks. Furthermore, the tools found at the site are not associated with the elephants but with the leg bones and mandibles of horses, deer, and wild cattle—the very parts of the animals that would be gathered by scavenging. At best, it appears that H. *erectus* was present at these sites and cut some meat off animal carcasses found there. There is no compelling evidence for cooperative big-game hunting.

Two other alleged kill sites, at Olduvai Gorge and Olorgesailie in Africa, similarly give rise to elaborate interpretations of cooperative big-game hunting, but they too are based on questionable evidence. The bones found at these sites are more indicative of scavenging than of large-scale hunting.

So, we may probably conclude that *Homo erectus* was a forager, collecting plant foods and scavenging for meat, who also hunted at least smaller animals when necessary or when the opportunity presented itself.

Language Finally, what about the linguistic skills of *H. erectus*? As noted, their average cranial capacity was just a little short of the modern human minimum, and individual *erectus* remains fall within the modern human range. It's difficult to be certain what this fact means. After all, the modern range of 1,000 to 2,000 ml means that some people have brains twice the volume of others, but there is no solid evidence that within this range brain size has anything to do with intelligence. Was *H. erectus*, then, just a little bit less intelligent than we are?

Because the inside of the skull reflects some of the features of the brain it once held, anthropologist Ralph Holloway (1980, 1981) has been able to look at the structure of *H. erectus* brains. By making **endocasts** of the inside surfaces of fossil crania, Holloway has produced images of the very brains of our ancestors (Figure 11.17). One intriguing find is that the brains of

FIGURE 11.17
Natural endocasts from South African australopithecines. Notice the degree of detail, particularly the blood vessels of the upper right cast. Such casts may also be made artificially and allow us to compare the brains of our ancestors with those of modern humans.

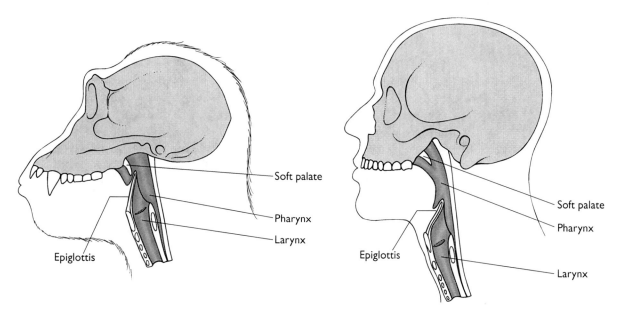

FIGURE 11.18
Vocal tract of a chimp compared with a modern human's. The high placement of the chimp's vocal tract makes it impossible for it to produce all of the sounds that are part of modern human languages.

H. erectus were asymmetrical—the right and left halves of the brain weren't the same shape. This is found to some extent in apes but to a greater extent in modern humans, because the halves of our brains perform different functions. Language and the ability to use symbols, for example, are functions of the left hemisphere, while spatial reasoning (such as the hand-eye coordination needed to make complex tools) is performed in the right hemisphere. This hints that *H. erectus* also had hemisphere specialization, perhaps even including the ability to communicate through a symbolic language.

Further evidence of language use by *H. erectus* is suggested by the reconstruction of the vocal apparatus based on the anatomy of the cranial base. Even though the vocal apparatus is made up of soft parts, those parts are connected to bone, and so the shape of the bone is correlated with the shape of the larynx, pharynx, and other features (Figure 11.18).

Reconstruction work on australopithecines indicates that their vocal tract was basically like that of apes, with the larynx and pharynx high up in the throat. While this would have allowed them to drink and breathe at the same time (as human infants can do up to 18 months), it would not have allowed for the precise manipulation of air that is required for modern human languages. The early hominins could make sounds, but they would have been more like those of chimpanzees.

Homo erectus, on the other hand, had vocal tracts more like those of modern humans, positioned lower in the throat and allowing for a greater

endocasts Natural or human-made casts of the inside of a skull.

range and speed of sound production. Thus, *erectus* could have produced vocal communication that involved many sounds with precise differences. Whether or not they did so is another question. But given their ability to manufacture fairly complex tools, to control fire, and to survive in different and changing environmental circumstances, *erectus* certainly had complex things to talk *about*. It is not out of the question that *erectus* had a communication system that was itself complex, although there are authorities who feel that a communication system with the attributes of modern human language is associated only with the sophisticated behavior of modern *Homo sapiens* (see Holden 1998 for a detailed discussion).

If we can consider it a separate species, *H. erectus*—although now extinct—was a smashing success by any standards. The species evolved nearly 2 mya in Africa, possibly from an earlier species, *H. ergaster*, and by perhaps 1.8 mya had spread as far as Java. By 500,000 ya, they had reached northern China and Europe. They lasted as an identifiable group in Africa and China until 250,000 ya and may have persisted in Java until less than 100,000 ya. Their adaptations—now focused on learning, technology, and the cultural transmission of information—allowed them to exploit a number of different environments.

There is some debate over just how much *H. erectus* changed during their tenure on earth. There is a small increase in average cranial capacity over this time (about 180 ml), as well as some refinement in their hand axe–making technique and variation in their flake tool production. These changes, however, are small and slow, so the overall impression is one of stability—not a bad thing in evolutionary terms.

Perhaps as early as 800,000 ya, there was another sudden surge in brain size, to an average matching our own. This marks the beginning of perhaps the most complex part of our story.

BIG BRAINS, ARCHAIC SKULLS

The next three hominin species—using the six-species model, illustrated in Figure 11.1—are marked by brain sizes within the modern human range that, indeed, match or approximate the modern human average; nonetheless, they have other features, especially of the cranium, that retain primitive characteristics. These hominin groups are sometimes collectively referred to as "archaic." The most recent of these, *Homo neanderthalensis*, will be considered separately in the next section. Here we will discuss the earlier *H. heidelbergensis* and the even earlier *H. antecessor* (Table 11.2 and Figure 11.19).

TABLE 11.2
Major Fossils of *Homo antecessor* and *Homo heidelbergensis*

Country	Locality	Fossils	Age (years)	Est. Brain Size (ml)
Homo antecessor				
Spain	Gran Dolina	More than 80 fragments	>780,000	>1,000
	Sima del Elefante	Mandible	1,100,000–1,200,000	—
Homo heidelbergensis				
China	Dali	Cranium	200,000	1,120
	Jinniushan(?)*	Nearly complete skeleton	200,000	1,350
	Maba(?)	Cranium	130,000–170,000	—
	Xujiayao(?)	Fragments of 11 individuals	100,000–125,000	—
England	Swanscombe	Occipital and parietals	276,000–426,000	1,325
	Boxgrove[†]	Tibia, teeth	362,000–423,000	—
Ethiopia	Bodo	Cranium	600,000(?)	1,250
France	Arago	Cranium and fragmentary remains of 7 individuals	250,000	1,200
Germany	Bilzingsleben(?)	Cranial fragments and tooth	320,000–412,000	—
	Mauer	Mandible	500,000	—
	Steinheim(?)	Cranium	200,000–240,000	1,200
Greece	Petralona	Cranium	160,000–240,000	1,200
Hungary	Vértesszöllös	Occipital fragment	250,000–475,000	1,250
India	Narmada	Cranium	200,000	1,300
Spain	Sima de los Huesos	2,500 fragments from at least 33 individuals	300,000	1,390
Tanzania	Ndutu (Olduvai)(?)	Cranium	400,000–700,000	1,100
Zambia	Kabwe (Broken Hill)	Cranium and additional cranial and postcranial remains of several individuals	400,000–700,000	1,280
			Mean	**1,247.00**

*The (?) indicates that the species identification of that fossil is in question.
[†] Some flint tools have recently been discovered at the site of Pakefield in southeast England. They are dated at 700,000 ya, but no fossil remains indicate that a hominin species is responsible for them (Parfitt et al. 2005).

Homo antecessor

The newest suggested hominin species, named in mid-1997, is *Homo antecessor* ("advance guard" or "explorer"). Many authorities do not recognize the fossils involved as a separate species, but the discoverers see sufficient

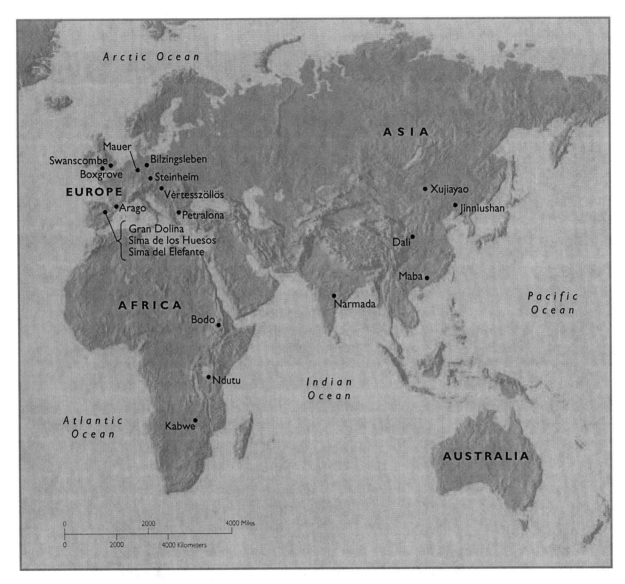

FIGURE 11.19
Map of major *Homo antecessor* and *Homo heidelbergensis* sites.

distinctions to warrant the new name (Bermúdez de Castro et al. 1997). Fossils have been discovered at two sites in the Atapuerca Hills in northern Spain. They consist of more than eighty fragments, including skulls, jaws, teeth, and other portions, as well as tools and animal bones. Gran Dolina, the first site found, is dated at more than 780,000 ya, and the most recent site, Sima del Elefante (Carbonell et al. 2008), is dated at 1.2 to 1.1 mya. Assuming these dates are correct, these would be the oldest well-accepted hominin fossils in Europe. Analysis of the cranial specimens estimates the brain size at more than 1,000 ml.

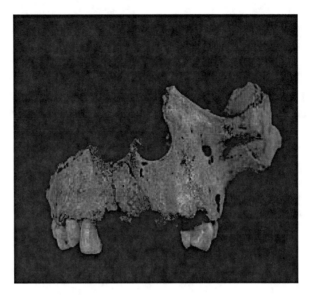

FIGURE 11.20
Fossil ATD6-69 from Gran Dolina cave, Atapuerca, Spain. This partial face of an 11-year-old boy who died perhaps more than 780,000 ya is fully modern in many features, including the hollowed cheekbone easily seen here.

The most striking fossil is the partial face of an 11-year-old boy (Figure 11.20). His features, described by the researchers as "fully modern," include a projecting nose region with a sharp lower margin, hollowed cheekbones (technically, the *canine fossae*), and several details of the dentition.

On the other hand, other fossils from this site show primitive features such as prominent brow ridges and premolars with multiple roots (modern human premolars have a single root). This unique mix of traits, especially the very modern appearance of the face, is what led the investigators to assign the new species name—and to further suggest that this species is the direct ancestor both of modern humans and of *H. heidelbergensis* and *H. neanderthalensis* (see Chapter 12).

A logical objection to the analysis of the Gran Dolina boy is that the modern-looking traits seen so clearly in the boy's face might be juvenile features, not present in adults of his group and, therefore, not of diagnostic value for species assignment. The investigators, however, report that some of the other fragmentary facial bones from the site also show these modern traits and that *later* fossils from a nearby site, Sima de los Huesos, do not (Gibbons 1997b).

The earliest-dated tools found at Gran Dolina resemble pre–hand axe tools from Africa, such as cores and simple cutting flakes. Later tools are more sophisticated. One long flake has a sharp edge on one side and a dulled flat edge on the other. It was presumably formed to be used as a knife. None of the tools at the sites, however, are as complex as some of the Acheulian tools being made by *H. erectus* and *H. ergaster* at the same time period or earlier.

Finally, there is some intriguing evidence of the diet of these people. Bison and deer bones, as well as some from other species, have been found that show stone-tool cut marks, implying that the people hunted. According to the investigators, there are also cut marks on some of the human bones that were mixed in with animal bones, suggesting cannibalism (Kunzig 1997).

Homo heidelbergensis

Table 11.2 and Figure 11.19 show that the fossils assigned to *Homo heidelbergensis* are geographically widespread and range over about 275,000 years in time (longer if one includes *H. antecessor*). The species was first named for a mandible found in 1907 at Mauer, near Heidelberg, Germany. Note that the inclusion of several of the fossils is questioned by those who recognize this group as a species.

Members of this group show an average brain size of nearly 1,300 ml, a more than 30 percent increase over the average for *H. erectus*. The brains are also differently proportioned than those of *H. erectus*, with greater emphasis on the forebrain, reflected by steeper foreheads. This may be important because the frontal lobes of the human brain are the areas thought to be most involved in the control of voluntary movements, speech, attention, social behavior, planning, and reasoning (see Figure 7.7).

The bones of the cranium, compared with those of *H. erectus*, are thinner; the overall size of the face is reduced; the profile is less prognathous; the brow ridges, though still present, are less pronounced; and the **postorbital constriction,** characteristic of *erectus*, is lessened (Figure 11.21). The postcranial skeletons, essentially modern in overall shape, are more rugged and muscular than in modern humans. The 362,000- to 423,000-year-old tibia from Boxgrove in southeast England, for example, is strikingly thicker in cross section than the tibia of a modern person. Figures 11.22 and 11.23 show two of the more complete examples of *H. heidelbergensis* crania.

We have evidence from Boxgrove of hand axes dated at 500,000 ya. And by about 200,000 ya, people included in *H. heidelbergensis* invented a new and imaginative way to make stone tools. The method appears first in Africa and later in Europe. Called the *prepared core*, or **Levallois technique** (after the suburb of Paris where it was first

postorbital constriction A narrowing of the skull behind the eyes, as viewed from above.

Levallois technique A tool technology involving striking uniform flakes from a prepared core.

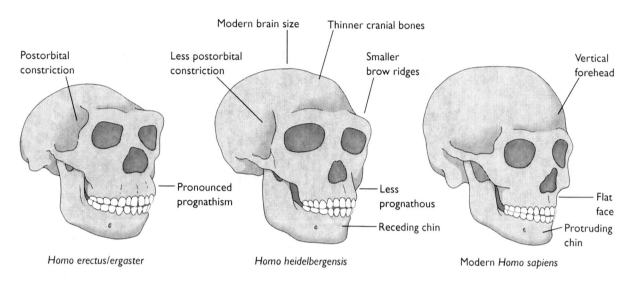

Postorbital
constriction

Less postorbital
constriction

Modern brain size

Thinner cranial bones

Smaller
brow ridges

Vertical
forehead

Pronounced
prognathism

Less
prognathous

Receding chin

Flat
face

Protruding
chin

Homo erectus/ergaster

Homo heidelbergensis

Modern *Homo sapiens*

FIGURE 11.21
Cranial features of *Homo
erectus/ergaster, Homo
heidelbergensis,* and modern
Homo sapiens.

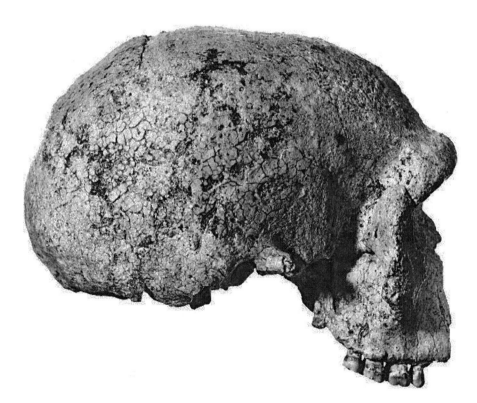

FIGURE 11.22
Skull of *Homo heidelbergensis*
from Steinheim, Germany.
Note the more rounded
shape and higher forehead
as compared with *H. erectus.*
At the same time, note the
retention of heavy brow
ridges.

FIGURE 11.23
The Kabwe (formerly called Broken Hill) specimen is one of the best-known examples of a premodern *Homo sapiens* from Africa. Note the extremely large brow ridges on this skull, which has a cranial capacity of 1,280 ml, quite close to the modern mean.

recognized), it involved the careful preparation of the rough stone core so that up to four or five flakes of a desired shape could be taken off. The flakes could then be used for cutting, scraping, or piercing. Figure 11.24 shows the steps involved and a replica of such a tool. There is also evidence of other materials used for manufacturing tools, such as some wooden spears from the 400,000-year-old site of Schöningen in Germany. The size and characteristics of these approximately 6-foot-long weapons suggest that they were meant to be thrown at fairly large animals (Thieme 1997).

Finally, an intriguing but still dim glimpse into the lives of the people of this era comes from another site in Atapuerca, Spain, near Gran Dolina (Kunzig 1997). Known as Sima de los Huesos ("pit of bones"), it is a shaft inside a cave, dated by electron spin resonance (see Chapter 9) at about 300,000 ya. It contains the bones of animals and the remains of at least thirty-three humans—many so well preserved that they include even fingertips and small inner ear bones. Most of the bones are from teenagers and young adults, both male and female. Although the bones show signs of chewing by a carnivore, it is unlikely that some predator would have selected just that age group, and the nonhuman remains in the pit are not those of prey animals but those of foxes and bears, which

Side Views   **Top Views**

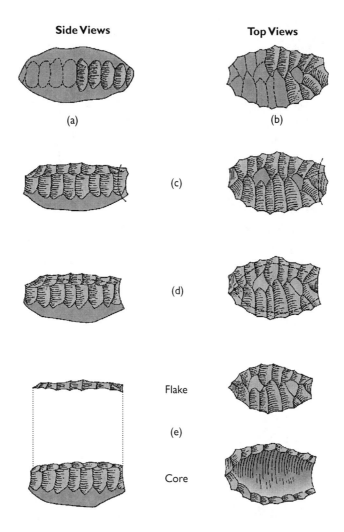

(a)   (b)

(c)   (c)

(d)   (d)

Flake

(e)

Core

FIGURE 11.24
The Levallois technique step-by-step: (*a*) produce a margin along the edge of the core, (*b*) shape the surface of the core, (*c*, *d*) prepare the surface to be struck (the "striking platform"), (*e*) remove the flake, and return to step (*b*) for additional flake removal. Shown below is a replica of a Levallois core and tool.

may have fallen in and chewed on the human bones before dying. Investigators think the bodies were thrown into the pit after death (one seems to have died from a massive infection), probably not as part of a formal funeral ritual (no artifacts were found) but more likely for simple disposal purposes. Perhaps they all died together in some catastrophe or at least over a short period of time. Many of the bones show signs of childhood malnourishment.

No doubt the peoples labeled *H. antecessor* and *H. heidelbergensis* had other mental, cultural, and perhaps physical adaptations to help them deal with the various and changeable environments they encountered as the Pleistocene continued. We certainly know this was true for one famous group of humans from Europe and the Near East. Some crania from Sima de los Huesos are said to show traits that might be ancestral to this next group, the Neandertals.

THE NEANDERTALS

The Neandertals—*Homo neanderthalensis* in the six-species model— were named after one of the first human fossils found and recognized as a human fossil, a skullcap from the Neander Valley in Germany recovered in 1856 (Figure 11.25). This was before Darwin wrote *Origin of Species*. (In German, *thal* means "valley" and is always pronounced *tal*. Recent

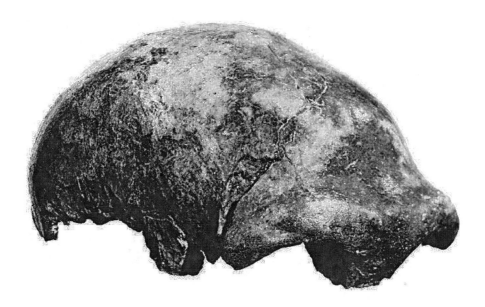

FIGURE 11.25
The original Neandertal skullcap from Germany. The cranial vault held a very large brain, but the brow ridges indicate an obvious difference from modern humans.

TABLE 11.3
Major Fossils of *Homo neanderthalensis*

Country	Locality	Fossils	Age (years)	Est. Brain Size (ml)
Belgium	Spy	2 skeletons	—	—
Croatia	Krapina	Cranial and postcranial fragments of >45 individuals	130,000	1,200–1,450
	Vindija	52 fossil fragments	28,000–42,000	—
France	Biache St. Vaast	2 crania	150,000–175,000	—
	Fontechévade	Cranial fragments of several individuals	100,000	1,500
	La Chaise	Cranium	126,000	—
	La Chapelle-aux-Saints	Skeleton	—	1,620
	La Ferrassie	8 skeletons	>38,000	1,680
	St. Césaire	Skeleton	36,000	—
Germany	Neandertal	Skullcap	—	>1,250
	Ehringsdorf	Cranial fragment	225,000	—
Gibraltar	Forbe's Quarry	Cranium	50,000	—
Iraq	Shanidar	9 partial skeletons	70,000	1,600
Israel	Amud	Skeleton	70,000	1,740
	Kebara Cave	Postcranial skeleton	60,000	—
	Tabun	Skeleton, mandible, postcranial fragments	100,000	1,270
Italy	Monte Circeo	Cranium	—	—
	Saccopastore	Cranium	—	—
			Mean	**1,478.89**

spelling drops the silent *h*, but some still use it. The formal species name retains its original spelling.) Table 11.3 and Figure 11.26 show the basic data for fossils of this species and the locations of these finds.

The Neandertals have had an interesting history in anthropology. At one time they were considered brutish, hunched-over, dim-witted members of a dead-end side branch of human evolution. At other times they have been thought of as just an ancient, slightly different-looking form of modern *Homo sapiens* (Figure 11.27). These are both exaggerations. We now recognize the sophistication of the Neandertals' intellectual and cultural achievements. They were certainly similar to modern humans physically but still different in significant ways. So debate at present centers on whether the similarities place them within our species or whether the

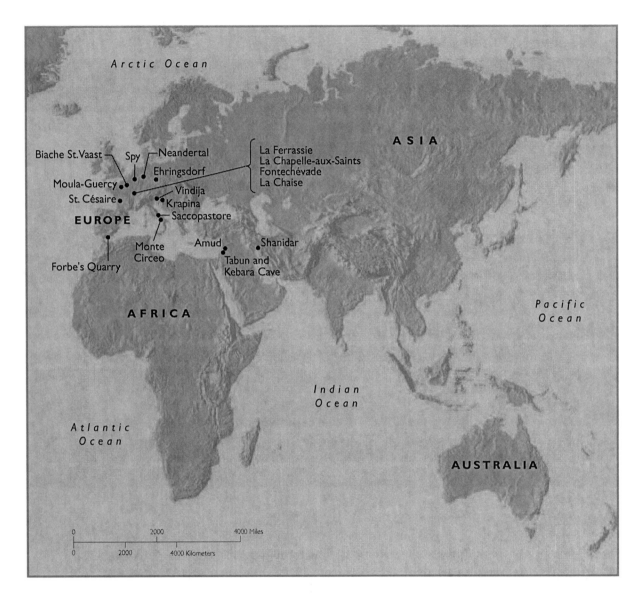

FIGURE 11.26
Map of major Neandertal sites.

differences make them a separate species (see Chapter 12). Figures 11.28 and 11.29 compare the skulls and skeletons of a Neandertal and a modern *Homo sapiens*.

Physical Features

The crania of the Neandertals are striking in appearance. They had, essentially, more pronounced versions of the cranial features of *Homo*

FIGURE 11.27

An old reconstruction from the Field Museum in Chicago (*left*) reinforces stereotypes of Neandertals as brutish, hairy, stooped-over distant cousins. In contrast, anthropologist Milford Wolpoff poses with a reconstructed Neandertal in modern dress to show that the differences between us and them were not that extreme.

heidelbergensis. Their cranial capacities ranged from about 1,200 ml to 1,740 ml, well within the modern range, but their foreheads were still sloped, the backs of their skulls broad, and the sides bulging. The brow ridges were still large, but smaller at the sides than in *H. erectus*, and they were filled with air spaces (called the *frontal sinuses*), unlike the solid ridges of *H. erectus*. The brow ridges of the Neandertals were also rounded over each eye, rather than forming a straight line, as in earlier archaics. The face was

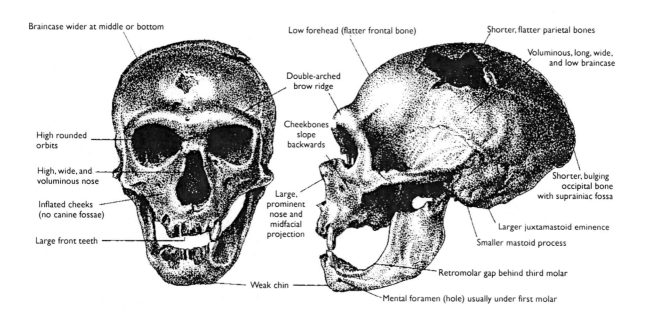

Braincase wider at middle or bottom

Low forehead (flatter frontal bone)

Shorter, flatter parietal bones

Voluminous, long, wide, and low braincase

Double-arched brow ridge

High rounded orbits

Cheekbones slope backwards

High, wide, and voluminous nose

Inflated cheeks (no canine fossae)

Large, prominent nose and midfacial projection

Large front teeth

Shorter, bulging occipital bone with suprainiac fossa

Larger juxtamastoid eminence

Smaller mastoid process

Weak chin

Retromolar gap behind third molar

Mental foramen (hole) usually under first molar

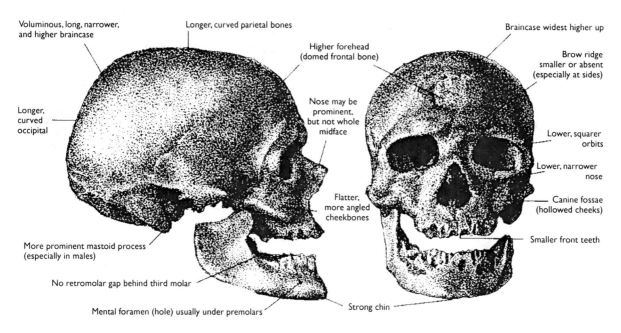

Voluminous, long, narrower, and higher braincase

Longer, curved parietal bones

Braincase widest higher up

Higher forehead (domed frontal bone)

Brow ridge smaller or absent (especially at sides)

Longer, curved occipital

Nose may be prominent, but not whole midface

Lower, squarer orbits

Lower, narrower nose

Canine fossae (hollowed cheeks)

Flatter, more angled cheekbones

More prominent mastoid process (especially in males)

Smaller front teeth

No retromolar gap behind third molar

Mental foramen (hole) usually under premolars

Strong chin

FIGURE 11.28
Cranial features of the La Chapelle-aux-Saints specimen of Neandertal (*above*) compared with modern *Homo sapiens*.

large and prognathous, with a broad nasal opening and wide-set eyes. The chin was receding.

From the neck down, there were striking features. The bones of the Neandertals, even the finger bones, were more robust and had heavier muscle markings than their modern counterparts. The Neandertals were

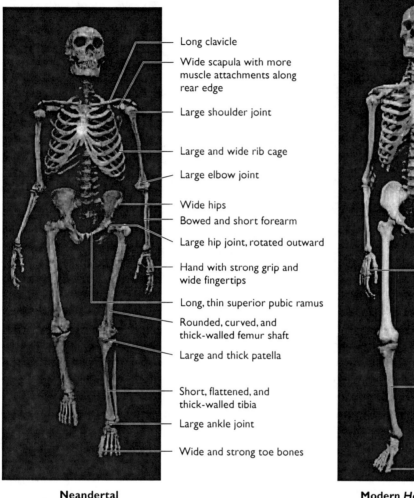

Long clavicle

Wide scapula with more muscle attachments along rear edge

Large shoulder joint

Large and wide rib cage

Large elbow joint

Wide hips

Bowed and short forearm

Large hip joint, rotated outward

Hand with strong grip and wide fingertips

Long, thin superior pubic ramus

Rounded, curved, and thick-walled femur shaft

Large and thick patella

Short, flattened, and thick-walled tibia

Large ankle joint

Wide and strong toe bones

Neandertal

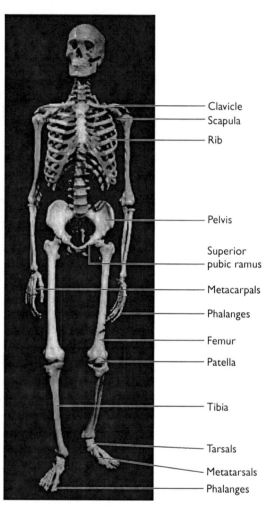

Clavicle
Scapula
Rib

Pelvis

Superior pubic ramus

Metacarpals

Phalanges

Femur

Patella

Tibia

Tarsals

Metatarsals

Phalanges

Modern *Homo sapiens*

FIGURE 11.29
Skeletal features of Neandertal compared with modern *Homo sapiens*.

stocky, muscular, powerful people. This is seen even in the bones of Neandertal children, so it is assumed to be a result of inheritance, not simply of a hard-working lifestyle.

Although very strong and stocky, the Neandertals were relatively short. Estimates put the average for males at 5 feet 6 inches and for females at 5 feet 3 inches. Their short stature was partially a result of relatively short lower legs. The lower arms were short as well. All these physical features hint at adaptations to a strenuous lifestyle and to cold climates. Shorter, heavier bodies with short limbs conserve heat better than narrow, long-limbed bodies (Holliday 1997; see also Chapter 13). As evidence, the limbs of the Neandertals from warmer Southwest Asia are relatively longer than the limbs of those living in ice-age Europe, who faced some of the extreme climates of the glacial advances.

Another possible adaptation to cold has been suggested by several investigators (see Menon 1997). In eight Neandertal skulls, they found triangular bony projections in the nasal cavity unlike anything seen in modern humans or in any other human ancestors. These projections are thought to have provided increased surface area for the nasal mucous membranes, which would have helped warm and moisten the cold, dry air of Europe during the Pleistocene glaciations. It has also been suggested that the large sinus cavities served a similar function. Moreover, it is thought that the larynx of the Neandertals was higher in the throat than in modern humans (see Figure 11.18), which would have prevented them from gulping in cold, dry air through the mouth.

Well-established Neandertal fossils date from 225,000 to 28,000 ya, and, as Table 11.3 and Figure 11.26 indicate, are found in Western Europe and the Middle East. There are some tools of the kind associated with Neandertals (see the next section) from Gibraltar that are younger than 28,000 years, but there are no human remains yet at that date (Finlayson et al. 2006).

There is also the possibility that the Neandertal range extended much farther east. A cave in Uzbekistan, dated at 70,000 ya, contained a partial skeleton of a child thought by some to be a Neandertal. Another cave in Siberia, dated at about 37,000 ya (Krause et al. 2007), revealed teeth and four postcranial bones, interpreted by DNA analysis (see Chapter 12) to be Neandertal. Both these extensions in time and space are still debated.

Culture

Among the well-established accomplishments of the Neandertals is an elaboration on the Levallois stone toolmaking technique. Called the **Mousterian technique,** after the site of Le Moustier in France, it involved the careful retouching of flakes taken off cores. These flakes were sharpened and shaped by precise additional flaking, on one side or both, to make specialized tools (Figure 11.30). One authority has identified no less than sixty-three tool types (Bordes 1972).

Several specific uses of Mousterian tools have been inferred from microscopic wear-pattern analysis on specimens from the Kebara Cave site in Israel. There are wear patterns that indicate animal butchering, woodworking, bone and antler carving, and working of animal hides (Shea 1989). There are also wear patterns like those produced by the friction of a wooden shaft against a stone spear point. The Neandertals may have been the first to **haft** a stone point.

Mousterian technique
A toolmaking tradition associated with the European Neandertals.

haft   To attach a wooden handle or shaft to a stone or bone point.

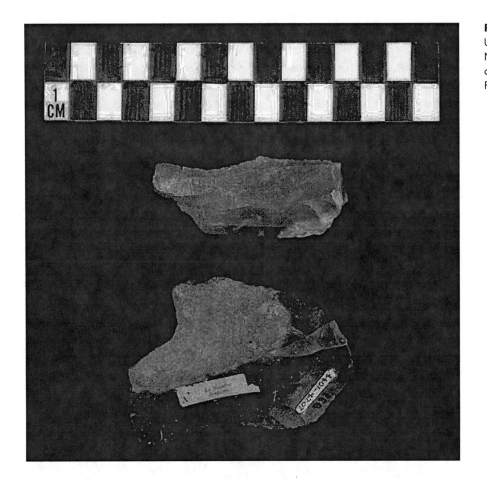

FIGURE 11.30
Unifacially retouched Mousterian flakes from the original site, Le Moustier, France.

Although there is still debate about whether the Neandertals were big-game hunters or mostly scavengers, there is no doubt that they were dependent on the animals that abounded during the Pleistocene—animals such as reindeer, deer, ibex (wild goat), aurochs (wild ox), horse, woolly rhinoceros, bison, bear, and elk. Bones of these creatures have been found in association with Neandertal remains.

While we now have earlier evidence of intentional human burials (discussed in the next section), the first and most famous evidence comes from the Neandertals. Although many of these "burials" have now been attributed to natural causes, at least thirty-six Neandertal sites show evidence of intentional interment of the dead, and in some graves there were remains of offerings—stone tools, animal bones, and, possibly, flowers (Figure 11.31).

Did the burials represent belief in an afterlife or reverence for the physical remains of the deceased, or were the people simply disposing of a corpse, as seems to have been the case much earlier at Sima de los Huesos? Were animal bones present in the graves as offerings, or did scavengers and predators drag them there, along with Neandertal bones, where they were subsequently buried by natural processes? Was the pollen found in a grave in Iraq from flowers placed in the grave, or was it brought in by burrowing rodents, carried in by water, or blown in by wind at the time of burial? The jury is still out on this issue. But we know the Neandertals did sometimes bury their dead, for whatever reason.

FIGURE 11.31
Neandertal burial from La Ferrassie, France. This body was interred in the flexed position, with the knees drawn up to the chest, perhaps to mimic sleep. (The basket belongs to the excavators.)

FIGURE 11.32
The famous "Old Man" of La Chapelle-aux-Saints, France. (See front view and labels in Figure 11.28.)

It has also been suggested that Neandertals were among the first to care for their elderly, ill, and injured. According to an early interpretation, the famous "Old Man" of La Chapelle-aux-Saints in France (Figure 11.32) was aged, lacked most of his teeth, and had a debilitating case of arthritis. That he survived for a time with these infirmities, according to the interpretation, indicates that he was cared for by his group.

Recent reexamination, though, shows that much of his tooth loss was after death and that his arthritis may not have been quite as debilitating as previously thought. Nor was he really old. He died when he was less than 40, probably rather quickly, as did the vast majority of Neandertals. Care of the elderly was probably not something they had to contend with very often.

On the other hand, there is a skeleton of a man from Shanidar, Iraq, that shows signs of injuries that may have resulted in blindness and the loss of one arm. He lived with this condition for some time and, therefore, was obviously cared for by his comrades.

But things may not have been completely peaceful among Neandertal populations. There is evidence of cannibalism from the Neandertal sites of Moula-Guercy in France (Defleur et al. 1999) and Krapina and Vindija in Croatia (White 2001). Fragmentary bones from at least six individuals show stone-tool cut marks in the same anatomical locations as those found on bones of wild goats and deer at the site. Some of the human long bones also show signs of having been smashed, in the way that would have allowed access to the rich bone marrow. Whether the inferred cannibalism was ritual (ingesting part of a group member at a funeral ceremony) or gustatory (eating the flesh as food) cannot be determined.

Finally, we have the question of the linguistic abilities of the Neandertals. Some investigators have reconstructed the vocal tract of Neandertals based on the structure of the underside of the cranium. They have concluded that because of the higher larynx noted before, Neandertals were not capable of making all the vowel sounds of modern humans. However, a recently found hyoid bone—a horseshoe-shaped bone in the throat—from the Neandertal site of Kebara in Israel appears fully modern. This would mean that the vocal tract of the Neandertals *was* like ours and that they *could* make all the sounds of which we are capable. The point, of course, is—as we said for *Homo erectus*—that the Neandertals had sufficiently complex things to talk *about*, and just how they did so is less important than the fact that they must have talked.

Archaic members of genus *Homo* were successful in adapting to different environments and, in the case of the Neandertals, harsh and demanding climates. They were clearly intelligent. We will no doubt find more fossils of archaics in new areas in the future. But the archaics have combinations of traits not found in humans alive today. To begin the story of so-called anatomically modern *Homo sapiens*, we once again return to Africa.

MODERN HUMANS

Beginning perhaps as early as 300,000 ya, fossils with what are considered to be near-modern or modern combinations of features appear, earliest in Africa and later in Southwest Asia, Europe, and East Asia. Later still, modern humans migrated to Australia, the islands of the Pacific, and North and South America. Under the six-species model, fossil forms with modern features are the only ones placed in *Homo sapiens*. There is no general agreement among proponents of this model about the exact species affiliation of some transitional forms—fossils with a mix of archaic and modern traits. Table 11.4 and Figure 11.33 give the basic information and locations of some of the more important fossils of early *H. sapiens*, as well as transitional forms.

We call these fossils "anatomically modern" because they lack some features characteristic of earlier hominins and possess features common in humans today. According to a widely accepted definition, the anatomically modern human does not exhibit a prognathous profile; the face is flat.

TABLE 11.4
Some Important Fossils of Early *Homo sapiens* (listed chronologically)

Country	Location	Age (years)
Kenya	Ileret	270,000–300,000 (trans.)*
South Africa	Florisbad	100,000–200,000 (trans.)
Ethiopia	Omo	195,000 (trans.)
Tanzania	Ngaloba	120,000 (trans.)
Morocco	Jebel Irhoud	100,000 (trans.)
Ethiopia	Herto	154,000–160,000
South Africa	Klasies River Mouth	84,000–120,000
	Langebaan Lagoon (footprints)	117,000
	Border Cave	62,000–115,000
	Hofmeyr	36,000
Israel	Qafzeh	92,000–120,000
	Skhul	81,000–101,000
Germany	Stetten	36,000
France	Cro-Magnon	<30,000
	Abri Pataud	>27,000
China	Zhoukoudian	10,000–18,000
Australia	Lake Mungo	40,000
United States	Midland, Texas	11,600

*The abbreviation *trans.* indicates those fossils that are considered transitional between archaic and modern *Homo.*

Further, there are no heavy brow ridges. The skull is globular rather than elongated, and the forehead is more nearly vertical. The face is smaller and narrower, and there is a protruding chin. The postcranial skeleton is less robust. Refer back to Figures 11.28 and 11.29, and then look in the mirror.

Note in Table 11.4 that the earliest fossils are all from eastern and southern Africa and that they are considered, at least by some authorities, as transitional between archaic and modern *Homo*. There is also a transitional form from Morocco (Figure 11.34). The implication is that modern humans—whether a new species or just the modern form of an existing species—arose in Africa. The earliest transitional forms are from Kenya, dated by several methods to 300,000 ya (Braüer et al. 1997).

By around 160,000 ya, we begin to find fossils that represent humans of fully modern appearance relative to their geographic area. The earliest of these are recent finds from Ethiopia (Clark et al. 2003; White et al. 2003). Three partial skulls, one fairly complete (Figure 11.35), show very modern features, including a large cranial capacity of up to 1,450 ml. They are

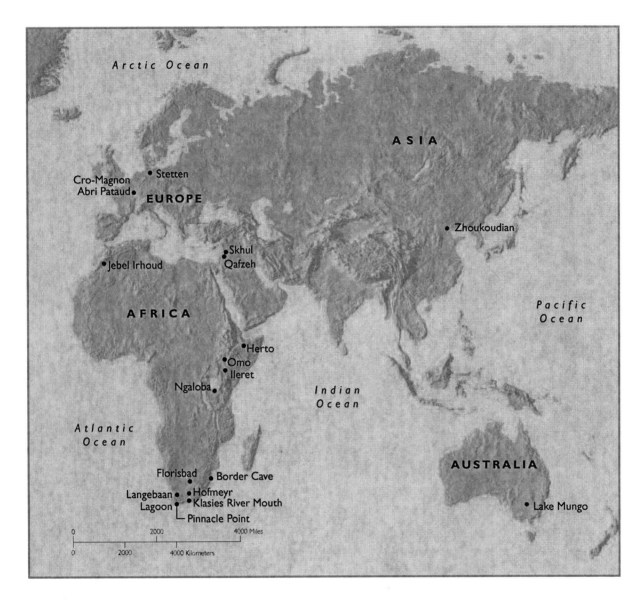

FIGURE 11.33

Map of major early *Homo sapiens* sites in Africa, Asia, Australia, and Europe noted in table or text.

thought to constitute the "oldest definite record of what we currently think of as modern *Homo sapiens*" (Stringer 2003). These remains are associated with a mix of primitive and more sophisticated stone tools, and the skulls show some signs of postmortem manipulation, possibly for ritual purposes.

Slightly more recent fossils are from South Africa and Israel (Figure 11.36). At the South African site of Langebaan Lagoon, a small human, possibly a female, left her footprints in rock claimed to be dated 117,000 ya—a moment frozen in time reminiscent of the Laetoli footprints from Tanzania

FIGURE 11.34
Cranium from Jebel Irhoud, Morocco. This skull, dated at about 100,000 ya, is considered by some to be transitional between archaic and modern *Homo*. The braincase is low, the face is relatively large, and it has distinct brow ridges. Otherwise, its features are modern.

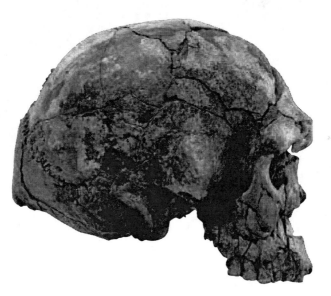

FIGURE 11.35
The most complete early *Homo sapiens* skull from Herto, Ethiopia, dated at 160,000 ya. The wide upper face, rounded forehead, divided brow ridge, flat midface, and large cranial capacity are all modern traits.

(see Chapter 10). As we move farther away from Africa and Southwest Asia, the dates for the early appearance of modern *H. sapiens* get more recent, a further indication that Africa is the birthplace of modern humans.

With modern anatomy came further advances in technology and expressions of modern behavior patterns. From the Pinnacle Point site, on the coast of South Africa and dated at 165,000 ya, we find evidence of shellfish used for food, of hematite used possibly as a pigment (with some of the pieces incised as decoration or maybe even a "notational system"), and of miniature stone tools called "bladelets" (Marean et al. 2007). A little later, from 120,000 ya at Klasies River Mouth, also on the South African coast, come long, bifacially worked spear points made from stone

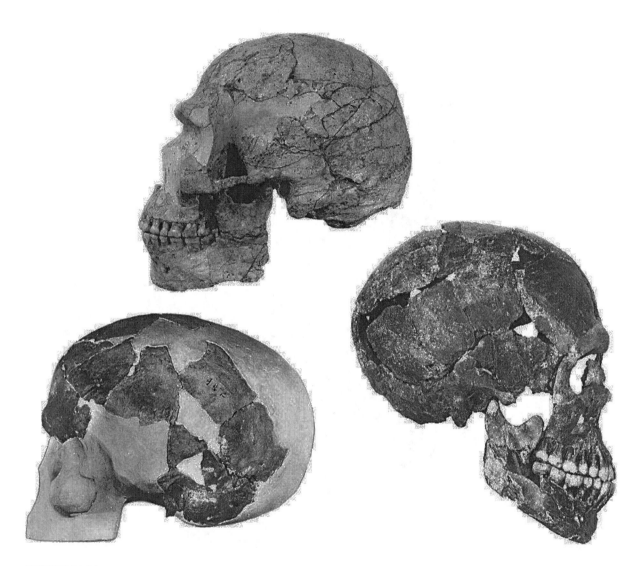

FIGURE 11.36

Examples of early modern *Homo sapiens* from (*counterclockwise from top*) Skhul, Israel; Border Cave, South Africa; and Qafzeh, Israel. Note the higher foreheads, protruding chins, and flatter faces compared with archaic *Homo*. Despite the rather prominent brow ridges in the Skhul specimen, it is still considered fully modern due to its other features.

blades. These were flaked from cores by the *punch technique* (Figure 11.37). Here a pointed punch, usually made from an antler, is placed on the core and then struck with a stone hammer. This method directs the force of the blow more precisely so that longer, narrower, thinner flakes of predictable shape may be taken off. The same technique shows up later in Europe.

The Klasies River site also provides evidence that the people there may have hunted adults of such large animals as cape buffalo and eland (a large antelope); both these animals can weigh up to a ton. The site contains a spear point lodged in a buffalo vertebra. Certainly these people also scavenged and may have hunted only weak or old individuals of these dangerous species. But there is good evidence of at least limited

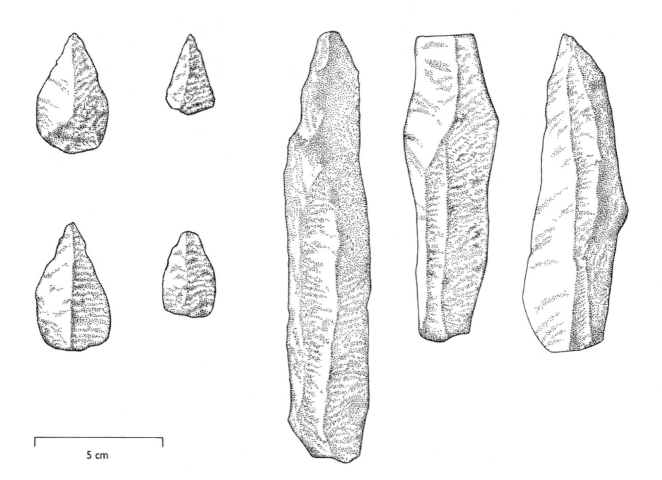

FIGURE 11.37
Blade tools from Klasies River Mouth, South Africa.

big-game hunting. That behavior, it seems, can be associated with the appearance of anatomically modern humans.

Although the Neandertal burials are perhaps the most famous examples of early human symbolic behavior, it is at two of the early *Homo sapiens* sites that we find the earliest examples. At Qafzeh and Skhul, there are graves, dated at between 120,000 and 80,000 ya, with bodies and grave goods carefully laid out. In one grave at Qafzeh, a child was buried with a deer antler. Another grave at the same site contained the body of a young woman with that of an infant, possibly hers, at her feet. At Skhul, a skeleton was found holding the jawbone of a wild boar.

By the time the Neandertals apparently disappeared, about 30,000 ya, modern *H. sapiens* had spread all over the Old World, even as far as Australia, and we enter a cultural period called the Upper Paleolithic, known first through finds in Europe. This period is marked by several important cultural innovations. Blades struck off cores become so precisely

FIGURE 11.38
Some typical Upper Paleolithic tools and examples of blades so finely made and thin they were probably used ritually.

FIGURE 11.39
Upper Paleolithic artifacts. Among the artifacts shown here are a shaft straightener with carved animals (*top*), a harpoon carved from antler (*upper left*), and an example of the famous Venus figurines (*lower right*) that may have served as fertility symbols.

and beautifully made as to be virtual works of art—in fact, some blades are so thin and delicate we think they may have been just that (Figure 11.38).

Tools in the Upper Paleolithic were also made from bone, antler, and ivory. Some are practical, such as harpoons, spear points, and shaft straighteners. Some have symbolic significance. Even some of the utilitarian items are decorated (Figure 11.39). Indeed, art is seen in the Upper Paleolithic in some of its most striking and beautiful forms. Over a hundred cave sites, mostly in France and Spain, have yielded paintings as aesthetically pleasing as anything produced today (Figure 11.40). There are also carvings in stone, bone, antler, and ivory, among the most famous of which are the

FIGURE 11.40
One of many beautiful paintings from the cave of Lascaux in southern France, this mural depicts an aurochs (an ancient ox) and several horses. There is an antlered animal, probably a deer, in the lower right. Notice that the left front leg of the red horse is separated from the body, adding a three-dimensional appearance. This photograph is really from Lascaux II, a replica near the actual cave, created because of damage to the original from bacteria and carbon dioxide given off by too many visitors. The walls of the replica cave are reproduced to within 5 mm of the contours of the original cave, and many of the pigments in the paintings are the same as those used by the original artists perhaps 17,000 ya.

Contemporary Reflections

Who Are the "Hobbits" from Indonesia?

In October 2004 an astonishing find was announced (Brown et al. 2004). A partial human skeleton, dated to 18,000 ya, was discovered on the Indonesian island of Flores. What makes this find remarkable is that the skeleton is of an adult female who stood a mere 106 cm tall (about 3 feet 5 inches) and had an estimated brain size of 380 ml, about the stature and cranial capacity of *Australopithecus afarensis*. And yet the physical features seem fairly clearly to assign the specimen to genus *Homo*, with particular similarities to *Homo erectus*. The discoverers gave the specimen the status of a new species, *Homo floresiensis* (Figure 11.41).

Since this initial discovery (Morwood et al. 2005), more specimens have been announced—including arm, wrist, and foot bones of the original skeleton, a mandible from a second individual, and assorted other bones—from an estimated nine individuals in all. Dates range from 74,000 (and possibly 95,000) to 12,000 ya.

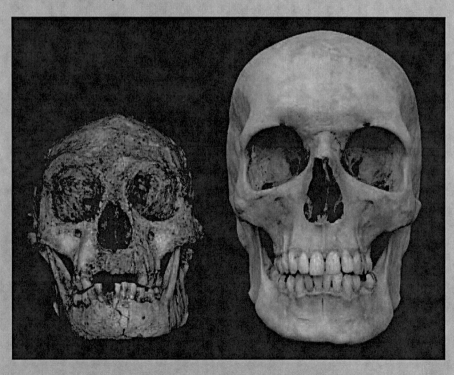

FIGURE 11.41
The skull of *Homo floresiensis* (*left*) compared to a modern human skull.

Even for those who propose multiple species of our genus over the last 2 million years, this is an amazing find, because as far as we know there have been no humans other than us—fully modern *Homo sapiens*—on earth for at least 27,000 years. And for those of us who feel that only one species of *Homo* has existed, the implications of this find and its interpretation are obvious.

What are we to make of these specimens, referred to in the popular press as Hobbits (a reference to the small characters in J. R. R. Tolkien's *Lord of the Rings*)? Given their body and brain size, could they be australopithecines, indicating that there were populations of this genus outside of Africa? Probably not. Although some authorities say the lack of a chin, features of the pelvis, and body proportions are australopithecine in nature (Balter 2004; Lieberman 2005), they have phenotypic characteristics that place them clearly in genus *Homo*. Moreover, the fossils were found in association with stone tools and evidence of hunting and possibly fire and cooking. None of these cultural features are associated with *Australopithecus*. And the game hunted was not small; it included pygmy elephants and Komodo dragons (the world's largest existing lizard). Certainly a high level of cooperation and communication would have been necessary to accomplish such hunting. Moreover, no fossils of australopithecines have been found outside of Africa.

Authorities are divided over the interpretation of these fossils, or, more accurately, over the original fossil, known as LB1, since it provides the vast majority of the data. Some contend it was an individual with a pathology, perhaps microcephaly, a genetic form of dwarfism (Eckhardt 2008). Other experts support the claim that LB1 represents a normal human of diminutive size but of a different species (Falk et al. 2008). The recently reported wrist bones are said to be "primitive" and thus indicative of a new species by some (Tocheri et al. 2007), while others disagree (Eckhardt 2008). Still others have concluded that because the feet are relatively long and not arched, as in modern humans, the Flores population represents a new species (Jungers 2008). The discussions over this issue at professional meetings are at least lively and can get quite heated. (For a summary of the arguments at a recent meeting, see Culotta 2008.)

So, there was either one, or several, individuals on Flores during the time range indicated that suffered from some anomaly, or there was a whole population of diminutive humans. If the latter, there are two questions: First, were they a different species? We can't, of course, experiment to see if they could interbreed with other human populations, so that will always remain an open question. Second, where did they come from? Did they descend from *Homo erectus* and respond to a phenomenon of dwarfing common to island species with restricted room and resources? Or did a hominin predating *H. erectus* get to Flores and evolve a more complex brain with no increase in size? Virtual images of the brain of LB1 indicate that it is not a miniaturized modern brain but more resembles *Paranthropus* in size and *H. erectus* in shape (Falk et al. 2005).

The debate continues and, of course, requires more data—specifically, more fossils. But one thing is certain: genus *Homo* is a lot more variable than we once imagined. And the story continues to unfold: on the island of Palau, Micronesia, researchers have found fossils of a possible small-bodied population with brains within the modern human range (Berger et al. 2008). Stay tuned.

so-called Venus figurines, often thought to be fertility symbols (see Figure 11.39, lower right). Some Venus figurines even depict clothing styles such as woven caps (Wong 2000a). An ivory "lion man" figurine from Germany, dated at 30,000 ya, may be the oldest figurative art in the world. There is also an engraved antler from France dated at about 32,000 ya that may have been a calendar based on phases of the moon.

There is some evidence of even older art from northern Australia. A hematite "crayon"—used to produce red ocher, a pigment—has been dated at almost 60,000 ya at the site of Malakunanja II, and painted ocher figures and carved holes at a rock shelter site called Jinmium may date to between 176,000 and 116,000 ya. Dating of these sites remains debatable (Gibbons 1997a).

As the Upper Paleolithic continued, big-game hunting became a way of life, especially for people living in glacial climates with limited plant resources. People no longer relied on caves or rock shelters for places of habitation but began manufacturing shelters. At Mal'ta, for example, an 18,000-year-old site in south-central Russia, scientists found the remains of a hut built on a wood frame supported by woolly mammoth bones and reindeer antlers and covered with animal hides.

Around 30,000 ya, and probably earlier, humans moved into North America, coming across a land bridge between Siberia and Alaska that was exposed when the sea level dropped during glacial periods. They soon moved throughout the continent and into South America. Modern *Homo sapiens* had populated every landmass on the planet except Antarctica.

SUMMARY

The record of the latest 2.5 million years of hominin evolution is complex. The fossils from the first 99 percent of this period are scarce, often fragmentary, scattered geographically, physically variable, and, in some cases, questionably dated. Not surprisingly, the interpretations of these fossils vary as greatly as do the fossils themselves. Our survey uses as a starting point an elaborate model for classifying and naming these fossils—the recognition of six species within genus *Homo* after the early *Homo* stage. I do not necessarily endorse this model but begin with it for the purpose of clearly organizing our discussion of a fairly complex topic.

The earliest species, *H. ergaster*, is found only in Kenya, but a possible branch of this group, *H. erectus*, spread through the rest of Africa and into Asia and possibly southern Europe. These two species are characterized by virtually modern postcranial skeletons, brain sizes close to and even overlapping the modern human range, and the invention of more sophisticated stone tools and other cultural innovations, including the use of fire. In Java, *H. erectus* may have persisted until as recently as 27,000 ya.

A geographically and chronologically scattered species, *Homo heidelbergensis*, appears next. The earliest examples of this group, from Spain, are placed by some authorities into a new species, *H. antecessor*. Located from England to South Africa to China, *H. heidelbergensis* displays brain sizes within the modern human range and at the modern human average, though their crania retain primitive features, giving them the label "archaic." They are known, starting about 200,000 ya, for the invention of the Levallois stone toolmaking technique—a sophisticated way of "mass producing" flake tools. They may have done some hunting as well.

The most famous of the "archaic" humans are the Neandertals, a separate species, *Homo neanderthalensis*, according to many. Living in Europe and Southwest Asia from 225,000 to 28,000 ya, this group exhibits traits that distinguish it from both *H. heidelbergensis* and later *H. sapiens*. These traits include a large, prognathous face, a ruggedly built skull, and a robust, muscular body—possibly adaptations to the cold glacial conditions many of their populations encountered. Neandertals are known for their retouched flake tools, which may have been used to carve bone and work wood, and for abstract cultural achievements such as burial of the dead and care of the elderly and infirm. They may also have been the first to haft stone points on wooden shafts.

Fossils transitional between archaic and modern *Homo* appear in Africa perhaps as early as 300,000 ya, and the first fully modern *Homo sapiens* are found in Africa and Southwest Asia beginning around 160,000 ya. From there, modern-appearing humans spread throughout the Old World and eventually to the islands of the Pacific and to the Americas. Archaic peoples—or archaic traits—disappear. During this time, big-game hunting develops, tool technology advances, sophisticated shelters are built, and humans create art.

This leads us to the following questions, which we will discuss in the next chapter: Just how many species of genus *Homo* are we actually dealing with? And, how are all these groups related evolutionarily?

QUESTIONS FOR FURTHER THOUGHT

1. We will discuss the debate over the evolution of genus *Homo* in greater detail in the next chapter. For now, however, does it matter to *you* how many species of our genus have existed? Why or why not? Why do you think it matters so much to professional scientists?

2. The issue of whether groups of organisms are separate species within one genus or are variable populations within a single species has ramifications for living things other than hominins. One related topic is the Endangered Species Act. Why might this issue matter with regard to the implementation of that legislation?

3. As a lead-in to the discussion in the next chapter, consider what the arguments might be in favor of lumping the Neandertals into *Homo sapiens*. What arguments might be made for splitting them into a separate species?

4. A little bit of science-fiction thinking: Suppose it was discovered that a population of *Homo floresiensis* still existed. What ethical questions would this bring up? How would your answer differ if they were a separate species or if they were members of *Homo sapiens* and thus capable of interbreeding with us?

KEY TERMS

Oldowan	glaciers	postorbital
core tools	tundra	constriction
flake tools	Acheulian technique	Levallois technique
sagittal keel	hand axe	Mousterian technique
torus	bifacial	haft
Pleistocene	endocasts	

SUGGESTED READINGS

For more on the Dmanisi finds, see a typically well-illustrated article in the August 2002 *National Geographic*: "New Find." See also "The Pathfinders," by Josh Fischman, in the April 2005 *National Geographic*. For more on the Atapuerca finds from Spain, see the also well-illustrated book *The First Europeans: Treasures from the Hills of Atapuerca*, published by Junta de Castilla y León.

An interesting article linking an increase in human brain size with dietary change is "Food for Thought," by William R. Leonard, in the December 2002 *Scientific American*. And for more on ancient cannibalism, see Tim D. White's "Once We Were Cannibals" in the August 2001 *Scientific American*.

For summaries of human evolution, see *The Last Neanderthal*, by Ian Tattersall, and *Extinct Humans*, by Ian Tattersall and Jeffrey Schwarz. Be aware that these authors are splitters, who advocate a maximum number of separate species for *Homo* and the other hominin genera. The books, however, are accurate and beautifully illustrated. For a more technical treatment, see *Human Evolution: Trails from the Past*, by Camilo J. Cela-Conde and Francisco J. Ayala.

For the fascinating story of Eugene Dubois and the discovery of "Java Man," see Pat Shipman's *The Man Who Found the Missing Link: Eugene Dubois and His Lifelong Quest to Prove Darwin Right*. The story of the missing "Peking Man" fossils is the topic of *The Search for Peking Man*, by C. Janus. A discussion of the African *H. erectus* sites is in *Lucy's Child: The Discovery of a Human Ancestor*, by Donald Johanson and James Shreeve. A discussion on early hominin diet is in "Diet and Food Preparation: Rethinking Early Hominid Behavior," by S. Ragir, in *Evolutionary Anthropology*.

An account of human evolution, with some interesting and debatable philosophical ideas, is *The Chosen Species: The Long March of Human Evolution*, by Juan Luis Arsuaga and Ignacio Martínez, both members of the Atapuerca team.

An interesting history of paleoanthropology is *Debating Humankind's Place in Nature, 1860–2000: The Nature of Paleoanthropology*, by Richard G. Delisle.

An interesting article on early art is "First Impressions," by Judith Thurman, in the 23 June 2008 *New Yorker*.

For more on the "Hobbits," see "The Littlest Human," by Kate Wong, in the February 2005 *Scientific American*, and "World of the Little People," by Mike Morwood et al., in the April 2005 *National Geographic*. For a recent summary of discussions about the identity of the "Hobbits" of Flores Island, see "When Hobbits (Slowly) Walked the Earth," by Elizabeth Culotta, in the 25 April 2008 *Science*.

12
CHAPTER

The Debate over Modern Human Origins

> *We carry within us the wonders we seek without us; There is all Africa and her prodigies in us.*
> *—Sir Thomas Browne*

One of the most contentious issues in bioanthropology concerns the origin of modern *Homo sapiens:* Are we a new and recent species, distinct from the other species of genus *Homo,* or are we the latest manifestation of an old species, with perhaps all members of genus *Homo* included?

An astounding number of articles and books advocate one point of view or another, summarize and evaluate the various hypotheses, or analyze and interpret the debate itself. And this debate is far from peaceful. Arguments get heated at times, with some accusing others of poor scholarship or hidden agendas. Comments can get downright nasty. Even impartial and dispassionate accounts can be detailed and confusing.

I will try in this chapter to reduce the competing models down to their essential elements in a way that relates them directly to the material we have covered so far. I hope that this approach will further illuminate the themes and data we have been examining.

As confusing as the issue might be, it is a good example of science in action, as both a scholarly and a very human endeavor. Even summarizing the debate—with its different interpretations, different theoretical points of view, related agendas, and sometimes rancorous rhetoric—is to catch scientific progress "in the act." Moreover, if you follow all the arguments presented in the discussion of this debate, you will, in fact, have grasped pretty much everything we've talked about so far. We will address the following questions in this chapter:

What have been the major competing models regarding the origin of modern *Homo sapiens*?

What evidence has been offered—from the fossil record, from genetics, and from evolutionary theory—for and against each model?

Is there an alternative model that resolves the debate?

THE MODELS

The separate but related questions that are addressed by the various models are these: First, did modern *Homo sapiens* evolve gradually and over a wide geographic area from a single archaic species that originated in Africa in the distant past and then spread across the Old World? Or, did modern *Homo sapiens* split from an existing archaic species in Africa more recently and then spread out?

Second, if the latter, did modern humans *replace* archaic populations in the other areas, or did we *interbreed* with them? This question, put another way, asks how the various populations of genus *Homo* are related: Was there one species, six, or some other number? You should recognize this as an extension of the lumper-splitter distinction introduced in Chapter 11.

We can name and discuss three general models in this debate. The single-species model is formally known as the **Multiregional Evolution (MRE) model**. The name implies that the evolution of modern *H. sapiens* took place across the Old World as existing populations of genus *Homo* exchanged genes. The model that recognizes *H. sapiens* as the most recent and only surviving species of genus *Homo* is called the **African Replacement (AR) model**. Here, the name implies that our new species dispersed over the Old World and replaced archaic species. A third model, which we will discuss later, is the **Primary African Origin (PAO) model** (Relethford 2008). There are some slightly different versions of this model, but they all combine an African origin for modern humans, with gene flow and thus interbreeding taking place between them and at least some archaic *Homo* populations that already had dispersed over the Old World.

Remember, all the evidence points to humans in general as having an African origin. So, the question is *when* our species arose. In terms of the two major models, was it around 200,000 years ago, or was it 2 million years ago? A tenfold difference is a big disagreement!

Multiregional Evolution (MRE) model   The hypothesis that *Homo sapiens* is about 2 million years old and that modern human traits evolved in geographically diverse locations and then spread through the species.

African Replacement (AR) model   The hypothesis that *Homo sapiens* evolved recently as a separate species in Africa and then spread to replace more archaic populations.

Primary African Origin (PAO) model   The hypothesis that modern *Homo sapiens* evolved first in Africa but then interbred with other populations as they dispersed over the Old World.

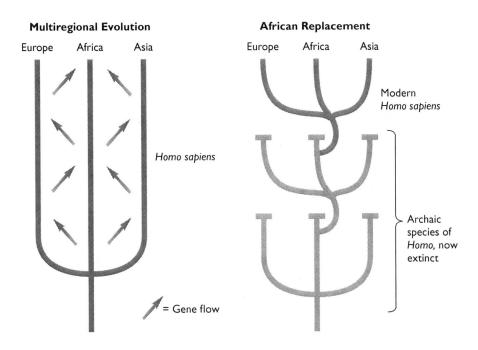

FIGURE 12.1
Generalized models for the origin of *Homo sapiens*.

Multiregional Evolution

Europe   Africa   Asia

Homo sapiens

= Gene flow

African Replacement

Europe   Africa   Asia

Modern
Homo sapiens

Archaic
species of
Homo, now
extinct

To summarize:

	AR	MRE	PAO
Modern *H. sapiens:*			
Originated in Africa	√		√
Evolved as it spread across the Old World		√	
Replaced archaic *Homo* species	√		
Interbred with archaic species		√	√

Figure 12.1 shows generalized diagrams of the first two models. Now, let's look at these models—the extremes—in detail. We'll examine the evidence for and against each and then look at the PAO model, which I believe nicely synthesizes the data into one unifying model.

The African Replacement (AR) Model

Major proponents of the African Replacement model are Christopher Stringer of the Natural History Museum in London (Stringer and McKie 1996) and Ian Tattersall of the American Museum of Natural History in New York (Tattersall 2001; Tattersall and Schwarz 2000). Although various supporters of this model recognize different numbers of species within genus *Homo*, they all share the view that modern *Homo sapiens* is a separate species that branched from a preexisting archaic *Homo* species in Africa around 200,000 to 150,000 ya. This new species then spread over the Old World, replacing archaic populations when they came in contact, presumably because *H. sapiens* was a better-adapted species.

If this model is correct, we must be able to find distinctions between modern humans and premodern (or archaic) humans that clearly distinguish us *as separate species*. (Keep in mind the definition we're using in this book of the term species: *a reproductively isolated biological unit, incapable of producing fertile offspring with another such unit*.) There must be an anatomical definition of modernity; in other words, there must be important traits that all *Homo sapiens* share that are not found in premoderns, as well as traits found in premoderns that are lacking in modern humans. We would also expect to find genetic distinctions that would indicate separate species.

If we can anatomically define and distinguish premodern from modern humans, then we can deduce that fossils transitional between premodern and modern humans should occur only in the single region in which moderns evolved, that is, Africa. Elsewhere, there should be evidence of premoderns and moderns coexisting in the same regions, once moderns spread out from their initial source area. Eventually, the premodern human forms would have become extinct, unable to compete with their anatomically modern cousins. Figure 12.2 shows one way this model interprets the relationships among the six species of *Homo* described in Chapter 11.

Multiregional Evolution (MRE) Model

The names most often associated with the Multiregional Evolution model are Milford Wolpoff and Rachel Caspari of the University of Michigan (Wolpoff and Caspari 1997). This model—a bit more complicated than the AR model—also claims that *Homo sapiens* arose in Africa, but it pushes back the date of *H. sapiens*'s appearance to as much as 2 mya. Members of this new species evolved and spread throughout the Old World, evolving genetic and phenotypic regional differences in response to the wide variety of environmental circumstances they encountered and to the complex population movements, isolations, mergings, and fissionings that must have taken place. Species mobility resulted in sufficient gene flow to maintain a single species, since no population was isolated long enough or to a great enough degree for speciation to occur. (Refer to Chapter 5 to review the requirements for speciation.) As successful advantageous adaptive features

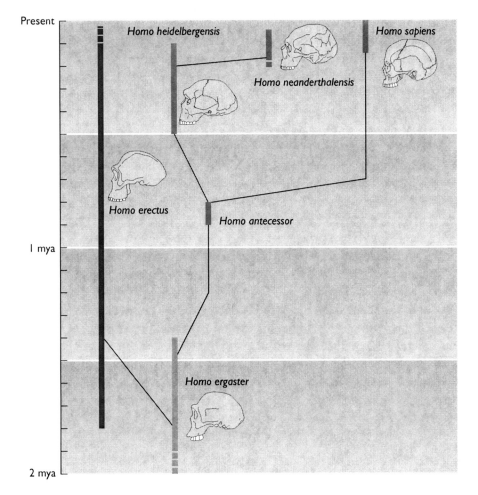

FIGURE 12.2
One possible set of relationships for the six proposed species of *Homo*, according to the AR model. The data are the same as in Figure 11.1.

Present — *Homo heidelbergensis* — *Homo neanderthalensis* — *Homo sapiens*

Homo erectus

Homo antecessor

1 mya

Homo ergaster

2 mya

arose, they were dispersed across the species through gene flow. Ideas and technologies spread and were exchanged as well (Wolpoff et al. 2001). Physical features we associate with modern humans eventually appeared everywhere but may have been manifested in different ways in different populations and in different environments. Thus, we are today and have always been a variable species—but a *single species*.

It is important to understand that this does *not* mean that *every* population survived to contribute genes to modern humans. Certainly, individual isolated populations could have become extinct with few or none of their genes passed down. Nor does this model deny the distinctive sets of traits that characterize some of the premodern (archaic) populations such as the Neandertals. The MRE model simply says that these populations were not separate species, that *Homo sapiens* did not arise in the recent past, and, thus, that it did not spread and become dominant by *replacing* other species of *Homo*.

If the MRE model is correct, we should find no clear evidence that modern *H. sapiens* is a separate species from any of the premodern groups. In other words, there should be no biologically meaningful definition of "modern"—no set of traits that is found among all populations classified as modern that is lacking among all premodern populations.

However, populations with transitional sets of traits should be found in many locations. Ideally, there should be some evidence of interbreeding in the form of a mix of traits in fossils from those areas where groups co-existed. Finally, there should be *regional continuity* of traits—features characteristic of geographic areas that appear not only in modern populations but premodern ones as well.

One conclusion of this model is that if premodern groups are in fact members of our species, then the rules of taxonomy dictate that the earliest name used for any of them must be applied to them all. Thus, if all six or more species of *Homo* are indeed the same species, they would all be *Homo sapiens*, the name first used by Linnaeus in 1758 (see Chapters 7 and 14). Figure 12.3 shows how the MRE model views the interrelationships among the various regional fossil populations discussed in Chapter 11.

The Key Requirements of Each Model

As we evaluate the evidence in this debate, here are the main points to keep in mind about each model:

AR

- Requires an anatomical definition of modernity that clearly distinguishes modern humans from premodern species
- Requires a degree of genetic distinctions that indicates modern humans are a separate species
- Requires that transitional forms appear only in the single region in which modern humans evolved

MRE

- Requires that there be no biologically meaningful definition of modernity—that is, no set of "modern" traits that is lacking among all premodern populations

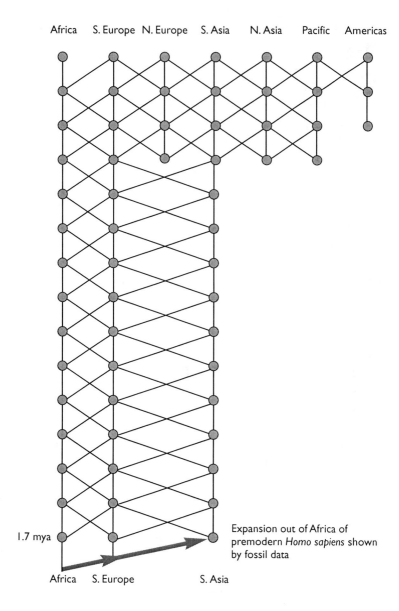

Africa   S. Europe   N. Europe   S. Asia   N. Asia   Pacific   Americas

FIGURE 12.3
Diagram of the MRE model. The red arrow represents the initial expansion out of Africa nearly 2 mya. Vertical lines represent direct regional descent. Diagonal lines represent gene flow among regional populations.
(Adapted from Templeton 2002:48)

1.7 mya

Expansion out of Africa of premodern *Homo sapiens* shown by fossil data

Africa   S. Europe   S. Asia

- Requires that populations with transitional sets of traits be found in many locations
- Requires a regional continuity of traits; that is, features characteristic of a given geographic area should appear in premodern and modern populations within that region

THE EVIDENCE

Clearly, the evidence for the past 2 million years of our evolution is limited. Fossils exist, but they are often fragmentary, and they are scattered across space and time. The same can be said for archaeological evidence of our ancestors' cultural activities. Genetic data are available, but only from fully modern populations living today—or at least in the recent past.

Thus, in reviewing the extensive literature on modern human origins, we find that different authorities have very different interpretations of the same data. Indeed, the same general data have been convincingly used to support both the MRE and AR models, but proponents differ in which specific pieces of data they emphasize. Following, then, is a general summary of the available evidence and interpretations by both the MRE and AR "camps." Keep in mind that to be relevant, *the evidence has to distinguish* between the two models or suggest an altogether different model.

The Fossil and Archaeological Records

Fossils   In using the multiple-species model for our discussion of genus *Homo* in Chapter 11, we have already presented the fossil evidence as interpreted by the African Replacement proponents. Look again at the tables and maps in that chapter.

As required by the AR model, forms considered transitional between archaic species (*H. heidelbergensis* and *H. neanderthalensis*) and *H. sapiens* are found only in Africa (see Table 11.4). Modern forms appear first in Africa and then show up at increasingly recent dates as one moves away from that continent. Archaics and moderns overlap in time in some areas. Note, for example, that the modern fossils from Skhul and Qafzeh in Israel actually predate the Neandertals in the same country and that the two groups shared the area for a time (see also Table 11.3).

In stark contrast, Wolpoff and Caspari assert that the variation seen within the fossil record of *Homo* does not warrant division into separate species. They claim, for example, that in broad perspective "just about every way *H. erectus* differs from its australopithecine ancestors also characterizes *H. sapiens*: virtually no features are unique to *H. erectus*" (1997:256). In other words, *H. sapiens* and *H. erectus* are the same species. They also contend that modern traits did not all arise in one location but in many and that they spread throughout the species through gene flow, to

FIGURE 12.4
Two Tiwi from Melville Island, northern Australia. Note their large, continuous brow ridges—a trait associated with archaic humans yet present here in fully modern *Homo sapiens*. (The man on the right is in mourning, which requires that he paint his body and not feed himself, so he is receiving water from a friend.)

be expressed differently in different geographic locations. As required by the MRE model, transitional forms are found in many locations.

Moreover, Wolpoff and Caspari feel that "it has proved impossible to provide an acceptable [physical] definition of modernity" in the first place (1997:313). Some features proposed to define modern humans *do not* include all recent or living peoples. For example, it has been suggested that the Neandertals' large, continuous brow ridges are a major diagnostic feature helping to distinguish them from modern humans. But some living indigenous people of Australia—fully modern biological humans in every sense of the word—also have large, continuous brow ridges (Figure 12.4). There is sufficient variation among modern humans, says Wolpoff, that modernity must be defined regionally, as no general definition includes all clearly modern humans and excludes all other proposed species.

The Neandertals are frequently used to establish a definition of modern. But to use the Neandertals in a comparison with modern populations is sort of "stacking the deck," since they are *more* different from moderns in some ways than are other archaics. Moreover, the Neandertals comprised small populations isolated by distance and ecology in an Old World backwater. Even if most of their populations, and thus their phenotypes, became extinct, that does not preclude their being members of our species, nor does it negate the MRE model. A physical definition of "modern" thus seems to be in the eye of the beholder, based on one's interpretation and choice of populations and characteristics.

Wolpoff and supporters (Wolpoff et al. 2001) also see continuity of individual traits in certain areas, especially Asia and Australia and between Neandertal and modern populations in Europe. In one study they compared anatomical features of skulls from both moderns and archaics from different parts of Europe, Africa, and Asia and found a series of similarities and differences that pointed to a mixed ancestry of the modern populations.

As further potential evidence of the MRE model, we have a 1998 find from Portugal of a 3½- to 5-year-old child who lived 24,500 ya (Duarte et al. 1999). The child's mandible displays a protruding chin and proportionately small front teeth, diagnostic of moderns. The postcranial bones, however, are robust, with proportionately short lower arms and legs, diagnostic of Neandertals. The investigators' interpretation is that the boy represents a hybrid, making those two groups, by definition, members of the same species. Not unexpectedly, of course, AR proponents reject this claim, suggesting that the child was simply a "chunky" anatomically modern human (Holden 1999).

So, in regard to this debate, the fossil record is ambiguous. It can clearly be interpreted to support either point of view, and there is wide disagreement between those points of view. Note that even AR proponents cannot agree on the exact number of premodern species of *Homo*. They only agree that *Homo sapiens* is a recent, separate species. The fossils that do exist are usually incomplete, not necessarily representative of the populations from which they came, and often of questionable age. Moreover, we don't know how much phenotypic traits tell us about actual genetic distinctions (Minugh-Purvis 1995). Finally, it is hard to translate physical features into species classification. As we saw in Chapters 4 and 5, some separate species look nearly identical, while other species can exhibit an amazing amount of phenotypic variation (see Figure 2.8).

Artifacts   Along with fossil evidence, archaeological data have also been cited in support of the two models. African Replacement supporters note the appearance of sophisticated toolmaking techniques and art (Henshilwood et al. 2002) earlier in Africa than elsewhere (see Figure 11.37 for an example). They also see evidence of the fairly rapid replacement in Europe of tools associated with Neandertals by those associated with modern *Homo sapiens*.

In contrast, MRE advocates claim that these early African tool forms are not all that different from the tools of Neandertals and that artifacts associated with modern fossils from Skhul and Qafzeh are virtually identical to those associated with nearby Neandertal finds. At Grotte XVI, in the French Dordogne Valley, investigators see a gradual change in cultural behavior over the course of many thousands of years, from

Neandertal to moderns, with a great degree of similarity in behavior between these two supposedly different groups. Based on analyses of tools and other archaeological evidence from these populations, researchers conclude that both moderns and Neandertals hunted, fished, smoked their catch to preserve it, and showed evidence of symbolic thinking (Wong 2000b, 2005). In other words, tool type is not necessarily diagnostic of species, and the variation, scattered nature, and questionable dating of some archaeological data present the same problems as does the paleontological record.

Neither the fossil nor archaeological evidence, then, helps us to distinguish between these models, nor do these data suggest another scenario.

Genetic Evidence

We mentioned genetic evidence in Chapter 9 regarding the relationship between humans and the nonhuman primates. Genetic data can also be used to compare living human populations and examine the question of modern human origins. Genetic lines of inquiry have usually been interpreted to support the African Replacement model, that is, a recent African source for modern humanity. As we will see, there are other possible interpretations.

There are three basic types of DNA that are used in this regard. **Nuclear DNA** is mostly noncoding and is therefore especially useful because it appears to be selectively neutral. Thus, mutations that accumulate in it are neither selected against, resulting in their disappearance, nor selected for, resulting in an increase in their frequency. Therefore, nuclear DNA may provide a more accurate record of the genetic history of two or more divergent lineages.

Mitochondria are the energy factories within the cells of plants and animals. They possess their own distinct DNA—**mitochondrial DNA (mtDNA)**—which, in complex interaction with the nuclear DNA, codes for the mitochondria's function of producing the biological fuel that energizes the cell. Most human cells contain hundreds to thousands of mitochondria. At some point in early cellular evolution, the ancestors of mitochondria were separate organisms. Through what may be the first example of **symbiosis,** they became functional elements within larger cells, maintaining their own genetic code. This code is particularly useful for some genetic studies because mtDNA accumulates mutations at a rate five to ten times faster than nuclear DNA, and there is evidence

nuclear DNA The genetic material in the nucleus of a cell.

mitochondrial DNA (mtDNA) The genetic material found in the cell's mitochondria rather than in the cell's nucleus.

symbiosis An adaptive relationship between two different species, often, but not necessarily, of mutual benefit.

that the mutation rate is fairly constant. In addition, the entire mtDNA genome is known; that is, all the base pairs have been identified, and there are large noncoding sequences. Finally, mtDNA is inherited only through the female line; although both human eggs and sperm contain mitochondria, the 50 to 100 mitochondria from the sperm disappear from the egg shortly after fertilization. Thus, one's mtDNA is not a combination of the mtDNA from two parents, as is nuclear DNA.

Y-chromosome DNA is inherited only from one's father and is passed on only by males. Thus Y-chromosome analysis, as with mtDNA, allows us to trace inheritance through one parental line with little or no influence from the other.

DNA from Living Humans   In general, living human beings exhibit very little genetic variation—in fact, less than that seen within ape species (Stringer and Andrews 1988:1264). Indeed, some chimpanzee DNA exhibits ten times the amount of variation as does human DNA (Wilson and Cann 1992:71; see Chapter 14 for more detail). This suggests a relatively recent, common source for all living humans, which is consistent with the AR hypothesis. In other words, if there is little genetic diversity, not much time has elapsed since the species first evolved.

On the other hand, the Multiregional Evolution model can also account for this genetic homogeneity. For a mobile species with a network of constant genetic exchange among populations, regional genetic differences would become increasingly lessened as the species increased its population and improved its ability to move around. In such a species, even a very old one, we would also expect relatively little *modern* genetic variation. Thus, our species' genetic homogeneity does not help us distinguish between the two models.

Although overall genetic variation is low in modern human beings, when some details of our DNA are compared across geographic populations, some interesting patterns emerge. Since evolution is the accumulation of genetic variation through mutation, the genetic differences among populations tell us how many mutations have taken place since they were a single population. We get a measure of relative evolutionary relationships, which allows us to construct "family trees."

Moreover, if we can estimate the mutation rate for a given type of DNA, we can turn these data into a "molecular clock." We ask how long it would take for a certain degree of difference to accumulate between two groups. This, we assume, is how long they have been evolving separately (if two species, such as chimps and humans) or relatively separately (if populations within a species). Then, we may add dates to the family tree.

Y-chromosome DNA
The genetic material found on the Y (male) chromosome.

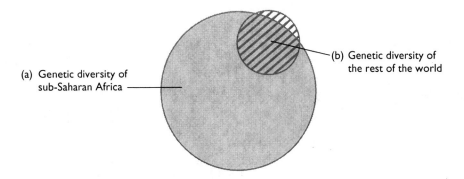

(a) Genetic diversity of
sub-Saharan Africa

(b) Genetic diversity of
the rest of the world

FIGURE 12.5
Comparative genetic
diversity. Circle (*a*)
represents the genetic
diversity of humans from
sub-Saharan Africa and (*b*)
the genetic diversity of the
rest of the world's peoples.
Note that African diversity is
much greater and that most
of the diversity of the rest
of the world is a subset of
African diversity. (Circles are
not drawn to scale.)

So what have the studies based on this reasoning told us about the
question of modern human origins? There are four conclusions from these
studies: First, the world's peoples tend to cluster into two genetic groups,
those from sub-Saharan Africa and those from everywhere else. Second,
Africa is more genetically diverse than the rest of the world put together,
with the genetic diversity of the rest of the world a subset of the genetic
diversity within Africa (Figure 12.5). Third, genetic and phenotypic diversity decreases as the distance away from Africa increases.

This evidence seems to support the AR model and a recent African
origin of modern humanity. If people have been evolving in Africa longer
than elsewhere and only recently spread to the rest of the world, then the
African population should be distinct from those of Europe and Asia and
should show greater genetic diversity.

Fourth, based on the comparative degrees of diversity among populations, the origin of modern human DNA is estimated by many studies at
150,000 to 200,000 ya. There is a fair amount of agreement among studies
of mtDNA, Y-chromosome DNA, and nuclear DNA.

The data from these studies could, however, also result if the species
were an old, single evolving lineage. Since most of hominin evolution occurred strictly in Africa, that continent has had the largest population for
most of human history. A large population on a large and environmentally
diverse continent would be expected to have a great deal of genetic diversity and thus be genetically different from the rest of humanity, which is
more recent (Relethford and Harpending 1995). Moreover, given the geography of the continents, there was more gene flow within Africa and within
populations in the rest of the world than *between* Africa and the rest of the
world (Figure 12.6). This would also contribute to a genetic distinction.

Fossil DNA   What about DNA from ancient remains? DNA is not a
very stable molecule, and scientists at one time doubted that it could be

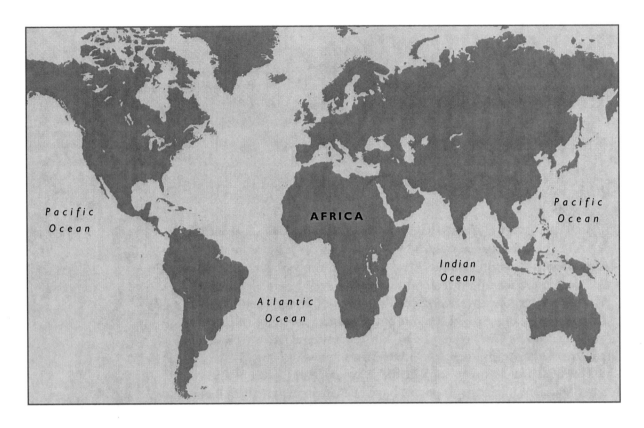

FIGURE 12.6
The relative size and location of Africa. The arrow shows the only way onto or off of the continent prior to modern transportation.

recovered from old bones. But this has proved possible. Perhaps the most famous ancient DNA samples have come from four Neandertal specimens. The first, from the original Neandertal (see Figure 11.25), consisted of a short sequence of 379 base pairs of mtDNA (out of a total of about 16,500 for human mtDNA). When compared with the same sequence in modern humans, there were more than three times the number of differences between the Neandertals and the moderns than between any two groups of moderns (Krings et al. 1997). Moreover, the sample showed no special similarity to modern Europeans, being equally distinct from all modern populations. The investigators concluded from this that the Neandertals made no contribution to modern human mtDNA and that our two lines diverged 690,000 to 550,000 ya. As of late 2007, mtDNA had been extracted from fourteen Neandertal specimens and nuclear DNA from several more (Hodgson and Disotell 2008). Most interpretations support the earlier conclusions of an ancient split between Neandertals and moderns, with no gene flow.

MRE proponents have questioned these conclusions. The DNA sequences are short, they note. And, says geneticist Simon Easteal, the fact that chimpanzees have much more mtDNA diversity than do humans shows that "the amount of diversity between Neanderthals and living humans is not exceptional" (Wong 1998). Moreover, one would expect there to be more genetic diversity in the human species in the past, before the larger populations, less isolation, and extensive gene flow of more recent times increased our genetic homogeneity. Clearly, more and larger ancient DNA samples will have to be obtained and studied.

As with the fossil and archaeological evidence, the genetic evidence, so far, does not distinguish between the two extreme models for modern human origins. Certainly, it points to an African origin; indeed, some Y-chromosome studies point to the Khoisan peoples of southern African as having the oldest versions of certain human genes (Figure 12.7). But the diversity and pattern of human genes can be accounted for by either model and so do not resolve the debate over replacement versus a single species with extensive gene flow (Relethford 2008).

Remember as well that the history of mtDNA or any other gene "does *not* reflect population history" (Wolpoff and Caspari 1997:302). Rather, it reflects the history of a specific genetic system, in the same way the history of "a single Scottish name might be different from the history of the Scottish people" (304). The evolutionary history of a population involves the histories of many genes. Again, larger samples are needed.

Evolutionary Theory

From the preceding discussion, it is clear that much of the haggling over these two major models focuses on details of the data. What about some of the broader considerations of evolutionary theory? What happens when we step back and look at the bigger picture? A major issue from this perspective is the plausibility of the gene flow required by the Multiregional Evolution model. Could such gene flow have taken place, and if so, how?

Christopher Stringer (Stringer and McKie 1996:142), representing the African Replacement view, thinks that such gene flow is unlikely, at best, for two reasons. First, he says, until recent times, hominin populations were too thinly spread across the three continents of the Old World to be so connected by gene flow. The gaps between groups were too large for genes to move around as much as MRE requires.

Second, there were too many geographic barriers. There were mountain, desert, and water barriers, and over the past million years or so, large portions of the world were in the grip of the Pleistocene ice ages, which caused extreme climatic disruptions and fluctuations. The flow of genes would have been severely limited by these geographic and climatic obstacles.

FIGURE 12.7
Recent studies have indicated that the oldest versions of certain genes on the male-inherited Y chromosome are found among Khoisan men, like this !Kung San hunter from the Kalahari Desert in southern Africa (the "!" indicates a click sound). These data are taken to mean that Khoisan may be the closest living populations, genetically, to the earliest modern humans.

There are—as you must suspect by now—responses to these issues from the MRE point of view. Two processes are involved in gene flow. One is the kind of genetic exchange Stringer cites, where "populations essentially sat still while genes passed through them" (144), that is, exchanged between neighboring groups. But genes also flow as a result of migration.

For the past 2 million years, we humans have been a migratory genus. In a short period of time, members of *Homo erectus* got all the way from Africa to Java. There is no reason why humans, having once arrived in these far-flung areas, would necessarily all stay put. Maps showing migration routes (see, for example, Shreeve 2006:64–65 and Stix 2008:59) are often over-simplified, making migrations seem one-way. People moved because they were following needed resources or looking for better conditions—and the Pleistocene climatic changes may have required a great deal of moving.

In response to the second issue, geographic barriers to human habitation and movement certainly existed and still do. They did not, however, prevent the spread of human populations. Even if there were six different species of *Homo,* the fossil record shows that most managed to move around a bit (see the tables and maps in Chapter 11). And the climatic disruptions of the Pleistocene fluctuated. Barriers changed in severity and location. Sea levels rose and isolated some land areas but then dropped again. Dry periods followed wet periods. Glaciers covered huge masses of land but then retreated. Spread over a 2-million-year period, such temporary and changeable barriers might not have presented severe limitations to gene flow.

We must also consider the evidence of possible hybridization between archaics and moderns. We've already discussed the young child from Portugal with both modern and Neandertal features. While some supporters of the AR model insist the child must be one species or the other, Christopher Stringer, a major AR proponent, has said that even if this child was a hybrid, hybridization between moderns and Neandertals was rare and had little impact on evolution (Bower 1999). Elsewhere, Stringer (1994) has claimed that interbreeding may have taken place between archaics and moderns in Eurasia but that it was limited and left no genetic or physical results in modern populations. In a later article, G. Bräuer and Stringer (1997) indicate they think interbreeding did occur, and O. M. Pearson (2000), writing on postcranial remains, admits the possibility of some admixture between moderns and Neandertals.

The problem here is that if there was *any* interbreeding between Neandertals and moderns that led to hybrid and fertile individuals, then, by definition, they were members of the same species. This is true even if few or no Neandertal genes or morphological features are still present in modern humans. Gene flow between archaics and moderns, no matter how limited, refutes the AR model and supports the MRE model (Wolpoff et al. 2001:296, n. 3).

Another relevant aspect of evolutionary theory involves the process of speciation (see Chapter 5). New species evolve when a portion of an existing species is completely isolated from the parent species long enough that

Contemporary Reflections

Is There a Connection between Modern Human Origins and Race?

"The Out-of-Africa [African Replacement] model makes mincemeat of racial difference" reads a quote on the back of Christopher Stringer and Robin McKie's *African Exodus: The Origins of Modern Humanity* (1996). The title of Milford Wolpoff and Rachel Caspari's (1997) book is *Race and Human Evolution: A Fatal Attraction*. What is the connection between race and the models we have been examining?

We will cover the topic of human biodiversity and the issue of race in detail in Chapter 14. For the moment, let me give away the punch line of that chapter and state that in the view of modern biological anthropology, the human species *is not* and *cannot* be divided into any number of clearly defined biological subgroups that warrant the title *race*. To be sure, we display phenotypic variation—in everything from skin color to relative frequencies of blood types—and this variation sometimes has geographic correlations. We can often accurately identify people's regional backgrounds from their visible physical features. But those correlations are merely the result of different percentages of alleles that have accumulated in different areas in response to some combination of environmental circumstances and population dynamics (in other words, in response to the operations of natural selection, gene flow, and genetic drift). Genetically, the whole species is remarkably homogeneous, and the genetic variation is relatively evenly spread. Nonetheless, it is these outward physical similarities and differences that cultures use to divide humans into races. Race is a cultural construct.

The biological unity of our species is now a well-documented fact, and it leads to certain socially relevant ideas and ideals—namely, that although individual humans vary in many ways, there exist no profound inherent differences *among human groups* that would warrant differential treatment in social and cultural environments. Skin color, for example, is no predictor of intellectual capabilities.

A majority of anthropologists in the past leaned toward the African Replacement model not only because many believed the data support it but also because it neatly explains our species' current homogeneity. If our species is very young—only a few hundred thousand years at most—and if it arose from one localized population, then it could not possibly display deep and profound variations among its populations. There simply hasn't been enough time. If the AR model is correct, human races could not exist. This makes the AR model attractive indeed.

subsequent genetic and phenotypic change eventually creates an absolute barrier to reproduction. Humans are and have been a mobile species, and our big brain has allowed our genus to experience increasing control over our environments and adaptations to those environments. We also have a proclivity for exchanging genes whenever we get the chance, or at least for the behavior that results in the exchange of genes. It would seem to be a rare event for any individual group of such a genus to be isolated long enough to evolve sufficient differences in reproductive behavior or biology to become a technically separate species. The most extreme AR model (see Lahr and Foley 2004) recognizes as many as *ten* species of *Homo* (including

Moreover, it has been stated by some AR supporters that one fatal problem with the Multiregional Evolution model is that it does "suggest, at face value, that modern humanity's constituent races are divided by fundamental and deep-rooted differences" (Stringer and McKie 1996:60). If, such arguments go, local populations show continuity of features into the distant past, that implies that modern racial groups are themselves very ancient and profoundly different. Such a suggestion goes against current social ideals, not to mention the scientific facts regarding our relative homogeneity.

There were, to be sure, earlier models of a multiregional perspective that did make such suggestions. In his 1962 book *The Origin of Races*, anthropologist Carleton Coon proposed that five subspecies, or races, of *Homo erectus* independently evolved into five major races of *Homo sapiens*, crossing "a critical threshold from a more brutal to a more *sapient* state" (658). To make matters worse, he claimed that the different races crossed the "sapiens threshold" at different times and that this accounted for some of the differences we see today in levels of cultural complexity. "If all races had a recent common origin," he asked, "why were the Tasmanians and many of the Australian aborigines still living during the nineteenth century in a manner comparable to that of Europeans of over 100,000 years ago?" (4). It is clear who Coon thought crossed the threshold first and last. Such ideas may well have sensitized anthropologists against any model of our evolution that included great time depth for the species and regional continuity of traits.

The modern MRE model, however, is quite different from Coon's and other early ideas. The MRE model does not claim that *populations* show continuity but that some regional *traits* do, especially traits that are found in fairly isolated areas, such as Australia and other places on the margins of the human geographic range. So-called racial groups are not now, nor were they ever, completely isolated. Rather, the species has displayed continual gene flow, enough to maintain species identity and spread physical features and their genes all over the world.

But this is all really a nonissue. Even if the extreme single-species MRE model proves correct, today's human species is *still* genetically and physically homogeneous. We know this because of well-established scientific studies of genetics and morphology. How we got to be this way doesn't change how we are, and either major model under debate could account for our current nature. As anthropologist Matt Cartmill puts it, "We are what we are, not what our ancestors were.... The truth of racial egalitarianism hinges on the facts about living people. Their genealogies are irrelevant" (1997:62).

H. habilis and *H. rudolfensis*). In terms of how new species evolve, and the nature of genus *Homo*, this appears highly unlikely indeed.

Perhaps we have been misled because we have examined every available minute genetic and phenotypic variation in living humans and our fossil ancestors through a microscope—literally and figuratively. A single species, as it responds to the processes of evolution through time, may change, of course, and it certainly may show regional variation. But over the long haul, the temporal changes and regional variation within a species occur around some central adaptive theme that defines that species ("oscillating selection"). Our central adaptive theme is our big brain and the resultant behaviors, especially culture, that such a brain makes possible. Evidence of this theme is found in all accepted members of genus *Homo*—and is absent in all other hominins.

So I see the burden of proof as being on the proponents of the view that there have been multiple species of our genus. Absent specific evidence of an inability to interbreed and, thus, justification for a different species name, the current data point to a taxonomically relevant similarity of all fossils and living individuals included in genus *Homo*. Thus, the "default" position is one species, *Homo sapiens*, unless proven otherwise.

Of course, I could be wrong. And that is the beauty and excitement of the self-correcting nature of science. But there is another model that I think resolves the debate.

PRIMARY AFRICAN ORIGIN (PAO) MODEL

So far, the debate has involved trying to force the data from the fossil and archaeological records and from genetics and evolutionary theory into one or the other of the standard models. But what about letting the data speak for themselves? What about generating a model that accounts for those data? (Recall, from Chapter 1, how science induces hypotheses from patterns.) This is what biologist Alan Templeton and anthropologist John Relethford have done. Templeton calls his idea "Out of Africa Again and Again" (Templeton 2002), and Relethford has coined the name "Primary African Origin" (Relethford 2001, 2008).

This model is a multiregional one in that it agrees that there is no reason to divide genus *Homo* into multiple species with different species names that indicate an inability to interbreed. The model also accepts the fossil and genetic evidence that points to Africa as the "birthplace" of our species. The difference is that it sees the origin of our species as occurring about 2 mya, and it accounts for the patterns of genetic diversity in a way that does not require a young species.

The model does so by proposing more than one major expansion out of Africa. The first was during *Homo erectus* times and the latest about the time proposed by AR for the origin and spread of modern *Homo sapiens*. There may have been other expansions as well, not all necessarily "out of Africa"; people migrate in all directions. These expansions spread collections of genes and traits across geographic space. Thus, the evolution of some features of modern humans—and the genes that coded for them—could have occurred first in Africa, but their spread around the world did not necessarily result in the replacement of an existing species by a new one. Rather, the features spread via gene flow among existing populations of a single species that descended from the first and subsequent expansions. Templeton's study (2002), using seven types of genetic data and a sophisticated statistical analysis, has even suggested times and directions of some of the expansions (Figure 12.8). And a more recent study by Templeton (2005), using even more sophisticated statistical analyses of genetic variation, concludes that the "out-of-Africa replacement [AR] hypothesis is strongly rejected" (56).

But what about the genetic data that show (1) very little genetic diversity within our species as a whole, (2) greater genetic diversity within sub-Saharan African populations than within the entire rest of the human population, and (3) genetic diversity among everyone else as a subset of the diversity within sub-Saharan Africa? Doesn't this argue for a young species that exploded out of Africa only recently?

Not necessarily. If our species has been characterized for 2 million years by movement and genetic exchange, the result would predictably be genetic homogeneity. Indeed, as time went on there were more of us, moving around more, and so genetic homogeneity would be expected to *increase* over time.

Why is the rest of the world's genetic diversity a small subset of African genetic diversity? Think about a map of the world (see again Figure 12.6). Africa is a big place, with a huge north-south axis. (For comparison, the northern tip of Africa is on the same latitude as Richmond, Virginia, and the southern tip on the same level as Montevideo, Uruguay. Put another way, Africa stretches the same distance as that between the Arctic Circle and Lima, Peru.) People would first have spread out within the African continent, responding, perhaps, to the great variety of environments there and so accumulating a relatively great degree of genetic diversity. Then, the rest of the world's human populations were founded (recall the founder effect) by the very small, and nonrepresentative, samples of Africans who just happened to migrate off the continent via that one fairly small strip of land in the northeast of the continent.

These founded populations spread around Eurasia, exchanging genes among themselves more easily than they would have exchanged them with Africans (it would have been just as rare an occurrence to migrate *back* to Africa as it was to leave in the first place). So the already small degree of genetic diversity of the rest of the world would become even smaller as genes were distributed by gene flow and with diversity decreasing even more as the distance from Africa increased.

So the PAO model nicely accounts for all the data from the various sources discussed before. In keeping with the scientific method, this model must now be deductively tested.

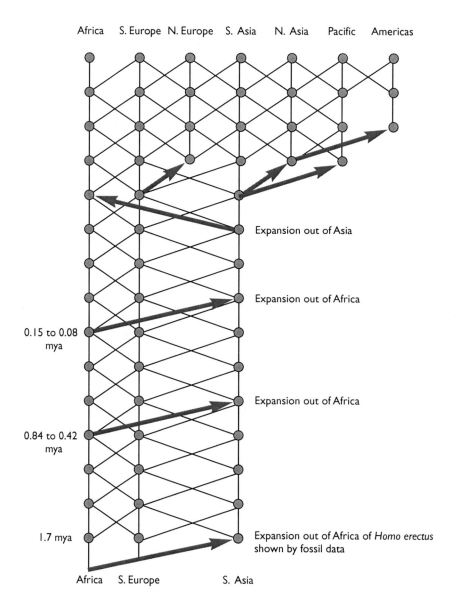

Africa   S. Europe   N. Europe   S. Asia   N. Asia   Pacific   Americas

Expansion out of Asia

Expansion out of Africa

0.15 to 0.08 mya

Expansion out of Africa

0.84 to 0.42 mya

1.7 mya

Expansion out of Africa of *Homo erectus* shown by fossil data

Africa   S. Europe   S. Asia

FIGURE 12.8

The multiple expansion, or Primary African Origin, model. Vertical lines represent direct regional descent, that is, regional continuity. Diagonal lines represent a network of recurrent gene flow among regional populations. (Actual gene flow, of course, would not have been this regular or even.) The red arrows represent major population expansions. In the original diagram, Templeton indicates that there is genetic evidence for the timing and direction of each of these expansions, as well as for certain sections of the network of gene flow. Note that, at least early on, Africa made major contributions to the gene pool and, thus, to the traits of the rest of the world. Also note that none of the expansions is a replacement or a speciation event, just the spread of a sample of genes among an existing, widespread species.

(Adapted from Templeton 2002:48)

SUMMARY

The hottest current debate in bioanthropology is over the origin of modern *Homo sapiens*. Many, if not most, authorities support either of two major models. One, the African Replacement (AR) model, proposes that modern humans evolved as a separate species 200,000 to 150,000 ya in Africa, having a set of characteristics that made them distinctly different from their ancestors and other contemporary species. They then spread throughout the Old World, replacing populations of archaic humans because of their better-adapted traits.

The other model, the Multiregional Evolution (MRE) model, claims that our species is as much as 2 million years old and incorporates other previously recognized species of genus *Homo* possibly back through *H. erectus*. After first evolving in Africa, the species spread throughout the Old World, developing regional differences but always maintaining species identity through gene flow. As new and successful adaptations arose in different areas, they were shared across the species. Thus, "modern" humans—all 6 billion of us living today—share a collection of traits that is the latest set of physical features in a very ancient species.

The data from paleontology, archaeology, and genetics are ambiguous on this issue. Either model may be supported by the same basic facts. But now a newer model, the Primary African Origin (PAO) model, or multiple expansion model, seems to reconcile all the evidence into a more satisfying scheme. It says that after an initial expansion out of Africa, nearly 2 mya, there were several other major expansions out of that more heavily populated continent that spread genes and traits across other geographic areas, already populated by descendants of earlier migrations and characterized by a network of recurrent gene flow. So most of our ancestors are African, but not all of them, and our species is an old one.

QUESTIONS FOR FURTHER THOUGHT

1. Having read about the debate over the evolution of genus *Homo*, go back to question 1 from Chapter 11. Now what are your thoughts on the issue? Is this debate interesting and important to you? Why or why not?

2. Aside from the alleged race implications, why do you think professionals are so emotional about this debate? Do you see any issues other than purely scientific ones—philosophical ones, perhaps—involved in this debate?

3. Some claim that the Multiregional Evolution model is potentially "racist." (Someone said it to me.) How would you respond to such an accusation?

KEY TERMS

Multiregional
  Evolution (MRE)
  model

African Replacement
  (AR) model

Primary African
  Origin (PAO)
  model

nuclear DNA

mitochondrial DNA
  (mtDNA)

symbiosis

Y-chromosome DNA

SUGGESTED READINGS

There is extensive literature about the AR/MRE debate. I would especially recommend the two books by the major proponents of each point of view: *Race and Human Evolution: A Fatal Attraction*, by Milford Wolpoff and Rachel Caspari, in support of the MRE model, and *African Exodus: The Origins of Modern Humanity*, by Christopher Stringer and Robin McKie, in support of the AR model. The Wolpoff and Caspari book includes a good historical review of the issue. For the newer PAO model, see Alan Templeton's "Out of Africa Again and Again" in the 7 March 2002 *Nature* and John Relethford's two highly readable books, the more technical *Genetics and the Search for Modern Human Origins* and the more popular and broader *Reflections of Our Past: How Human History Is Revealed in Our Genes*. A more recent, very technical article by Relethford is "Genetic Evidence and the Modern Human Origins Debate" in the 5 March 2008 issue of *Heredity*. A nice summary piece is "Traces of a Distant Past," by Gary Stix, in the July 2008 *Scientific American*.

On the fascinating topic of mitochondria, see "Symbionts and Assassins," by Guy C. Brown, in the July/August 2000 issue of *Natural History*.

For an interesting article on the possible intellectual differences between archaics and modern humans, see "The Morning of the Modern Mind," by Kate Wong, in the June 2005 *Scientific American.*

On the topic of the race connection, see Matt Cartmill's "The Third Man" in the September 1997 issue of *Discover,* and have a look at Carleton Coon's *The Origin of Races* to see why that book caused such a furor.

For a collection of twenty-nine technical articles on all aspects of the debate, see *Conceptual Issues in Modern Human Origins Research,* edited by G. A. Clark and C. M. Willermet. And for a more recent collection, see *The Speciation of Modern* Homo sapiens, edited by T. J. Crow.

Back Matter

REFERENCES

Aiello, L., and C. Dean. 1990. *An introduction to human evolutionary anatomy*. London: Academic Press.

Aiello, L. C. 1993. The fossil evidence for modern human origins in Africa: A revised view. *American Anthropologist* 95 (1): 73–96.

Aldhous, P., and A. Abbot. 2000. Battling the killer proteins. *Nature* 408:902–3.

Alemseged, Z., F. Spoor, W. H. Kimbel, R. Bobe, D. Geraads, D. Reed, and J. G. Wynn. 2006. A juvenile early hominin skeleton from Dikika, Ethiopia. *Nature* 443:296–301.

Alexander, R. McN. 1995. Standing, walking and running. In *Gray's anatomy*. 38th ed. New York: Churchill Livingston.

Allard, W. A. 2006. Solace at Surprise Creek. *National Geographic* 209 (6): 120–147.

Allen, T. B. 1996. The silk road's lost world. *National Geographic* 189 (3): 44–51.

Anderson, D. 2005. *How do we know the nature of human origins*. New York: Rosen Publishing Group.

Appleman, P. 1979. *Darwin: A Norton critical edition*. 2nd ed. New York: Norton.

Armelagos, G. 1998. The viral superhighway. *The Sciences* 38 (1): 24–29.

Armelagos, G., K. C. Barnes, and J. Lin. 1996. Disease in human evolution: The re-emergence of infectious disease in the third epidemiological transition. *AnthroNotes* 18 (3): 1–7.

Arsuaga, J. L., and I. Martínez. 2006. *The chosen species: The long march of human evolution*. Malden, MA: Blackwell.

Asfaw, B., T. White, O. Lovejoy, B. Latimer, S. Simpson, and G. Suwa. 1999. *Australopithecus garhi*: A new species of early hominid from Ethiopia. *Science* 284:629–35.

Ast, G. 2005. The alternative genome. *Scientific American*, April: 59–65.

Attenborough, D. 1979. *Life on earth*. Boston: Little, Brown.

Bahn, P. G. 1995. Last days of the Iceman. *Archaeology*, May–June, 66–70.

Balter, M. 2001a. Anthropologists duel over modern human origins. *Science* 291:1728–29.

——— 2001b. Scientists spar over claims of earliest human ancestor. *Science* 291:1460–61.

———. 2004. Skeptics question whether Flores hominid is a new species. *Science* 306:1116.

———. 2005. Expression of endorphin gene favored in human evolution. *Science* 310:1257.

———. 2008. Why we're different: Probing the gap between apes and humans. *Science* 319:404–5.

Balter, M., and A. Gibbons. 2002. Were "little people" the first to venture out of Africa? *Science* 297:26–27.

Barfield, A. 1976. Biological influences on sex differences in behavior. In *Sex differences*, ed. M. S. Teitelbaum. Garden City, NY: Anchor Press/Doubleday.

Barinaga, M. 1992. "African Eve" backers beat a retreat. *Science* 255:686–87.

Barluenga, M., K. N. Stölting, W. Salzberger, M. Muschick, and A. Meyer. 2005. Sympatric speciation in Nicaraguan crater lake cichlid fish. *Nature* 439:719–23.

Bass, W. 1971. *Human osteology: A laboratory and field manual of the human skeleton*. Columbia: Missouri Archaeological Society.

Beall, C. M., and A. T. Steegmann, Jr. 2000. Human adaptation to climate: Temperature, ultraviolet radiation, and altitude. In *Human biology: An evolutionary and biocultural perspective*, ed. S. Stinson et al., 163–224. New York: Wiley-Liss.

Becker, L. 2002. Repeated blows. *Scientific American*, March: 77–83.

Begun, D. R. 2003. Planet of the apes. *Scientific American*, August: 74–83.

Behe, M. J. 1996. *Darwin's black box*. New York: Touchstone.

Bellantoni, N., R. Thompson, D. Cooke, M. Park, and C. Trayling. 2007. The life, death, archaeological exhumation and reinterment of Opukahaʻia (Henry Obookiah), 1792–1818. *Connecticut History* 46, 2 (Fall): 206–26.

Benedict, J. 2003. *No bone unturned: The adventures of a top Smithsonian forensic scientist and the legal battle for America's oldest skeletons.* New York: HarperCollins.

Berger, L. R., S. E. Churchill, B. De Klerk, and R. L. Quinn. 2008. Small-bodied humans from Palau, Micronesia. *PLoS ONE* 3 (3): e1780, doi:10.1371/journal.pone.0001780, http://www.plosone.org/article/info:do:%2F10.1371%2Fjournal.pone.0001780.

Bermejo, M., J. D. Rodriguez-Teijero, G. Illera, A. Barroso, C. Vilá, and P. D. Walsh. 2006. Ebola outbreak killed 5000 gorillas. *Science* 314:1564.

Bermúdez de Castro, J. M., J. L. Arsuaga, E. Carbonell, A. Rosas, I. Martínez, and M. Mosquera. 1997. A hominid from the Lower Pleistocene of Atapuerca, Spain: Possible ancestor to Neandertals and modern humans. *Science* 276:1392–95.

Binford, L. 1985. Ancestral life ways: The faunal record. *Anthroquest* 32 (1): 15–20.

Binford, L., and K. Chuan. 1985. Taphonomy at a distance: Zhoukoudian, "The cave home of Beijing Man." *Current Anthropology* 26:413–43.

Binford, L., and N. M. Stone. 1986. Zhoukoudian: A closer look. *Current Anthropology* 27:435–76.

Binford, L. R. 1987. *Bones: Ancient men and modern myths.* Orlando, FL: Academic Press.

Bloch, J. I., and D. M. Boyer. 2002. Grasping primate origins. *Science* 298:1606–9.

Blumenschine, R. J., et al. 2003. Late Pliocene *Homo* and hominid land use from Western Olduvai Gorge, Tanzania. *Science* 299:1217–21.

Boaz, N. T., and R. L. Ciochon. 2001. The scavenging of "Peking Man." *Natural History* 110 (2): 46–51.

Boesch, C. 1999. A theory that's hard to digest. *Nature* 399 (17 June): 653.

Boesch, C., and H. Boesch-Achermann. 1991. Dim forest, bright chimps. *Natural History*, September: 50–57.

Bogin, B. 2001. Book review. *Evolutionary Anthropology* 114 (2): 172–74.

Bolnick, D. A., et al. 2007. The science and business of genetic ancestry testing. *Science* 318:399–400.

Bordes, F. 1972. *A tale of two caves.* New York: Harper & Row.

Bower, B. 1997. Ancient ape shuffles to prominence. *Science News* 152 (18 October): 244.

———. 1999. Fossil may expose humanity's hybrid roots. *Science News* 155:295.

Bowlby, J. 1990. *Charles Darwin: A new life.* New York: Norton.

Boyd, R., and J. B. Silk. 1997. *How humans evolved.* New York: Norton.

Brace, C. L. 2005. *"Race" is a four-letter word: The genesis of the concept.* New York: Oxford.

Bramble, D. M., and D. E. Lieberman. 2004. Endurance running and the evolution of *Homo*. *Nature* 432:345–51.

Bramblett, C. A. 1994. *Patterns of primate behavior.* 2nd ed. Prospect Heights, IL: Waveland.

Bräuer, G., and C. Stringer. 1997. Models, polarization, and perspectives on modern human origins. In *Conceptual issues in modern human origins research*, ed. G. A. Clark and C. M. Willermet. New York: Aldine de Gruyter.

Bräuer, G., Y. Yokoyama, C. Falguères, and E. Mbua. 1997. Modern human origins backdated. *Nature* 386:337.

Brown, G. C. 2000. Symbionts and assassins. *Natural History* 109 (6): 66–71.

Brown, P., et al. 2004. A new small-bodied hominin from the Late Pleistocene of Flores, Indonesia. *Nature* 431:1055–61.

Brown, R. A., and G. J. Armelagos. 2001. Apportionment of racial diversity: A review. *Evolutionary Anthropology* 10 (1): 34–40.

Browne, J. 1995. *Charles Darwin: Voyaging.* Princeton, NJ: Princeton University Press.

———. 2002. *Charles Darwin: The power of place.* Princeton, NJ: Princeton University Press.

Brunet, M. 2002. Reply to Wolpoff et al. 2002. *Nature* 419:582.

Brunet, M., et al. 2002. A new hominid from the Upper Miocene of Chad, Central Africa. *Nature* 418:145–55.

Brunet, M., et al. 2005. New material of the earliest hominid from the Upper Miocene of Chad. *Nature* 434:752–55.

Buchan, J. C., S. C. Alberts, J. B. Silk, and J. Altmann. 2003. True paternal care in a multi-male primate society. *Nature* 425:179–81.

420 References

Campbell, C. J., A. Fuentes, K. C. Mackinnon, M. Panger, and S. K. Bearder. 2007. *Primates in perspective.* New York: Oxford.

Cann, R. L., M. Stoneking, and A. C. Wilson. 1987. Mitochondrial DNA and human evolution. *Nature* 325:31–36.

Carbonell, E., et al. 2008. The first hominin of Europe. *Nature* 452:465–69.

Carroll, S. B., B. Prud'homme, and N. Gompel. 2008. Regulating evolution. *Scientific American,* May: 61–67.

Cartmill, M. 1992. New views on primate origins. *Evolutionary Anthropology* 1 (3): 105–11.

———. 1997. The third man. *Discover,* September: 56–62.

Cavalieri, P., and P. Singer. 1993. *The great ape project: Equality beyond humanity.* New York: St. Martin's.

Cavalli-Sforza, L. L. 1991. Genes, peoples, and languages. *Scientific American* 265:104–10.

Cavalli-Sforza, L. L., and F. Cavalli-Sforza. 1995. *The great human diasporas: The history of diversity and evolution.* Reading, MA: Addison-Wesley.

Cavalli-Sforza, L. L., P. Menozzi, and A. Piazza. 1994. *The history and geography of human genes.* Princeton, NJ: Princeton University Press.

Cela-Conde, C. J., and F. J. Ayala. 2007. *Human evolution: Trails from the past.* Oxford: Oxford University Press.

Chaplin, G. 2004. Geographic distribution of environmental factors influencing human skin coloration. *American Journal of Physical Anthropology* 125:292–302.

Check, E. 2004. Geneticists study human-chimp divergence. *Nature* 928:242.

Chimpanzee Sequencing and Analysis Consortium. 2005. Initial sequence of the chimpanzee genome and comparison with the human genome. *Nature* 437:69–87.

Cibelli, J. 2007. A decade of cloning mystique. *Science* 316:990–2.

Ciochon, R., J. Olsen, and J. James. 1990. *Other origins: The search for the giant ape in human prehistory.* New York: Bantam Books.

Ciochon, R. L., and J. G. Fleagle, eds. 1993. *The human evolution source book.* Englewood Cliffs, NJ: Prentice Hall.

Clark, G. A., and C. M. Willermet, eds. 1997. *Conceptual issues in modern human origins research.* New York: Aldine de Gruyter.

Clark, J. D., et al. 2003. Stratigraphic, chronological and behavioral contexts of Pleistocene *Homo sapiens* from Middle Awash, Ethiopia. *Nature* 423:747–52.

Cohen, J. 2007a. Relative differences: The myth of 1%. *Science* 316:1836.

———. 2007b. The world through a chimp's eyes. *Science* 316: 44–45.

Cohen, J. E. 1996. Ten myths of population. *Discover,* April: 42–47.

Conroy, G. C. 1997. *Reconstructing human origins: A modern synthesis.* New York: Norton.

Conway Morris, S. 1998. *The crucible of creation: The Burgess Shale and the rise of animals.* New York: Oxford.

Conway Morris, S., and S. J. Gould. 1998–1999. Showdown on the Burgess Shale. *Natural History* 107 (10): 48–55.

Coon, C. 1962. *The origin of races.* New York: Knopf.

Cooper, R. S., C. N. Rotimi, and R. Ward. 1999. The puzzle of hypertension in African-Americans. *Scientific American,* February: 56–63.

Coppens, Y. 1994. East side story: The origin of humankind. *Scientific American* 270:88–95.

Cowen, R. 1995. *History of life.* 2nd ed. Boston: Blackwell Scientific Publications.

Crossette, B. 2001. Against a trend, U.S. population will bloom, U.N. says. *New York Times,* 28 February, A6.

Crow, T. J., ed. 2002. *The speciation of modern* Homo sapiens. Oxford: Oxford University Press (for The British Academy).

Culotta, E. 1999a. Anthropologists probe bones, stones, and molecules. *Science* 284:1109–11.

———. 1999b. A new human ancestor? *Science* 284:572–73.

———. 2008. When Hobbits (slowly) walked the earth. *Science* 320:433–35.

Cummins, H., and C. Midlo. 1961. *Finger prints, palms, and soles: An introduction to dermatoglyphics.* New York: Dover.

Dalton, R. 2006. Neanderthal DNA yields to genome foray. *Nature* 441:260–61.

Darwin, C. 1869. *On the origin of species by means of natural selection or the preservation of favoured races in the struggle for life.* London: John Murray.

Dawkins, R. 2005. The illusion of design. *Natural History* 114 (November): 35–37.

De Bonis, L., and G. D. Koufos. 1994. Our ancestor's ancestor: *Ouranopithecus* is a Greek link in human ancestry. *Evolutionary Anthropology* 3 (3): 75–83.

Defleur, A., T. White, P. Valensi, L. Slimak, and E. Crégut-Bonnoure. 1999. Neanderthal cannibalism at Moula-Guercy, Ardèch, France. *Science* 286:128–31.

de Heinzelin, J. J., D. Clark, T. White, W. Hart, P. Renne, G. Wolde-Gabriel, Y. Beyene, and E. Vrba. 1999. Environment and behavior of 2.5-million-year-old Bouri hominids. *Science* 284:624–29.

Delisle, R. G. 2007. *Debating humankind's place in nature, 1860–2000: The nature of paleoanthropology.* Upper Saddle River, NJ: Pearson/Prentice Hall.

Dennell, R., and W. Roebroeks. 2005. An Asian perspective on early human dispersal from Africa. *Nature* 438:1099–1103.

de Waal, F., and F. Lanting (photographer). 1997. *Bonobo: The forgotten ape.* Berkeley: University of California Press.

de Waal, F. B. M. 1995. Bonobo sex and society. *Scientific American*, March: 82–88.

Diamond, J. 1991. Curse and blessing of the ghetto. *Discover*, March: 60–65.

———. 2004. *Collapse: How societies choose to fail or succeed.* New York: Viking.

Dickson J. H., K. Oeggl, and L. L. Handley. 2003. The Iceman reconsidered. *Scientific American*, May: 70–79.

DiPietro, L. 2000. Tackling race and sports. *Scientific American*, May: 73–76.

Dobzhansky, T. 1970. *Genetics of the evolutionary process.* New York: Columbia University Press.

Dolhinow, P., and A. Fuentes 1999. *The nonhuman primates.* Mountain View, CA: Mayfield.

Donnelly, C. A. 2000. Likely size of the French BSE epidemic. *Nature* 408:787–88.

Donnelly, P., S. Tavaré, D. J. Balding, and R. C. Griffiths. 1996. Technical comments: Estimating the age of the common ancestor of men from the ZFY intron. *Science* 272:1357–58.

Dorit, R. L., H. Akashi, and W. Gilbert. 1995. Absence of polymorphism at the ZFY locus on the human Y chromosome. *Science* 268:1183–85.

Duarte, C., J. Mauricio, P. B. Pettiee, P. Souto, E. Trinkhaus, H. Van der Plicht, and J. Zilhão. 1999. The early Upper Paleolithic human skeleton from the Abrigo od Lagar Velho (Portugal) and modern human emergence in Iberia. *Proceedings of the National Academy of Sciences* 96:7604–9.

Dunham, I., N. Shimizu, B. A. Roe, S. Chissoe, et al. 1999. The DNA sequence of human chromosome 22. *Nature* 402:489–95.

Eaton, S. B., and M. Konner. 1985. Diet: Paleolithic genes and twentieth-century health. *Anthroquest*, The L. S. B. Leakey Foundation, 1985.

Eckhardt, R. B. 2008. Developmental anomalies of the wrist in LB1 from Flores, Indonesia. Paper and talk delivered at the 77th annual meeting of the American Association of Physical Anthropologists, Columbus, OH.

Ehrlich, P. R., and R. W. Holm. 1964. A biological view of race. In *The concept of race*, ed. A. Montagu. New York: Collier.

Eldredge, N. 1991. *The miner's canary: Unraveling the mysteries of extinction.* New York: Prentice Hall.

———. 1995. *Dominion.* New York: Holt.

Entine, J. 2000. *Taboo: Why black athletes dominate sports and why we're afraid to talk about it.* New York: PublicAffairs Books.

Epstein, P. R. 2000. Is global warming harmful to health? *Scientific American*, August: 50–57.

Espinasa, L., and M. Espinasa. 2005. Why do cave fish lose their eyes? *Natural History*, June: 44–49.

Fagan, B. 1994. *In the beginning: An introduction to archaeology.* 8th ed. New York: HarperCollins.

Fagan, B. M. 1990. *The journey from Eden: The peopling of our world.* London: Thames and Hudson.

Falk, D., et al. 2005. The brain of LB1, *Homo floresiensis. Science* 308:242–45.

———. 2008. LB1 did not have Laron Syndrome. Paper and talk delivered at the 77th annual meeting of the American Association of Physical Anthropologists, Columbus, OH.

Fausto-Sterling, A. 1993. The five sexes. *The Sciences*, March–April: 20–24.

———. 2000. The five sexes, revisited. *The Sciences* July–August: 18–23.

Feder, K. L. 1997. Indians and archaeologists: The conflicting views of myth and science. *Skeptic* 5 (3): 74–80.

———. 1999. *Lessons from the past: An introductory reader in archaeology.* Mountain View, CA: Mayfield.

———. 2007. *The past in perspective: An introduction to human prehistory.* 4th ed. New York: McGraw-Hill.

———. 2008. *Frauds, myths, and mysteries: Science and pseudoscience in archaeology.* 6th ed. New York: McGraw-Hill.

Feder, K. L., and M. A. Park. 2007. *Human antiquity: An introduction to physical anthropology and archaeology.* 5th ed. New York: McGraw-Hill.

Fedigan, L. M., and L. Fedigan. 1988. *Gender and the study of primates: Curricular module for the Project on Gender and Curriculum.* Washington, DC: American Anthropological Association.

Ferris, Timothy. 1988. *Coming of age in the Milky Way.* New York: Morrow.

Finlayson, C., et al. 2006. Late survival of Neanderthals at the southernmost extreme of Europe. *Nature* 443:850–53.

Fischman, J. 2005. The pathfinders. *National Geographic* 207:16–27.

Fleagle, J. G. 1988. *Primate adaptation and evolution.* San Diego: Academic Press.

Fortey, R. 1998. *Life: A natural history of the first four billion years of life on earth.* New York: Knopf.

Fossey, D. 1983. *Gorillas in the mist.* Boston: Houghton Mifflin.

Fouts, R., with S. T. Mills. 1997. *Next of kin: What chimpanzees have taught me about who we are.* New York: Morrow.

Fouts, R. S., and D. H. Fouts. 1999. Chimpanzee sign language research. In *The nonhuman primates,* ed. P. Dolhinow and A. Fuentes. Mountain View, CA: Mayfield.

Francione, G. L. 1996. *Rain without thunder: The ideology of the animal rights movement.* Philadelphia: Temple University Press.

Frayer, D. W., M. H. Wolpoff, A. G. Thorne, F. H. Smith, and G. G. Pope. 1993. Theories of modern human origins: The paleontological test. *American Anthropologist* 95 (1): 14–50.

———. 1994. Getting it straight. *American Anthropologist* 96:424–38.

Frisancho, A. R. 1993. *Human adaptation and accommodation.* Ann Arbor: University of Michigan Press.

Gaffney, E. S., L. Dingus, and M. K. Smith. 1995. Why cladistics? *Natural History* 104 (6): 33–35.

Galdikas, B. 1995. *Reflections of Eden: My years with the orangutans of Borneo.* Boston: Little, Brown.

Gebo, D. L., L. MacLatchy, R. Kityo, A. Deino, J. Kingston, and D. Pilbeam. 1997. A hominoid genus from the early Miocene of Uganda. *Science* 276:401–4.

Gee, H. 2001. Return to the planet of the apes. *Nature* 412:131–32.

Gibbons, A. 1997a. Doubts over spectacular dates. *Science* 278:220–22.

———. 1997b. A new face for human ancestors. *Science* 276 (30 May): 1331–33.

———. 1998a. Genes put mammals in age of dinosaurs. *Science* 289:675–76.

———. 1998b. Which of our genes makes us human? *Science* 281:1432–34.

———. 2001. The peopling of the Pacific. *Science* 291:1735–37.

Giere, R. N. 1997. *Understanding scientific reasoning.* Belmont, CA: Wadsworth/Thomson.

Gish, Duane T. 1979. *Evolution: The fossils say no!* San Diego: Creation-Life Publishers.

Gladwell, M. 2007. None of the above. *New Yorker,* 17 December: 92–96.

Glausiusz, J. 1995. Unfortunate drift. *Discover,* June: 34–35.

Goldman, E. 2003. Puzzling over the origin of species in the depths of the oldest lakes. *Science* 299:654–55.

Goodall, J. 1971. *In the shadow of man.* Boston: Houghton Mifflin.

———. 1986. *The chimpanzees of Gombe: Patterns of behavior.* Cambridge, MA: Belknap.

———. 1990. *Through a window: My thirty years with the chimpanzees of Gombe.* Boston: Houghton Mifflin.

Gore, R. 1989. Extinctions. *National Geographic* 175 (6): 662–99.

———. 1993. The Cambrian period: Explosion of life. *National Geographic* 184 (4): 120–36.

———. 1997a. Expanding worlds. *National Geographic* 191 (5): 84–109.

———. 1997b. The first Europeans. *National Geographic* 192 (1): 96–113.

———. 2002a. The first pioneer? *National Geographic* 202 (August): xxxvii–xlvii.

———. 2002b. New find. *National Geographic* (August).

Goudsmit, J. 1997. *Viral sex: The nature of AIDS*. New York: Oxford University Press.

Gould, S. J. 1977. *Ever since Darwin*. New York: Norton.

———. 1980. *The panda's thumb*. New York: Norton.

———. 1983. *Hen's teeth and horse's toes*. New York: Norton.

———. 1985. *The flamingo's smile*. New York: Norton.

———. 1989. *Wonderful life: The Burgess Shale and the nature of history*. New York: Norton.

———. 1991. *Bully for brontosaurus*. New York: Norton.

———. 1992. What is a species? *Discover*, December: 40–45.

———, ed. 1993a. *The book of life*. New York: Norton.

———. 1993b. *Eight little piggies*. New York: Norton.

———. 1994a. The evolution of life on the earth. *Scientific American* 271 (4): 84–91.

———. 1994b. In the mind of the beholder. *Natural History* 103 (2): 14–23.

———. 1995a. *Dinosaur in a haystack: Reflections in natural history*. New York: Harmony.

———. 1995b. Evolution by walking. *Natural History* 104 (3): 10–15.

———. 1995c. Of tongue worms, velvet worms, and water bears. *Natural History* 104 (1): 6–15.

———. 1996a. *Full house: The spread of excellence from Plato to Darwin*. New York: Harmony.

———. 1996b. *The mismeasure of man*. 2nd ed. New York: Norton.

———. 1997–1998. The paradox of the visibly irrelevant. *Natural History* 106 (11): 12–18, 60–66.

———. 1998. *Leonardo's mountain of clams and the Diet of Worms: Essays on natural history*. New York: Harmony.

———. 1999. *Rocks of ages: Science and religion in the fullness of life*. New York: Ballantine.

———. 2000. *The lying stones of Marrakech: Penultimate reflections in natural history*. New York: Harmony.

———. 2002a. *I have landed: The end of a beginning in natural history*. New York: Vintage.

———. 2002b. *The structure of evolutionary theory*. Cambridge, MA: Belknap.

Grant, P., and R. Grant. 2000. Non-random fitness variation in two populations of Darwin's finches. *Proceedings of the Royal Society of London* 267 (1439): 131–38.

Grant, P. R., and B. R. Grant. 2002. Unpredictable evolution in a 30-year study of Darwin's finches. *Science* 296:707–11.

———. 2008. *How and why species multiply: The radiation of Darwin's finches*. Princeton, NJ: Princeton University Press.

Greene, J. C. 1959. *The death of Adam*. New York: Mentor.

Groves, C. P. 1997. Thinking about evolutionary change: The polarity of our ancestors. In *Conceptual issues in modern human origins research*, ed. G. A. Clark and C. M. Willermet, 319–26. New York: Aldine de Gruyter.

Guth, A. H. 2000. Genesis: The sequel. *Natural History* 109 (1): 77–79.

Hahn, B. H., G. M. Shaw, K. M. De Cock, and P. M. Sharp. 2000. AIDS as a zoonosis: Scientific and public health implications. *Science* 287:607–14.

Haile-Selassie, Y. 2001. Late Miocene hominids from the Middle Awash, Ethiopia. *Nature* 412:178–81.

Haile-Selassie, Y., G. Suwa, and T. D. White. (2004). Late Miocene teeth from Middle Awash, Ethiopia, and early hominid dental evolution. *Science* 303 (5663): 1503–5.

Hammer, M. F., and S. L. Zegura. 1996. The role of the Y chromosome in human evolutionary studies. *Evolutionary Anthropology* 5 (4): 116–34.

Hansen, J. P., J. Meldgaard, and J. Nordqvist. 1985. The mummies of Qilakitsoq. *National Geographic* 167 (2): 191–207.

Harpending, H., and J. Relethford. 1997. Population perspectives on human origins research. In *Conceptual issues in modern human origins research*, ed. G. A. Clark and C. M. Willermet. New York: Aldine de Gruyter.

Harris, C. L. 1981. *Evolution: Genesis and revelations*. Albany: State University of New York Press.

Harrison, G. A., and A. J. Boyce, eds. 1972. *The structure of human populations*. Oxford: Clarendon.

Harrison, G. A., J. S. Weiner, J. M. Tanner, and N. A. Barnicot. 1977. *Human biology: An introduction to human evolution, variation, growth, and ecology*. 2nd ed. Oxford: Oxford University Press.

Harvey, P. H., R. D. Martin, and T. H. Clutton-Brock. 1987. Life histories in comparative perspective. In *Primate Societies*, ed. B. B. Smits et al., 181–96. Chicago: University of Chicago Press.

Hawks, J., and M. H. Wolpoff. 2001. Brief communication: Paleoanthropology and the population genetics of ancient genes. *American Journal of Physical Anthropology* 114:269–72.

Hedges, S. B., S. Kumar, K. Tamura, and M. Stoneking. 1992. Technical comments. *Science* 255:737–39.

Henshaw, S. K. 1998. Unplanned pregnancies in the United States. *Family Planning Perspectives* 30 (1).

Henshilwood, C. S., F. d'Errico, R. Yates, A. Jacobs, C. Tribolo, G. A. T. Duller, N. Mercier, J. C. Sealy, H. Valladas, I. Watts, and A. G. Wintle. 2002. Emergence of modern human behavior: Middle Stone Age engravings from South Africa. *Science* 295:1278–80.

Hern, W. M. 1993. Is human culture carcinogenic for uncontrolled population growth and ecological destruction? *BioScience* 43 (11): 768–73.

Herrnstein, R. J., and C. Murray. 1994. *The bell curve: The reshaping of American life by difference in intelligence*. New York: Free Press.

Hodgson, J. A., and T. R. Disotell. 2008. No evidence of a Neandertal contribution to modern human diversity. *Genome Biology* 9:206.

Holden, C. 1998. No last word on language origins. *Science* 282:1455–58.

———. 1999. Patrimony debate gets ugly. *Science* 285:195.

———. 2001a. Dinner in a mound. *Science* 291:587.

———. 2001b. Oldest human DNA reveals Aussie oddity. *Science* 291:230–31.

Holliday, T. W. 1997. Postcranial evidence of cold adaptation in European Neandertals. *American Journal of Physical Anthropology* 104:245–58.

Holloway, R. 1980. Indonesian "Solo" (Ngandong) endocranial reconstructions: Preliminary observations and comparisons with Neandertal and *Homo erectus* groups. *American Journal of Physical Anthropology* 53:285–95.

———. 1981. The Indonesian *Homo erectus* brain endocasts revisited. *American Journal of Physical Anthropology* 55:503–21.

Hostetler, J. A. 1974. *Hutterite society*. Baltimore: Johns Hopkins University Press.

Huyghe, P. 1988. No bone unturned. *Discover*, December: 9, 38–45.

Ingman, M., H. Kaessmann, S. Pääbo, and U. Gyllensten. 2000. Mitochondrial genome variation and the origin of modern humans. *Nature* 408:708–13.

Ingmanson, E. 1996. Tool-using behavior in wild *Pan paniscus*: Social and ecological considerations. In *Reaching into thought: The minds of the great apes*, ed. A. Russon, K. Bard, and S. Taylor. Cambridge: Cambridge University Press.

Ingmanson, E., and H. Ihobe. 1992. Predation and meat eating by *Pan paniscus* at Wamba, Zaire. Paper delivered at the 61st Annual Meeting of the American Association of Physical Anthropologists, Las Vegas, NV.

Ingmanson, E., and T. Kano. 1993. Waging peace. *International Wildlife*, November–December: 30–37.

International HapMap Consortium. 2003. The international HapMap project. *Nature* 426:789–96.

———. 2005. A haplotype map of the human genome. *Nature* 437:1299–1320.

International SNP Map Working Group. 2001. A map of human genome sequence variation contains 1.42 million single nucleotide polymorphisms. *Nature* 409:928–33.

Jablonski, N. G., and G. Chaplin. 2000. The evolution of human skin coloration. *Journal of Human Evolution* 39 (1): 57–106.

———. 2002. Skin deep. *Scientific American*, October: 74–81.

Janus, C. 1975. *The search for Peking Man*. New York: Macmillan.

Jegalian, K., and B. T. Lahn. 2001. Why the Y is so weird. *Scientific American*, February: 56–61.

Jensen, A. R. 1969. How much can we boost IQ and scholastic achievement? *Harvard Educational Review* 39 (1, Winter): 1–123.

Jobling, M. A., and C. Tyler-Smith. 1995. Fathers and sons: The Y chromosome and human evolution. *Trends in Genetics* 11:449–56.

Johanson, D., and J. Shreeve. 1989. *Lucy's child: The discovery of a human ancestor*. New York: Morrow.

Johanson, D. C., and M. A. Edey. 1981. *Lucy: The beginnings of humankind*. New York: Simon & Schuster.

Johnson, T. C., C. A. Scholz, M. R. Talbot, K. Kelts, R. D. Ricketts, G. Ngobi, K. Beuning, I. Ssemmanda, and J. W. McGill. 1996. Late Pleistocene dessication of Lake Victoria and rapid evolution of cichlid fishes. *Science* 273 (23 August): 1091–93.

Jolly, A. 1985. *The evolution of primate behavior.* New York: Macmillan.

———. 1988. Madagascar's lemurs: On the edge of survival. *National Geographic* 174 (2): 132–61.

Jones, K. E., N. G. Patel, M. A. Levy, A. Storeygard, D. Balk, J. L. Gittleman, and P. Daszak. 2008. Global trends in emerging infectious diseases. *Nature* 451:990–93.

Judson, O. 2008. Inside the code. *Natural History* (March): 31–34.

Jungers, W. L., W. E. H. Harcourt-Smith, S. G. Larson, M. J. Morwood, and T. Djubiantono. 2008. Hobbit bipedalism: Functional anatomy of the foot of *Homo floresiensis.* Paper delivered at the 77th annual meeting of the American Association of Physical Anthropologists, Columbus, OH.

Junta de Castilla y León. 2003. *The first Europeans: Treasures from the hills of Atapuerca.* New York: Junta de Castilla y León.

Kano, T. 1990. The bonobos' peaceable kingdom. *Natural History,* November: 62–71.

Ke, Y., et al. 2001. African origin of modern humans in East Asia: A tale of 12,000 Y chromosomes. *Science* 292:1151–53.

Keith, A. 1927. *Concerning man's origin.* London: Watts.

Kennedy, K. A. R. 1976. *Human variation in space and time.* Dubuque, IA: Brown.

Kerr, R. A. 2001. Evolutionary pulse found, but complexity as well. *Science* 293:2377.

King, M.-C., and A. Motulsky. 2002. Mapping human history. *Science* 298:2342–43.

Kirkpatrick, M. 2000. Fish found in *flagrante delicto. Nature* 408:298–99.

Kirkpatrick, M., and T. Price. 2008. In sight of speciation. *Nature* 455:601–2.

Korber, B., M. Muldoon, J. Theiler, F. Gao, R. Gupta, A. Lapedes, B. H. Hahn, S. Wolinsky, and T. Bhattacharya. 2000. Timing the ancestor of the HIV-1 pandemic strains. *Science* 288:1789–96.

Krause, J., et al. 2007. Neandertals in central Asia and Siberia. *Nature* 449:902–4.

Krings, M., H. Geisert, R. W. Schmitz, H. Krainitzki, and S. Pääbo. 1999. DNA sequence of the mitochondrial hypervariable region II from the Neandertal type specimen. *Proceedings of the National Academy of Sciences* 96 (10): 5581–85.

Krings, M., A. Stone, R. W. Schmitz, H. Krainitzki, M. Stoneking, and S. Pääbo. 1997. Neandertal DNA sequences and the origin of modern humans. *Cell* 90 (1): 19–30.

Kunzig, R. 1997. The face of an ancestral child. *Discover* 18 (12): 88–101.

Lack, D. 1947. *Darwin's finches: An essay on the general biological theory of evolution.* Cambridge: Cambridge University Press.

Lahr, M. M., and R. Foley. 2004. Human evolution writ small. *Nature* 431:1043–44.

Langdon, J. H. 2005. *The human strategy: An evolutionary perspective on human anatomy.* New York: Oxford University Press.

Leakey, M. G., C. S. Feibel, I. McDougall, and A. Walker. 1995. New four-million-year-old hominid species from Kanapoi and Allia Bay, Kenya. *Nature* 376:565–71.

Leakey, M. G., F. Spoor, F. H. Brown, P. N. Gathogo, C. Kiarie, L. N. Leakey, and I. McDougall. 2001. New hominid genus from eastern Africa shows diverse Middle Pliocene lineages. *Nature* 410: 433–40.

Leakey, M. G., F. Spoor, F. H. Brown, P. N. Gathogo, and L. N. Leakey. 2003. A new hominin calvaria from Ileret (Kenya). Paper delivered at the 72nd Annual Meeting of the American Association of Physical Anthropologists, Tempe, AZ.

Leakey, R., and R. Lewin. 1992. *Origins reconsidered: In search of what makes us human.* New York: Doubleday.

———. 1995. *The sixth extinction: Patterns of life and the future of humankind.* New York: Doubleday.

Lehrman, S. 2006. Trace elements: Reconnecting African-Americans to an ancestral past. *Scientific American,* June: 16–18.

Lemonick, M. D. 1994. One less missing link. *Time,* 3 October: 68–69.

Leonard, W. R. 2002. Food for thought. *Scientific American,* December: 106–15.

Lewin, R. 1991. The biochemical route to human origins. *Mosaic* 22 (3): 46–55.

Lewontin, R. 1982. *Human diversity.* New York: Scientific American Books.

Li, J. Z., et al. 2008. Worldwide human relationships inferred from genome-wide patterns of variation. *Science* 319:1100–4.

Li, W.-H., and M. A. Saunders. 2005. The chimpanzee and us. *Nature* 437:50–51.

Lieberman, D. E. 2005. Further fossil finds from Flores. *Nature* 437:957–58.

Linz, B., et al. 2007. An African origin for the intimate association between humans and *Helicobacter pylori*. *Nature* 445:915–18.

Livingstone, F. B. 1958. Anthropological implications of sickle cell gene distribution in West Africa. *American Anthropologist* 60:533–62.

Lordkipanidze, D., et al. 2007. Postcranial evidence from early *Homo* from Dmanisi, Georgia. *Nature* 449:305–10.

Luo, Z.-X. 2007. Transformation and diversification in early mammal evolution. *Nature* 450:1011–19.

Lyell, C. 1873. *The geological evidences of the antiquity of man.* London: Murray.

Malik, K. 2000. Sporting colours. *Nature* 407:131–32.

Malthus, T. R. 1789. *An essay on the principles of population as it affects the future improvement of society with remarks on the speculations of Mr. Godwin, M. Condorcet and other writers* (facsimile of the first edition, 1926). London: Macmillan.

Maples, W. R., and M. Browning. 1994. *Dead men do tell tales.* New York: Doubleday.

Marean, C. W., et al. 2007. Early human use of marine resources and pigment in South Africa during the Middle Pleistocene. *Nature* 449:905–8.

Marks, J. 1994. Book reviews. *Human Biology* 66:1113–17.

———. 1995. *Human biodiversity: Genes, race, and history.* New York: Aldine de Gruyter.

———. 2002. *What it means to be 98% chimpanzee: Apes, people, and their genes.* Berkeley: University of California Press.

———. Phylogenetic trees and evolutionary forests. *Evolutionary Anthropology* 14:49–53.

Marks, J., and R. B. Lyles. 1994. Rethinking genes. *Evolutionary Anthropology* 3 (4): 139–46.

Martin, M. K., and B. Voorhies. 1975. *Female of the species.* New York: Columbia University Press.

Martin, R. D. 1993. Primate origins: Plugging the gap. *Nature* (20 May): 223–24.

McCollum, M. A. 1999. The robust australopithecine face: A morphogenic perspective. *Science* 284:301–4.

McGrew, W. C. 1998. Culture in nonhuman primates? *Annual Review of Anthropology* 27:301–28.

McKenna, J. J. 1996. Babies need their mothers beside them. *World Health*, March–April: 14–15.

Meier, R. J. 2003. *The complete idiot's guide to human prehistory.* New York: Alpha.

Menon, S. 1997. Neanderthal noses. *Discover*, March: 30.

Mercader, J., M. Panger, and C. Boesch. 2002. Excavation of a chimpanzee stone tool site in the African rainforest. *Science* 296:1452–55.

Mettler, L. E., T. G. Gregg, and H. E. Schaffer. 1988. *Population genetics and evolution.* Englewood Cliffs, NJ: Prentice Hall.

Mielke, J. H., L. W. Konigsberg, and J. H. Relethford. 2006. *Human biological variation.* New York: Oxford University Press.

Miller, G. 2007. All together now—pull! *Science* 317:1338–40.

Miller, K. R. 1999. *Finding Darwin's god.* New York: HarperCollins.

Mills, C. 1997. The deadliest virus. The *Sciences*, January–February: 34–38.

Minugh-Purvis, N. 1995. The modern human origins controversy: 1984–1994. *Evolutionary Anthropology* 4 (4): 140–47.

Molnar, S. 1992. *Human variation: Races, types, and ethnic groups.* 3rd ed. Englewood Cliffs, NJ: Prentice Hall.

Montagu, A., ed. 1964. *The concept of race.* New York: Collier.

———. 1997. *Man's most dangerous myth: The fallacy of race.* Walnut Creek, CA: Altamira.

Morris, H. M. 1974. *The troubled waters of evolution.* San Diego, CA: Creation-Life Publishers.

Morwood, M., T. Sutikna, and R. Roberts. 2005. World of the little people. *National Geographic* 207:2–15.

Morwood, M. J., et al. 2005. Further evidence for small-bodied hominins from the Late Pleistocene of Flores, Indonesia. *Nature* 437:1012–17.

Mosko, S., C. Richard, J. McKenna, S. Drummond, and D. Mukai. 1997. Maternal proximity and infant CO_2 environment during bedsharing and possible implications for SIDS research. *American Journal of Physical Anthropology* 103 (3): 315–28.

Mowat, F. 1987. *Woman in the mists*. New York: Warner.

Muchmore, E. A., S. Diaz, and A. Varki. 1998. A structural difference between the cell surfaces of humans and great apes. *American Journal of Physical Anthropology* 107:187–98.

Müller, W., H. Fricke, A. N. Halliday, M. T. McCulloch, and J.-A. Wartho. 2003. Origin and migration of the Alpine Iceman. *Science* 302:862–65.

Nafte, M. 2000. *Flesh and bone*. Durham, NC: Carolina Academic Press.

Nanda, S. 1990. *Neither man nor woman: The hijras of India*. Belmont, CA: Wadsworth.

National Center for Health Statistics. 2004. Deaths: Preliminary data for 2004. www.cdc.gov/nchs/products/pubs/pubd/hestats/prelimdeaths04/preliminarydeaths04.htm.

Nesse, R. M., and G. C. Williams. 1998. Evolution and the origins of disease. *Scientific American*, November: 52–58.

Nichols, M., J. Goodall, G. B. Schaller, and M. G. Smith. 1993. *The great apes: Between two worlds*. Washington, DC: National Geographic Society.

Normile, D. 2001. Gene expression differs in human and chimp brains. *Science* 292:44–45.

O'Brien, S. J., and R. Stanyon. 1999. Ancestral primate revealed. *Nature* 402 (25 November): 356–66.

Oliwenstein, L. 1995. Dr. Darwin. *Discover*, October: 111–17.

Omohundro, J. T. 2001. *Careers in anthropology*. 2nd ed. Mountain View, CA: Mayfield.

Orgel, L. E. 1994. The origin of life on the earth. *Scientific American* 271 (4): 76–83.

Orr, H. A. 2005a. Devolution. *New Yorker*, 30 May: 40–52.

———. 2005b. Turned on. *New Yorker*, 24 October: 85–88.

Ovchinnikov, I., A. Götherström, G. Romanova, V. Kharitonov, K. Lindén, and W. Goodman. 2000. Molecular analysis of Neandertal DNA from the northern Caucasus. *Nature* 404:490–92.

Pääbo, S. 2001. The human genome and our view of ourselves. *Science* 291:1219–20.

Padian, K. 2008. Darwin's enduring legacy. *Nature* 451 (7): 632–34.

Parfitt, S. A., et al. 2005. The earliest record of human activity in northern Europe. *Nature* 438:1008–12.

Park, M. A. 1979. Dermatoglyphics as a tool for population studies: An example. Ph.D. dissertation, Department of Anthropology, Indiana University, Bloomington.

———. 1982–1983. Palmistry: Science or hand-jive? *Skeptical Inquirer* 7 (2): 21–32.

———. 1999. The homegoing. In *Lessons from the past*, ed. K. L. Feder, 80–83. Mountain View, CA: Mayfield.

———. 2009. *Biological anthropology: An introductory reader*. 6th ed. New York: McGraw-Hill.

———. 2008. *Introducing anthropology: An integrated approach*. 4th ed. New York: McGraw-Hill.

Parker, I. 2007. Swingers. *New Yorker*, 30 July: 48–61.

Parra, E. J. 2007. Human pigmentation variation: Evolution, genetic basis, and implications for public health. *Yearbook of Physical Anthropology* 50:85–105.

Partridge, T. C., D. E. Granger, M. W. Caffee, and R. J. Clarke. 2003. Lower Pliocene hominid remains from Sterkfontein. *Science* 300:607–12.

Passingham, R. 1982. *The human primate*. New York: Freeman.

Pearson, H. 2006. What is a gene? *Nature* 441:339–401.

Pearson, O. M. 2000. Postcranial remains and the origin of modern humans. *Evolutionary Anthropology* 9 (6): 229–47.

Pennisi, E. 2001. Malaria's beginnings: On the heels of hoes? *Science* 293:416–17.

———. 2006. Competition drives big beaks out of business. *Science* 313:156.

Perry, W., and M. Blakey. 1999. Archaeology as community service: The African Burial Ground Project in New York City. In *Lessons from the past*, ed. K. L. Feder, 45–51. Mountain View, CA: Mayfield.

Pfeiffer, J. 1966. When *Homo erectus* tamed fire, he tamed himself. *New York Times Magazine*, 11 December.

Pilbeam, D. 1984. The descent of the hominoids and hominids. *Scientific American* 250 (3): 84–96.

———. 1986. Human origins. *David Skomp Distinguished Lecture in Anthropology*. Bloomington: Indiana University.

Podolefsky, A., and P. J. Brown, eds. 1994. *Applying anthropology: An introductory reader*. 5th ed. Mountain View, CA: Mayfield.

Podos, J. 2001. Correlated evolution of morphology and vocal signal structure in Darwin's finches. *Nature* 409:185–87.

Pollack, A. 2008. The promise and power of RNA. *New York Times,* 11 November, D1, D3.

Post, P. W., F. Daniels, Jr., and R. T. Binford. 1975. Cold injury and the evolution of "white" skin. *Human Biology* 47:65–80.

Potts, R. 1984. Home bases and early hominids. *American Scientist* 72:338–47.

Power, M. 1991. *The egalitarians—human and chimpanzee: An anthropological view of social organization.* Cambridge: Cambridge University Press.

Prag, J., and R. Neave. 1997. *Making faces: Using forensic and archaeological evidence.* College Station: Texas A&M University Press.

Prum, R. O., and A. H. Brush. 2003. Which came first, the feather or the bird? *Scientific American,* March: 84–93.

Prusiner, S. B. 1997. Prion diseases and the BSE crisis. *Science* 278 (10 October): 245–51.

Quammen, D. 2004. Darwin's big idea. *National Geographic* 206 (5): 2–35.

Raby, P. 1996. *Bright paradise: Victorian scientific travellers.* Princeton, NJ: Princeton University Press.

Reinhard, J. 1996. Peru's ice maidens. *National Geographic* 189 (6): 62–81.

———. 1997. Mummies of Peru. *National Geographic* 191 (1): 36–43.

———. 1999. Frozen in time. *National Geographic* 196 (5): 36–55.

Relethford, J. H. 2001. *Genetics and the search for modern human origins.* New York: Wiley-Liss.

———. 2003. *Reflections of our past: How human history is revealed in our genes.* Boulder, CO: Westview.

———. 2008. *The human species: An introduction to biological anthropology.* 7th ed. New York: McGraw-Hill.

———. 2008. Genetic evidence and the modern human origins debate. *Heredity* 100:555–63.

Relethford, J. H., and H. C. Harpending. 1995. Ancient differences in population size can mimic a recent African origin of modern humans. *Current Anthropology* 36 (4): 667–74.

Rhine, S. 1998. *Bone voyage: A journey in forensic anthropology.* Albuquerque: University of New Mexico Press.

Rhodes, R. 1997. *Deadly feasts: Tracking the secrets of a terrifying new plague.* New York: Simon & Schuster.

Richmond, B. G., and W. L. Jungers. 2008. *Orrorin tugenensis* femoral morphology and the evolution of hominin bipedalism. *Science* 319:1662–65.

Ridley, Mark. 1996. *Evolution.* 2nd ed. Boston: Blackwell Scientific Publications.

Ridley, Matt. 1999. *Genome: The autobiography of a species in 23 chapters.* New York: HarperCollins.

Roberts, D. 1993. The Ice Man. *National Geographic* 183 (6): 36–67.

Robey, B., S. O. Rutstein, and L. Morris. 1993. The fertility decline in developing countries. *Scientific American,* December: 60–67.

Robins, A. 1991. *Biological perspectives on human pigmentation.* Cambridge: Cambridge University Press.

Rosen, J. 2007. Missing link. *New Yorker,* 12 February: 76–81.

Rosenberg, N. A., J. K. Pritchard, J. L. Weber, H. M. Cann, K. K. Kidd, L. A. Zhivotovsky, and M. W. Feldman. 2002. Genetic structure of human populations. *Science* 298:2381–85.

Rowe, N. 1996. *The pictorial guide to the living primates.* East Hampton, NY: Pogonius.

Rowen, L., G. Mahairas, and L. Hood. 1997. Sequencing the human genome. *Science* 278 (24 October): 605–7.

Ryan, F. 1997. *Virus X: Tracking the new killer plagues out of the present and into the future.* Boston: Little, Brown.

Sabeti, P. C., et al. 2006. Positive natural selection in the human lineage. *Science* 312:1614–20.

Sagan, C. 1977. *The dragons of Eden: Speculations on the evolution of human intelligence.* New York: Random House.

———. 1996. *The demon-haunted world: Science as a candle in the dark.* New York: Random House.

Sargis, E. J. 2002. Primate origins nailed. *Science* 298:1564–65.

Savage-Rumbaugh, E. S., S. Shanker, T. J. Taylor, and S. Savage-Rumbaugh. 1998. *Apes, language, and the human mind.* Oxford: Oxford University Press.

Savage-Rumbaugh, S., and R. Lewin. 1994a. Ape at the brink. *Discover,* September: 91–98.

———. 1994b. *Kanzi: The ape at the brink of the human mind.* New York: Wiley.

Schadewald, R. 1981–1982. Scientific creationism, geocentricity and the flat earth. *Skeptical Inquirer* 6 (2): 41–48.

———. 1986. Creationist pseudoscience. In *Science confronts the paranormal*, ed. Kendrick Frazier. Buffalo, NY: Prometheus.

Schick, K. D., and N. Toth. 1993. *Making silent stones speak: Human evolution and the dawn of technology.* New York: Morrow.

Schoeninger, M. J. 1995. Stable isotope studies in human evolution. *Evolutionary Anthropology* 4 (3): 83–98.

Scholz, M., L. Bachmann, G. J. Nicholson, J. Bachmann, I. Giddings, B. Rüschoff-Thale, A. Czarnetzki, and C. M. Pusch. 2000. Genomic differentiation of Neanderthals and anatomically modern man allows a fossil DNA-based classification of morphologically indistinguishable hominid bones. *American Journal of Human Genetics* 66:1927–32.

Schultz, E., and R. Lavenda. 1998. *Anthropology: A perspective on the human condition.* 2nd ed. Mountain View, CA: Mayfield.

Schuster, A. M. H. 2001. World's oldest woodworking? *Archaeology Online News*, 31 January. www.archaeology. org/online/news.

Schwartz, J. H. 1995. *Skeleton keys: An introduction to human skeletal morphology, development, and analysis.* New York: Oxford University Press.

———. 2004. Getting to know *Homo erectus. Science* 305:53–54.

Science. 2003. Iceman fights back. *Science* 301:1043.

Scientific American and Financial Times. 2005. The future of stem cells. *Scientific American*, July: Special Report.

Self, S., S. Blake, K. Sharma, M. Widdowson, and S. Sephton. 2008. Sulfur and chlorine in Late Cretaceous Deccan magmas and eruptive gas release. *Science* 319:1654–57.

Service, R. F. 2000. Where dead men really do tell tales. *Science* 289:855–57.

Sewa, G., B. Asfaw, Y. Beyene, T. D. White, S. Katoh, S. Nagaoka, H. Nakaya, K. Uzawa, P. Renne, and G. WoldeGabriel. 1997. The first skull of *Australopithecus boisei. Nature* 389 (2 October): 489–92.

Sharer, R. J., and W. Ashmore. 1993. *Archaeology: Discovering our past.* 2nd ed. Mountain View, CA: Mayfield.

Shea, J. 1989. A functional study of the lithic industries associated with hominid fossils in Kebara and Qafzeh Caves, Israel. In *The human revolution: Behavioural and biological perspectives in the origins of modern humans*, ed. P. Mellars and C. Stringer, 611–25. Princeton, NJ: Princeton University Press.

Shermer, M. 2002. *In Darwin's shadow: The life and science of Alfred Russel Wallace.* New York: Oxford University Press.

Sherwood, R. J. 2000. The status of early *Homo.* Paper delivered at the 69th Annual Meeting of the American Association of Physical Anthropologists, San Antonio, TX.

Shipman, P. 1981. *Life history of a fossil: An introduction to taphonomy and paleoecology.* Cambridge, MA: Harvard University Press.

———. 1984. Scavenger hunt. *Natural History* 93 (4): 20–27.

———. 1986. Scavenging or hunting in early hominids: Theoretical frameworks and tests. *American Anthropologist* 88:27–43.

———. 2001. *The man who found the missing link: Eugene Dubois and his lifelong quest to prove Darwin right.* New York: Simon & Schuster.

Shipman, P., and J. Rose. 1983. Evidence of butchery and hominid activities at Torralba and Ambrona: An evaluation using microscopic techniques. *Journal of Archaeological Science* 10:465–74.

Shreeve, J. 1994. *Erectus* rising. *Discover*, September: 80–89.

———. 1995. The Neanderthal peace. *Discover*, September: 70–81.

———. 1999. Secrets of the gene. *National Geographic* 196 (4): 42–75.

———. 2006. Human journey. *National Geographic* 209:60–73.

Silk, J. B., et al. 2005. Chimpanzees are indifferent to the welfare of unrelated group members. *Nature* 437:1357–59.

Simerly, C., et al. 2003. Molecular correlates of primate nuclear transfer failures. *Science* 300:297.

Simons, E. L., and T. Rasmussen. 1994. A whole new world of ancestors: Eocene anthropoideans from Africa. *Evolutionary Anthropology* 3 (4): 128–39.

Simons, M. 1996. New species of early human reported found in Africa. *New York Times*, 23 May, A8.

Simpson, G. G. 1961. *Principles of animal taxonomy.* New York: Columbia University Press.

Smail, J. K. 1999. Beyond population stabilization: The case for dramatically reducing global human numbers. *Politics and Life Sciences* 16 (2):183–92.

Small, M. F. 1992. A reasonable sleep. *Discover,* April: 83–88.

Smith, B. H. 1993. Life history and the evolution of human maturation. *Evolutionary Anthropology* 1 (4): 134–42.

Smith, F. H. 1994. Samples, species, and speculations in the study of modern human origins. In *Origins of anatomically modern humans,* ed. M. Nitecki and D. Nitecki, 227–52. New York: Plenum.

Smith, F. H., A. B. Falsetti, and S. M. Donnelly. 1989. Modern human origins. *Yearbook of Physical Anthropology* 32:35–68.

Smith, J. M. 1984. Science and myth. *Natural History* 93 (11): 10–24.

Smith, S. L., and F. B. Harrold. 1997. A paradigm's worth of difference? Understanding the impasse over modern human origins. *Yearbook of Physical Anthropology* 40:113–38.

Smuts, B. 1985. *Sex and friendship in baboons.* Hawthorne, NY: Aldine de Gruyter.

———. 1995. Apes of wrath. *Discover,* August: 35–37.

Snow, C. C., and J. L. Luke. 1970. The Oklahoma City child disappearances: Forensic anthropology in the identification of skeletal remains. In *Applying anthropology,* ed. A. Podolefsky and P. J. Brown. Mountain View, CA: Mayfield.

Sokolove, M. 2004. The lab animal. *New York Times Magazine,* 18 January: 28–33, 48, 54, 58.

Specter, M. 1999. Decoding Iceland. *New Yorker,* 18 January: 40–51.

Sponheimer, M., and J. A. Lee-Thorp. 1999. Isotopic evidence for the diet of an early hominid, *Australopithecus africanus. Science* 283:368–69.

Sponheimer, M., B. H. Passey, D. J. deRuiter, D. Guatelli-Steinberg, T. E. Cerling, and J. A. Lee-Thorp. 2006. Isotopic evidence for dietary variability in the early hominin *Paranthropus robustus. Science* 314:980–81.

Stanford, C. 1999. *The hunting apes: Meat eating and the origins of human behavior.* Princeton, NJ: Princeton University Press.

Stanford, C. B. 1995. To catch a colobus. *Natural History* 104 (1): 48–55.

———. 2006. Arboreal bipedalism in wild chimpanzees: Implications for the evolution of hominid posture and locomotion. *American Journal of Physical Anthropology* 129:225–31.

Stedman, H. H., et al. 2004. Myosin gene mutation correlates with anatomical changes in the human lineage. *Nature* 428:415–18.

Stern, J. T., Jr. 2000. Climbing to the top: A personal memoir of *Australopithecus afarensis. Evolutionary Anthropology* 9 (3): 113–33.

Steudel, K. 1996. Limb morphology, bipedal gait, and the energetics of hominid locomotion. *American Journal of Physical Anthropology* 99 (2): 345–56.

Stinson, S. 2000. Growth variation: Biological and cultural factors. In *Human biology: An evolutionary and biocultural perspective,* ed. S. Stinson et al. New York: Wiley-Liss.

Stinson, S., B. Bogin, R. Huss-Ashmore, and D. O'Rourke, eds. 2000. *Human biology: An evolutionary and biocultural perspective.* New York: Wiley-Liss.

Stix, G. 2008. Traces of a distant past. *Scientific American,* July: 56–63.

Stone, R. 2000. Ice Man warms up for European scientists. *Science* 289:2253–54.

Stoneking, M. 1993. DNA and recent human evolution. *Evolutionary Anthropology* 2 (2): 60–73.

———. 2001. From the evolutionary past . . . *Nature* 409:821–22.

Strait, D. S., and F. E. Grine. 1999. Cladistics and early hominid phylogeny. *Science* 285:1210.

Stringer, C. 1994. Out of Africa: A personal history. In *Origins of anatomically modern humans,* ed. M. H. Nitecki and D. V. Nitecki, 149–72. New York: Plenum.

———. 2003. Out of Ethiopia. *Nature* 423:692–95.

Stringer, C., and P. Andrews. 1988. Genetic and fossil evidence for the origin of modern humans. *Science* 239:1263–68.

Stringer, C., and C. Gamble. 1993. *In search of the Neanderthals: Solving the puzzle of human origins.* London: Thames and Hudson.

Stringer, C., and R. McKie. 1996. *African exodus: The origins of modern humanity.* New York: Holt.

Strum, S. 1987. *Almost human.* New York: Random House.

Summers, A. 2005. Born to run. *Scientific American,* April: 34–35.

Sussman, R. W. 1997. Exploring our basic human nature: Are humans inherently violent? *AnthroNotes* 19 (3).

———, ed. 1999. *The biological basis of human behavior: A critical review.* 2nd ed. Upper Saddle River, NJ: Prentice Hall.

Suwa, G., et al. 1997. The first skull of *Australopithecus boisei. Nature* 389:489–92.

Suwa, G., R. T. Kono, S. Katoh, B. Asfaw, and Y. Beyene. 2007. A new species of great ape from the Late Miocene epoch in Ethiopia. *Nature* 448:921–24.

Takai, M., F. Anaya, N. Shigehara, and T. Setoguchi. 2000. New fossil materials of the earliest New World monkey, *Branisella boliviana*, and the problem of platyrrhine origins. *American Journal of Physical Anthropology* 111:263–81.

Tattersall, I. 1992. The many faces of *Homo habilis. Evolutionary Anthropology* 1 (1): 33–37.

———. 1993. *The human odyssey: Four million years of human evolution.* New York: Prentice Hall.

———. 1994. What do we mean by human—and why does it matter? *Evolutionary Anthropology* 3 (4): 114–16.

———. 1995. *The last Neanderthal: The rise, success, and mysterious extinction of our closest human relatives.* New York: Macmillan.

———. 1997. Out of Africa again . . . and again? *Scientific American,* April: 60–67.

———. 2001. How we came to be human. *Scientific American,* December: 56–63.

———. 2003. Stand and deliver: Why did early hominids begin to walk on two feet? *Natural History,* November: 61–64.

Tattersall, I., and J. Schwarz. 2000. *Extinct humans.* Boulder, CO: Westview.

Tavaré, S., C. R. Marshall, O. Will, C. Soligo, and R. D. Martin. 2002. Using the fossil record to estimate the age of the last common ancestor of extant primates. *Nature* 416:726–29.

Teitelbaum, M. S., ed. 1976. *Sex differences.* Garden City, NY: Anchor Press/Doubleday.

Templeton, A. R. 1993. The "Eve" hypothesis: A genetic critique and reanalysis. *American Anthropologist* 95:51–72.

———. 1996. Gene lineages and human evolution. *Science* 272:1363.

———. 1997. Testing the Out of Africa replacement hypothesis with mitochondrial DNA data. In *Conceptual issues in modern human origins research,* ed. G. A. Clark and C. M. Willermet. New York: Aldine de Gruyter.

———. 2002. Out of Africa again and again. *Nature* 416:45–51.

———. 2005. Haplotype trees and modern human origins. *Yearbook of Physical Anthropology* 48:33–59.

Thieme, H. 1997. Lower Paleolithic hunting spears from Germany. *Nature* 385:807–10.

Thompson, M. J., and D. W. Harsha. 1984. Our rhythms still follow the African sun. *Psychology Today,* January: 50–54.

Thorpe, S. K. S., R. L. Holder, and R. H. Crompton. 2007. Origin of human bipedalism as an adaptation for locomotion on flexible branches. *Science* 316:1328–31.

Thurman, J. 2008. First impressions. *New Yorker,* June 23: 58–67.

Time-Life Books, eds. 1973. *The first men.* New York: Time-Life Books.

Tocheri, M. W., et al. 2007. The primitive wrist of *Homo floresiensis* and its implications for hominin evolution. *Science* 317:1743–45.

Todd, T. W. 1920. Age changes in the pubic bone. *American Journal of Physical Anthropology* 3:285–384.

Toth, N. 1985. The Oldowan reassessed: A close look at early stone tools. *Journal of Archaeological Science* 2:101–20.

Tuchman, B. W. 1978. *A distant mirror: The calamitous fourteenth century.* New York: Knopf.

Tullar, R. M. 1977. *The human species: Its nature, evolution, and ecology.* New York: McGraw-Hill.

Turner, A., P. J. Makovicky, and M. A. Norell. 2007. Feather quill knobs in the dinosaur *Velociraptor. Science* 317:1721.

Ubelaker, D., and H. Scammell. 1992. *Bones: A forensic detective's casebook.* New York: HarperCollins.

UNAIDS/WHO. 2008. AIDS epidemic update. www.unaids.org/en.

Underwood, J. H. 1979. *Human variation and human microevolution.* Englewood Cliffs, NJ: Prentice Hall.

Unger, P. S., and R. S. Scott. 2008. Investigating the importance of fallback foods in early hominins using dental microwear. Paper delivered at the 77th annual meeting of the American Association of Physical Anthropologists, Columbus, OH.

Van Blerkom, L. M. 2003. Role of viruses in human evolution. *Yearbook of Physical Anthropology* 46: 14–46.

van Schaik, C. P., et al. 2003. Orangutan cultures and the evolution of material culture. *Science* 299:102–5.

Vekua, A., et al. 2002. A new skull of early *Homo* from Dmanisi, Georgia. *Science* 297:85–89.

Venter, J. C., et al. 2001. The sequence of the human genome. *Science* 291:1304–51.

Verheyen, E., W. Salzburger, J. Snoeks, and A. Meyer. 2003. Origin of the superflock of cichlid fishes from Lake Victoria, East Africa. *Science* 300:325–29.

Vogel, G. 2006. Tracking Ebola's deadly march among wild apes. *Science* 314:1522–23.

Wade, N. 1998. Human or chimp? 50 genes are the key. *New York Times*, 20 October, F1, 4.

Walsh, P. D., et al. 2003. Catastrophic ape decline in western equatorial Africa. *Nature* 422:611–14.

Ward, C., M. Leakey, and A. Walker. 1999. The new hominid species *Australopithecus anamensis. Evolutionary Anthropology* 7 (6): 197–205.

Watson, A. 2000. A new breed of high-tech detectives. *Science* 289:850–54.

Weaver, K. F. 1985. The search for our ancestors. *National Geographic* 168:560–623.

Weaver, R. F. 1984. Changing life's genetic blueprint. *National Geographic*, December: 818–47.

Weiner, J. 1994. *The beak of the finch: A story of evolution in our time.* New York: Knopf.

Weiss, K. M., and A. V. Buchanan. 2000. Rediscovering Darwin after a Darwinian century. *Evolutionary Anthropology* 9 (5): 187–200.

Wells, J. C. K., and J. T. Stock. 2007. The biology of the colonizing ape. *Yearbook of Physical Anthropology* 50:199–222.

White, F. J. 1996. *Pan paniscus* 1973 to 1996: Twenty-three years of field research. *Evolutionary Anthropology* 5 (1): 11–17.

White, T. D. 2001. Once we were cannibals. *Scientific American*, August: 58–65.

———. 2003. Early hominids—diversity or distortion? *Science*, 299:1994–97.

White, T. D., B. Asfaw, D. DeGusta, H. Gilbert, G. D. Richards, G. Suwa, and F. C. Howell. 2003. Pleistocene *Homo sapiens* from Middle Awash, Ethiopia. *Nature* 423:742–47.

White, T. D., and P. A. Folkens. 1991. *Human osteology.* San Diego: Academic Press.

White, T. D., G. Suwa, and B. Asfaw. 1994. *Australopithecus ramidus,* a new species of early hominid from Aramis, Ethiopia. *Nature* 371 (22 September): 306–12.

Whiten, A. 2005. The second inheritance system of chimpanzees and humans. *Nature* 437:52–55.

Whiten, A., and C. Boesch. 2001. The cultures of chimpanzees. *Scientific American,* January: 60–67.

Whiten, A., J. Goodall, W. C. McGrew, T. Nishida, V. Reynolds, Y. Sugiyama, C. E. G. Tutin, R. W. Wrangham, and C. Boesch. 1999. Cultures in chimpanzees. *Nature* 399 (17 June): 682–85.

Whiten, A., V. Horner, and F. B. M. de Waal. 2005. Conformity to cultural norms of tool use in chimpanzees. *Nature* 437:737–40.

Wilford, J. N. 1994. Fog thickens on climate and origin of humans. *New York Times,* 17 May, C1, 8.

Wilmut, I. 1998. Cloning for medicine. *Scientific American,* December: 58–63.

Wilmut, I., A. E. Schnieke, J. McWhir, A. J. Kind, and K. H. S. Campbell. 1997. Viable offspring derived from fetal and adult mammalian cells. *Nature* 385 (27 February): 810–13.

Wilson, A. C., and R. L. Cann. 1992. The recent African genesis of humans. *Scientific American* 266 (4): 68–73.

Wilson, E. O. 1992. *The diversity of life* (College edition with study materials). New York: Norton.

———. 1998. *Consilience: The Unity of Knowledge.* New York: Knopf.

Winchester, S. 2002. *The map that changed the world: William Smith and the birth of modern geology.* New York: HarperCollins/Perennial.

Wolpoff, M. 1989. Multiregional evolution: The fossil alternative to Eden. In *The human revolution: Behavioural and biological perspectives in the origins of modern humans,* ed. P. Mellars and C. Stringer, 62–108. Princeton, NJ: Princeton University Press.

———. 1994. What do we mean by human—and why does it matter? *Evolutionary Anthropology* 3 (4): 116–17.

Wolpoff, M., and R. Caspari. 1997. *Race and human evolution: A fatal attraction.* New York: Simon & Schuster.

Wolpoff, M. H., J. Hawks, D. W. Frayer, and K. Hunley. 2001. Modern human ancestry at the peripheries: A test of the replacement theory. *Science* 291:293–97.

Wolpoff, M. H., B. Senut, M. Pickford, and J. Hawks. 2002. Brief communication. *Nature* 419:581–82.

Wong, K. 1998. Ancestral quandary. *Scientific American* 278 (1): 30–32.

———. 2000a. The caveman's new clothes. *Scientific American*, November: 32–34.

———. 2000b. Paleolithic pit stop. *Scientific American*, December: 18–20.

———. 2003. An ancestor to call our own. *Scientific American*, January: 54–63.

———. 2005a. The littlest human. *Scientific American*, February: 56–65.

———. 2005b. The morning of the modern mind. *Scientific American*, June: 86–95.

———. 2006. Lucy's baby. *Scientific American* (December): 78–85.

Wood, B. 2002. Hominid revelations from Chad. *Nature* 418:133–35.

Wood, B., and M. Collard. 1999. The human genus. *Science* 284:65–71.

Wood, J. N., D. D. Glynn, B. C. Phillips, and M. D. Hauser. 2007. The perception of rational goal-directed action in nonhuman primates. *Science* 317:1402–5.

Woodruff, D. S., and P. A. Morin. 1995. Geneticists out on a limb. *Natural History* 104 (1): 54.

Yoon, C. K. 1996a. Lake Victoria's lightning-fast origin of species. *New York Times*, 27 August, C1, 4.

———. 1996b. Parallel plots in classic evolution. *New York Times*, 12 November, C1, 7.

———. 1998. Iguanas sail from Guadeloupe to Anguilla and into history. *New York Times*, 8 October.

Zhu, R. X., et al. 2001. Earliest presence of humans in northeast Asia. *Nature* 413:413–17.

Zimmer, C. 1995. Tooling through the trees. *Discover*, November: 46–47.

———. 2001. After you, Eve. *Natural History* 110 (2): 32–35.

———. 2008. What is a species? *Scientific American*, June: 72–79.

Zollikofer, C. P. E., et al. 2005. Virtual cranial reconstruction of *Sahelanthropus tchadensis*. *Nature* 434:755–59.

PHOTO CREDITS

Chapter 1 CO1, Courtesy of the author; 1.2, © Momatiuk/ Eastman/Woodfin Camp & Associates; 1.3, 1.4, Courtesy of the author; 1.5, © William F. Keegan/Keegan Associates; 1.6, Photograph by Michael Kodas/The Hartford Courant, 7/25/93.

Chapter 2 CO2, Courtesy K.L. Feder; 2.1, © Julia Margaret Cameron/National Portrait Gallery, London; 2.3, British Geological Survey © NERC. All rights reserved. (IPR/109-20CX); 2.4, Courtesy K.L. Feder; 2.5, Courtesy NASA; 2.8, © Robert F. Sisson/National Geographic Society Image Collection.

Chapter 3 CO3, 3.4, © David Robert Austen; 3.4, © David Robert Austen; 3.6, © CNRI/SPL/Science Source/Photo Researchers, Inc.

Chapter 4 CO4, © G. Merlen/OSF/Animals Animals; 4.1 (left), © Goodshoot/PunchStock; 4.1 (right), © Image Source/PunchStock; 4.2, © March of Dimes; 4.3, © G. Merlen/OSF/Animals Animals; 4.8, © Meckes/Ottawa/ Photo Researchers, Inc.

Chapter 5 CO5, © Tom and Theresa Stack/Tom Stack & Associates; 5.2, Courtesy of the author; 5.4, © Tom and Theresa Stack/Tom Stack & Associates; 5.6, Courtesy J.M. Beatty.

Chapter 6 CO6, © Reg Morrison; 6.2 (top), © Fred Bavendam/Peter Arnold, Inc.; 6.2 (bottom), © Reg Morrison; 6.5, © Marvin Mattelson/National Geographic Society Image Collection; 6.7, "The Age of Reptiles," a mural by Rudolph F. Zallinger. © 1966, 1975, 1985, 1989, Peabody Museum of Natural History, Yale University, New Haven, Connecticut; 6.8, Courtesy of the author.

Chapter 7 CO7, 7.4, © 2004 Frans Lanting/www.lanting. com; 7.6, Courtesy Marine World Africa USA/Darryl Bush; 7.8 (top left), 7.8 (top right), 7.8 (bottom left), © Noel Rowe; 7.8 (bottom right), Courtesy of the author; 7.9, Courtesy of the author; 7.10, © Noel Rowe; 7.13, 7.14, 7.15, 7.16, 7.17, 7.18 (top left), © Noel Rowe; 7.18 (top right), Courtesy of the author; 7.18 (bottom right), © Steve Turner/Animals Animals; 7.18 (bottom left), © Ron Garrison/Zoological Society of San Diego; 7.19, © Jane Goodall/National Geographic Society Image Collection; 7.20, Courtesy of the author.

Chapter 8 CO8, © Frans Lanting/www.lanting.com; 8.1, © Peter Johnson/Corbis; 8.2, © Timothy Ransom/Biological Photo Service; 8.3, © Irven DeVore/Anthro-Photo; 8.4, © Zig Leszczynski/Animals Animals; 8.5, © Kennan Ward/ DRK Photo; 8.6, © Frans Lanting/www.lanting.com; 8.7, © Noel Rowe.

Chapter 9 CO9, © Enrico Ferorelli; 9.1, Gorilla illustration by Enid Kotschnig. Cat illustration by Rudolf Freund; 9.4, © Karen Huntt Mason/Corbis; 9.6, Reprinted from *Identification of Pathological Conditions in Human Skeletal Remains*, Orter and Putschar (Washington, DC: Smithsonian Institution Press), pages 195,198, by permission of the publisher. © 1985; 9.7, © E.E. Kingsley 1984/ Science Source/Photo Researchers, Inc.; 9.8, © Enrico Ferorelli; 9.11, © Stephen Alvarez/National Geographic Society Image Collection.

Chapter 10 CO10, © 1985 David L. Brill; 10.4, © David L. Brill, 1985; 10.6, Courtesy Dr. Ian Tattersall, American Museum of Natural History; 10.9, © 1985 David L. Brill; 10.11, © Kenneth Garrett/National Geographic Society Image Collection; 10.12, From *Lucy: The Beginnings of Humankind*, © 1981 Luba Dmytryk Gudz/Brill Atlanta; 10.13, © John Reader/Science Photo Library/ Photo Researchers, Inc.; 10.14, © Institute of Human Origins, photography by W.H. Kimbel. Used with permission; 10.16 (left), © John Reader/Science Photo Library/Photo Researchers, Inc.; 10.16 (right), Neg. #4744(5). Photo by D. Finnin/C. Chesek. Courtesy Department of Library Services, American Museum of Natural History; 10.17, Courtesy Transvaal Museum, D.C. Panagos; 10.18, Micrographs courtesy of Dr. Frederick E. Grine, SUNY, Stony Brook. Photographed by Chester Tarka; 10.19, © Alan Walker/National Geographic Society Image Collection; 10.20, Courtesy Transvaal Museum, D.C. Panagos; 10.21, © The National Museums of Kenya; 10.22, © Tim D. White/Brill Atlanta; 10.23, © National Museums of Kenya; 10.24, © Patrick Robert/Sygma Collection/Corbis.

Chapter 11 CO11, Courtesy Comité Départemental du Tourisme de la Dordogne; 11.2, © Eric Delson; 11.4, © The National Museums of Kenya; 11.5, Courtesy

Dr. Pat Shipman; 11.7 (top), © Museum Naturalis; 11.7 (middle), Neg. #319781. Courtesy Department of Library Services, American Museum of Natural History; 11.8, Neg. #315446. Photo by Charles H. Coles. Courtesy Department of Library Services, American Museum of Natural History; 11.9, © The National Museums of Kenya; 11.11, © David L. Brill, 1985; 11.12, © Geoffrey Clifford/ Woodfin Camp and Associates; 11.14, © AP/Wide World Photos; 11.15 (left), © Boltin Picture Library/Bridgeman Art Library; 11.15 (middle), 11.15 (right), Courtesy K.L. Feder; 11.16, Illustration by Patricia J. Wynne; 11.17, © John Reader/Science Photo Library/Photo Researchers, Inc.; 11.20, © Javier Trueba/Madrid Scientific Films; 11.22, © Dr. Christopher B. Stringer/Natural History Museum, London; 11.23, © The Natural History Museum, London; 11.24, Courtesy Dr. Ian Tattersall, From *The Human Odyssey*; 11.25, © H. Lilienthal/Landschaftsverband Rheinland; 11.27 (left), © The Field Museum, Neg. #A66700; 11.27 (right), © Paul Jaronski/University of Michigan Photo Services; 11.28, From *In Search of the Neanderthals* by Clive Gamble and Christopher Stringer. Published by Thames and Hudson, Inc., New York, 1995.; 11.29, Courtesy American Museum of Natural History Library; 11.30, Courtesy K.L. Feder; 11.31, Courtesy Phototheque du Musée de l'Homme, Paris. M. Lucas, photographer; 11.32, © John Reader/Science Photo Library/ Photo Researchers, Inc.; 11.34, Courtesy Phototheque du Musée de l'Homme, Paris; 11.35, © David L. Brill; 11.36 (top), © 2006 Peabody Museum, Harvard University. 2004.24.26470; 11.36 (bottom left), Photo by A.R. Hughes. Courtesy Professor P.V. Tobias, University of

the Witwatersrand, Johannesburg, South Africa; 11.36 (bottom right), Courtesy B. Vandermeersch, Laboratoire d'Anthropologie, Universite de Bordeaux; 11.37, From Singer and Wymer, *The Middle Stone Age at Klasies River*. Reprinted by permission of The University of Chicago Press; 11.38 (left), Courtesy K.L. Feder; 11.38 (right), © Peter A. Bostrom/Lithic Casting Lab; 11.39, Neg. #39686. Photo by Kirschner. Courtesy Department of Library Services, American Museum of Natural History; 11.40, Courtesy Comité Départmental du Tourisme de la Dordogne; 11.41, © Dr. Peter Brown, University of New England, Armdale, Australia.

Chapter 12 CO12, © Anthony Bannister/Animals Animals/Earth Scenes; 12.4, © Charles P. Mountford/National Geographic Society Image Collection; 12.7, © Anthony Bannister/Animals Animals/Earth Scenes.

Chapter 13 CO13, © Bruce Dale/NGS Image Collection; 13.4 (left), Neg. #231604. Photo by D.B. MacMillan. Courtesy Department of Library Services, American Museum of Natural History; 13.4 (right), © Bruce Dale/ NGS Image Collection; 13.5 (left), © Paul Zahl/National Geographic/Getty Images; 13.5 (right), Kevin Peterson/ Getty Images; 13.6, © Ariel Skelley/Photographer's Choice/Getty Images.

Chapter 14 CO14, 14.1, © 1996 George Steinmetz; 14.3, Courtesy Dr. Serena Nanda; 14.6, © The Granger Collection, New York.

Chapter 15 CO15, © Kenneth Garrett/NGS Image Collection; 15.1, © Gerha Hinterleitner/Gamma; 15.2, © Kenneth Garrett/NGS Image Collection; 15.3, © Irven DeVore/Anthro-Photo.

INDEX

CPSIA information can be obtained
at www.ICGtesting.com
Printed in the USA
FFOW03n0629161113
2373FF